Industrial Arts

And

Technology

Industrial Arts

And

Technology

Delmar W. Olson

Professor of Industrial Arts
Coordinator of Graduate Study for Industrial Arts
Kent State University, Kent, Ohio

PRENTICE-HALL, INC.
Englewood Cliffs, N. J.

To every industrial arts teacher
who sees industrial arts
as fundamental education
for every American boy and girl

PRENTICE-HALL INTERNATIONAL, INC., London
PRENTICE-HALL OF AUSTRALIA, PTY., LTD., Sydney
PRENTICE-HALL OF CANADA, LTD., Toronto
PRENTICE-HALL OF JAPAN, INC., Tokyo

© 1963 by
PRENTICE-HALL, INC.
Englewood Cliffs, N. J.

Printed in the United States of America
45921-C

Library of Congress Catalog No.
63-11097

Current printing (last digit):
11   10   9   8   7   6   5   4   3

Frontispiece: Courtesy, Ford Motor Company

To My Colleagues:

A Foreword

Many of us at one time or another have wondered about the curriculum for industrial arts, because at the same time that we saw it in its common form of woodworking, mechanical drawing, and metalworking, we also saw that it could be crafts, power, graphic arts, transportation, auto mechanics, or other. We personally know teachers who support the narrower curriculum and others who insist on the expanded. Who is right?

Industrial arts has traditionally been a disciplinary subject in that it insisted on routing a youngster through a series of prescribed experiences leading to a mastery of a tool or a machine tool under the assumption that this mastery was the essence of its goodness. It seems to me that it is time for us to reconsider what the mastering of materials, energies, tools, machines, and products by man has done for him; to reflect on the control he has created for himself over his natural environment; and to look at the environment he is creating out of this mastery; and to study all of this mastery as the source of its subject matter. In my opinion all of this stands as a challenge: it is the challenge of technology and the great mission for industrial arts. With this kind of industrial arts man can learn about this materials mastery as he discovers and develops his own native aptitudes for having better ideas with materials. He can find value in his technology beyond that of tool skills and can gain even greater control of what happens to him in his time.

This proposal suggests a rather clear direction for a new industrial arts. My hope is that it will help you to envision a great new program, too, and that each of us will take it upon himself to study, experiment, and to share his findings. I can see the possibility of a magnificent new education for every American and a golden age for industrial arts in the years ahead.

DELMAR W. OLSON

Preface

The concept of industrial arts described in this book is a proposal that originated with an attempt to place today's industrial arts within the context of today's technology. The influence of such an environment projects change for the industrial arts. Necessarily imaginative and idealistic, the proposal creates a new ideal for industrial arts. In this idealism it seeks to discover meaning, purpose, and excellence in a technology that is commonly assumed to be materialistic. Idealism and materialism, essentially divergent philosophies, have seemed sufficiently reconcilable to me to be brought together.

The hypotheses on which the proposal is based are simple and logical. First, the purpose of the school in any society is to acquaint the young with the nature of their culture. Second, man by nature is facile in reasoning, problem-solving, creating, and constructing with the materials and energies provided by nature. Third, the ultimate goal and good in technology is the liberation of man from enslavement to materials, freeing him for higher purpose and achievement. Fourth, the technology originated through man's creativity; the continuing change in technology evidences a continuing creativity. Fifth, all men possess a measure of creativity, but not necessarily the same measure. The creative imagination is the highest level of the human intellect, the greatest of man's gifts, and is of greater significance than knowledge. Sixth, in the American pattern of civilization there is more than one road to wisdom and culture, and among them the study of the technology is fully as liberating as the liberal arts. And last, it is the responsibility of the school to acquaint its students with the nature of technological culture and to assist them in discovering and developing their talents therein. This should be the province of the industrial arts.

A proposal for a new industrial arts might possibly have entirely different bases than these. It might follow from a study of the psychological nature and needs of man, or it might be drawn from a scientific-mathematical-engineering analysis of materials, processes, and machines. This study, however, is essentially socio-economic-cultural in origin and development, since the material culture, the technology, derives from men and materials.

Two sources should be read before studying this proposal. The first, an address given by Alfred North Whitehead in 1917, is Chapter 4 in his *The Aims of Education* (89, 52-68) and is entitled "Technical Education and its Relation to Science and Literature." This essay, teeming with significant concepts, permits the industrial arts teacher to idealize and then to realize his visions. Especially meaningful to us in industrial arts, Whitehead's idealism of 1917 now approaches common logic.

The second source is Chapter 8 in *Goals for Americans* (63, 193-204). Thomas J. Watson, Jr. describes national goals as he analyzes technological change. He stands in a key position for influencing such change, and seems to speak directly to the industrial arts teacher. These two sources, each in its own way, envision a technology released from restriction to materialism. They prepare the teacher for his search for a greater industrial arts.

The total proposal evolves through five stages. The first, Chapter I, provides the historical and evolutionary background of industrial arts and identifies forces which have tended to shape its curriculum. The second, Chapters II and III, studies the technology itself, identifying its elements and outlining results. A perspective of contemporary industry as an institution is also developed. Technology and industry are seen as the primary sources of subject matter for industrial arts. The third stage, Chapters IV, V, VI, and VII, derives and classifies subject matter originating in industry and makes an analysis of the functions of industrial arts. The fourth stage, Chapters VIII and IX, identifies the new industrial arts as a complete program and describes essential facilities. The last stage, Chapter X, reviews the entire proposal pointing out implications which may become principles or generalizations from within the over-all concept. These serve as guides to a clarification of the concept, to implementation of the program at any level, to a rethinking of teaching method, to measures for evaluation, and as issues for debate.

May I express my appreciation to my colleagues throughout the profession who through the years have assisted in their own unique ways in the development of this proposal for a new industrial arts. I am even indebted to those who have said, "It is a good idea, but it won't work." The testing because of this resistance has caused me to broaden my thinking about industrial arts. I am sure that if it is a good idea, someone can make it work.

I wish also to express my gratitude to the many students who, captive as they may be in my classes, have been willing to reflect on the contents of the proposal and to take parts of it for study and experimentation in their own schools. Some of these stand out today as bright spots in the progress of the profession.

May this also acknowledge our men who have been moved to stimulate the profession with their vision and their hope, and who have persisted in their faith that there is much more good in industrial arts than we have sensed. I am reminded of a letter from George A. Bowman, President of Kent State University, in which he pointed out to me that the hand must reach farther than it can grasp. I wish I could acknowledge all of those who have shared in this proposal for a new industrial arts.

D.W.O.

Acknowledgements

The author is grateful to the following for the illustrative material reproduced in this text:

American Vocational Association, Inc.: the selection from "A Guide to Improving Instruction in Industrial Arts," used by permission of the American Vocational Association, Inc.

Appleton-Century-Crofts, Inc.: from *Technology and Social Change*, by Francis R. Allen, Hornell Hart, Delbert C. Miller, William F. Ogburn and Meyer F. Nimkoff. Copyright (c) 1957. Used by permission of Appleton-Century-Crofts, Inc.

Chas. A. Bennett Co., Inc.: the selection from the editorial by Charles Richards in Volume VI, No. 1, October, 1904, of the *Manual Training Magazine*, the selection from Charles A. Bennett's *The Manual Arts*, the selection from Bennett's *History of Manual and Industrial Education 1870 to 1917*, used by permission of Chas. A. Bennett Co., Inc.

Bonser, Frederick G. and Lois C. Mossman: from *Industrial Arts for The Elementary School*, used by permission.

The Bruce Publishing Company: from Bawden's *Leaders in Industrial Education*, 1950, by permission of the Bruce Publishing Company.

Columbia University Press: from *Modern Science and Modern Man* by James B. Conant, copyright 1955, used by permission of Columbia University Press, and David Snedden and W. E. Warner, *Reconstruction of Industrial Arts Courses*, 1927, used by permission of Bureau of Publications, Teachers College, Columbia University.

Crown Publishers, Inc.: the selection from *The Power Age* by Walter Polakov, used by permission of Crown Publishers, Inc.

Epsilon Pi Tau, Inc.: the selection from *Industrial Arts and The American Tradition* by Boyd H. Bode, used by permission of Epsilon Pi Tau, Inc.

Harcourt, Brace & World, Inc.: from *Technics and Civilization* by Lewis Mumford, copyright, 1934, by Harcourt, Brace & World, Inc., used by permission of the above.

Harper & Row, Publishers: the selection from *America's Next Twenty Years* by Peter F. Drucker, in *Harper's Magazine*, March, April, May, June, 1955, used by permission of Harper & Row, Publishers.

D. C. Heath and Company: the selection from *The Manual Training School*, 1887, by Calvin M. Woodward.

International Textbook Company: from *Industrial Arts and General Education* by Gordon O. Wilber, used by permission of International Textbook Company

Liveright Publishing Corporation: from *The Story of Mankind* by Hendrick W. Van Loon, by permission of LIVERIGHT, Publishers. N.Y.

The Macmillan Company: from *The Aims of Education* by Alfred N. Whitehead, by permission of The Macmillan Company.

McGraw-Hill Book Company, Inc.: from *Modern Technology and Civilization* by Charles R. Walker. Copyright 1962. McGraw-Hill Book Company, Inc. Used by permission.

National Industrial Conference Board: *Road Map* No. 1080, used by permission of National Industrial Conference Board.

Prentice-Hall, Inc.: the selection from T. J. Watson, Jr., in *Goals for Americans, The Report of the President's Commission on National Goals.* © 1960, by The American Assembly. Prentice-Hall. Inc., Publisher. Used by permission.

The Ronald Press Company: the selection from *History of American Technology* by John W. Oliver, Copyright 1956. Used by permission of The Ronald Press Company.

Scientific American: from *Automatic Control*, September, 1952, used by permission of Scientific American.

Simon and Schuster, Inc.: from *American Science and Invention*, Copyright 1954 by Mitchell Wilson, by permission of Simon and Schuster, Inc.

The Twentieth Century Fund: from *America's Needs and Resources* by J. Frederick Dewhurst and Associates, used by permission of The Twentieth Century Fund.

The University of Chicago Press: from *School and Society* by John Dewey, Copyright 1916 by the University of Chicago, used by permission of The University of Chicago Press.

C. A. Watts & Co. Ltd.: from *Man Makes Himself* by V. Gordon Childe, used by permission of C. A. Watts & Co. Ltd.

Wilkie Brothers Foundation: from *Civilization Through Tools*, used by permission of Wilkie Brothers Foundation.

Table of Contents

Industrial Arts

And

Technology

(Above) A typical scene in the shop of the early wheelwright—a builder of wheels. Before the automobile, horse carriage wheels were light, beautifully finished, and tired with solid rubber. The wheels shown were made of wood with the felloe, or outer rim, shaped in sections. An iron band, heated red was placed around the felloe and shrunk tight. (Courtesy: The DoAll Company.)

(Right) A beryllium shield for a space capsule. Note the aluminum foil suits protecting the workers from heat radiated by the forging. The wagon wheel and the beryllium shield, both circular, both man-made, and both components of transportation, represent levels of intellect far apart. (Courtesy: Aluminum Company of America.)

I

The Industrial Arts
Curriculum
In Transition

*. . . there are, however, three main roads along which we
can proceed with good hope of advancing towards the best
balance of intellect and character: these are the way of
literary culture, the way of scientific culture, the way of
technical culture. No one of these methods can be exclusively
followed without grave loss of intellectual activity and of
character. . . .*
—Alfred North Whitehead, *The Aims of Education.*
(New York: The Macmillan Company, 1929).

Industrial arts education had its beginning with
the acceptance of the concept of *work as education.* But pinpointing
in the history of education when this acceptance occurred is difficult. Work was considered moral, righteous, and spiritually uplifting
long before it was considered to be educative. The experiments and
theories of Johann Heinrich Pestalozzi and Philip Emanuel von
Fellenberg in Switzerland during the latter part of the eighteenth
and the early part of the nineteenth centuries are considered pioneer
developments in the implementation of the concept of work as
education. Pestalozzi has been called the father of manual training

1

as well as the father of modern elementary education, so great was his influence on later trends in education.

During the first part of the nineteenth century a technical instruction system was developed in Russia for the training of engineers and technicians. It was revolutionary in that it employed a *class* type of training in contrast to the *apprentice* method. This was officially launched in 1830 with the establishment of the School of Trades and Industries in Moscow. At the same time a system of educational handwork was being developed in the Scandinavian countries, to be known as Scandinavian *sloyd*. By the middle of the nineteenth century sloyd schools were common in Norway and Sweden. In Finland, an improved type of sloyd under the leadership of a teacher, Uno Cygnaeus, was introduced during the second half of the century and was recognized by law as a part of the public elementary school program in 1866. Sloyd was introduced into the common school because of its acceptance as education for all children. Instruction concentrated upon the making of articles useful in the home, generally of wood—although other materials were added in some schools.

At this point in history these concepts of educative handwork found their way across the Atlantic to the United States. Historians claim that the Russian plan was introduced in 1870 and the sloyd plan in 1888; but for purposes of studying their contributions to the development of industrial arts, we can assume that they arrived simultaneously. These systems, influenced by an expanding American industrialization, developed into a type of educative shopwork which was shortly to be known as *manual training*.

MANUAL TRAINING

The great American champion of manual training was Calvin M. Woodward, dean of the polytechnic faculty at Washington University, St. Louis, Missouri. Because of his leadership and the support of other prominent educators, manual training came to be the first form of organized, shop-type education in American public schools. Industrial drawing instruction was introduced at the Massachusetts Institute of Technology in 1870 by John D. Runkle, president of the institution, and Woodward also began his first experiments with manual training at the college level. In 1880, Woodward opened the country's first manual training high school, known as The Manual

Training School of Washington University. In 1886 he described his manual training:

> The object of the introduction of manual training is not to make mechanics. I have said that many times, and I find continued need of repeating the statement. We teach banking, not because we expect our pupils to become bankers; and we teach drawing, not because we expect to train architects or artists or engineers; and we teach the use of tools, the properties of materials, and the methods of the arts, not because we expect our boys to become artisans. We teach them the United States Constitution and some of the Acts of Congress not because we expect them all to become congressmen. But we do expect that our boys will at least have something to do with bankers, and architects, and artists, and engineers, and artisans; and we expect all to become good citizens. Our great object is educational: other objects are secondary. That industrial results will surely follow, I have not the least doubt; but they will take care of themselves. Just as a love for the beautiful follows a love for the true, and as the high arts cannot thrive except on the firm foundation of the low ones, so a higher and finer development of all industrial standards is sure to follow a rational study of the underlying principles and methods. Every object of attention put into the schoolroom should be put there for two reasons—one educational, the other economic. Training, culture, skill come first; knowledge about persons, things, places, customs, tools, methods comes second. It is only by securing both objects that the pupil gains the great prize, which is power to deal successfully with the men, things, and activities which surround him (99, p. 229).[1]

American educators experimented with the Russian system, the sloyd methods, and manual training, devising numerous variations and combinations of these. For years Woodward's manual training provided the basic pattern for high school shopwork in programs of general education. Manual trainers themselves, however, began to point out weaknesses in it. Among the criticisms were that manual training was too formal, too rigid, and not truly liberal because it confined the pupil to exercises in narrow fields and ignored relationships with the sciences. One stricture is particularly significant for this study. Some educators expressed concern over the lack of attention paid to aesthetic design in exercises, projects, and models. This criticism was echoed by reformers who were championing the arts and crafts movement. The latter was a crusade dedicated to

---

[1] For full citation of this and other references that follow, see the Bibliography at the end of the book.

preserving handwork as an American institution. Machine production in the last half of the nineteenth century was rapidly replacing hand methods in industry, and many felt that handcraft skills and artistry in materials would soon be lost.

At this time the curriculum in manual training included woodworking, mechanical drawing, and metalworking in that order of acceptance. Woodworking, as the textbooks of the period show, involved joinery (the making of joints), cabinetmaking, finishing, wood turning, and often patternmaking. Mechanical drawing was largely the drawing of blocks as well as plain and solid geometric forms and patterns. Metalworking included forging, founding, machining, bench and sheet metalworking.

MANUAL ARTS

As the machine age advanced, Charles A. Bennett was much concerned with the possibilities of a national loss of hand skills and artistry with materials. In 1917 he wrote a book—*The Manual Arts*—and in it described a proposal for a system of education bearing the same title. He did not choose to define manual arts as clearly and specifically as Frederick G. Bonser had identified industrial arts several years earlier, but he apparently envisioned in his manual arts much of what Bonser had held for industrial arts. Bennett wrote the following concerning the effects of the development of industry on living:

> A very important result of this development in the industries is the need of men with a wider knowledge of the materials and processes of industry and the principles upon which the processes and the use of the materials rest. This knowledge is not being handed down from father to son to any great extent, nor from master to apprentice, partly because the factory system does not easily lend itself to education, and partly because the knowledge needed is so new that even the masters themselves find it difficult to keep up with the development. But this need for a wider knowledge of the principles and processes of industry is not confined to the workers in these producing industries. Every man who would intelligently use the modern conveniences of his own home, or the labor-saving devices and conveniences of business life, must know something of the materials and principles of industry; and if he is to have any adequate appreciation of the product—if he is to judge the quality of the thing he purchases or uses, he must know something of the process that produced it. In fact, industrial develop-

ment has been so rapid and so varied in our country—it has affected every man's life to such an extent that if he is to retain sufficient mastery of his environment to make it serve his needs, he is forced to acquire considerable practical knowledge of the materials, principles and processes of industry. And if the school is to furnish it, the school must be equipped with the tools of industry (*17*, p. 15).

When Bennett faced the question of which manual arts should be taught, he attempted a classification based on a survey of industry. He decided on the graphic arts, the mechanic arts, the plastic arts, the textile arts, and the bookmaking arts. It is of interest to note how Bennett justified his selection of subject matter. He reasoned that the five categories of work represented were fundamental to civilization and, therefore, should have a place in the school. Being a prolific writer, editor, and—eventually—a publisher in the field, he came to be known as the father of the manual arts movement.

INDUSTRIAL ARTS

Industrial arts can be called the third stage in the evolution of shopwork instruction in the public school. The origin of the term is credited to Charles R. Richards, editor of the *Manual Training Magazine*, published by the Charles A. Bennett Co., Inc., Peoria, Illinois. Richards made the following statements in 1904:

> Have we not come to the time when a change is urgently needed in the term applied to constructive work in the schools? Is there a manual training teacher in the country who does not increasingly feel the need for a more explicit and dignified title for his professional work? In short, is it not time that the term Manual Training, never fully expressing the meaning of school handiwork, has now come to be thoroughly inadequate and even misleading?

> . . . . .

> It is no longer merely a question of improving an indefinite title, but of replacing one that is inappropriate and incorrect in its implication. The old term is now not only vague, it has become misleading as an indication of the aim and character of our work.

> Now that we are beginning to see that the scope of this work is nothing short of the elements of the industries fundamental to modern civilization, such a term becomes at once a stumbling block and a source of weakness.

> . . . . .

> Behind every other subject in the curriculum is a body of ideas of fundamental meaning and importance. The industrial arts which stand for one of the most vital phases of modern civilization,

throw away their claim to recognition by masquerading under a term at once inappropriate and misleading. Such a term is both an obstacle to the full and free development of our work and to its recognition and appreciation on the part of the public.

.   .   .   .   .

In the hope of enlisting consideration and discussion, the writer proposes the term suggested above, Industrial Art. Such a term indicates a definite field of subject matter. The word Art is inclusive of both the technical and aesthetic elements, and the qualifying work points specifically and comprehensively to the special field of our material (65, pp. 32-33).

The terms *industrial art* and *the industrial arts* had been used much earlier than 1904 in connection with schools for teaching art as applied to industry in England, France, and Germany. The important issue here is not the authorship or the origin of the term *industrial arts*, but rather the changing educational concept which it was to identify. Richards pointed out the need for a change in terminology, but in so doing he did not furnish a new type of instruction and a new curriculum to accompany the new name. We can fairly presume that he invented a new label in hope and anticipation that a new program would emerge to fit it. Since 1904, the term *art* has been changed from the singular to the plural in our usage. Perhaps this suggests an increase in the number of the arts.

THE BONSER CONCEPT OF INDUSTRIAL ARTS. Both American historians, Charles A Bennett and William T. Bawden, attribute the original definition and clarification of the purposes of industrial arts to Frederick Gordon Bonser. Although he was neither an industrial arts teacher nor a tradesman, Bonser saw in industrial arts a means for improving elementary education. He may have been inspired by John Dewey, who proposed industrial arts as both subject matter and teaching method. The following statement made by Dewey in *The School and Society* shows some similarity in thought to Bonser's interpretations of the industrial arts:

> When we turn to the school, we find that one of the most striking tendencies at present is toward the introduction of so-called manual training, shopwork, and the household arts—sewing and cooking.
> This has not been done "on purpose," with a full consciousness that the school must now supply that factor of training formerly taken care of in the home, but rather by instinct, by experimenting and finding that such work takes a vital hold of pupils and gives

them something which was not to be got in any other way. We must conceive of work in wood and metal, of weaving, sewing, and cooking, as methods of living and learning, not as distinct studies.

We must conceive of them in their social significance, as types of the processes by which society keeps itself going, as agencies for bringing home to the child some of the primal necessities of community life, and as ways in which these needs have been met by the growing insight and ingenuity of man; in short, as instrumentalities through which the school itself shall be made a genuine form of active community life, instead of a place set apart in which to learn lessons (38, pp. 10-11).[2]

During the early part of the current century Bonser developed a concept of industrial arts which even today may be considered as frontier thinking. He was primarily concerned with industrial arts for the elementary school—grades one through six. However, his definition of industrial arts was surely appropriate for the senior high school, just as arithmetic, geography, English, and other subjects need but one basic definition for all grade levels. Following is the now classic definition given in his *Industrial Arts for Elementary Schools:*

> The industrial arts are those occupations by which changes are made in the forms of materials to increase their values for human usage. As a subject for educative purposes, industrial arts is a study of the changes made by man in the forms of materials to increase their values, and of the problems of life related to those changes. (20, p. 15).

Bawden reports that Bonser was presenting this concept in his classes at Columbia University at least as early as 1912.

Bonser illustrated his concept of industrial arts with examples of industrial change in the forms of materials.

> Few of the materials which we use are used just as nature produces them. We change the form of the trees of the forest into lumber, then into furniture, parts of buildings, and other products of wood. We change wheat and corn by milling and cooking processes into foods more palatable and wholesome than these grains are as produced by nature. We take the crude iron ore as it comes from the mines and through various changes make it into final forms serving uses so numerous that we sometimes speak of this as the iron age. We change masses of native clays into jars, jugs, vases, and china, both useful and beautiful. We take numerous

---

[2] Copyright 1916 by the University of Chicago Press.

> fibers produced by nature, and through many changes in their
> form we furnish ourselves with garments suited to every purpose
> of climate or occasion. All of these changes which we make in the
> forms of materials, that they may be more useful, we call *industrial*
> changes. We speak collectively of the occupations devoted to the
> making of these changes as *industries*, or *industrial arts*. The general
> term manufactures means about the same thing, but industrial arts
> is preferable as it is more inclusive (20, p. 3).

Agriculture, mining, transportation, and communications were not
included in Bonser's industrial arts since they involved no changing
of the form of materials. He saw fine arts as an integral part of the
design and development of industrial products.

Bonser advocated the general educational purpose of industrial
arts in the elementary school, as opposed to any vocational purpose.
His statement on "Outcomes of the Study of Industrial Arts" (20,
pp. 14-16) is essentially a statement of functions. Six outcomes are
included: health, economic, aesthetic, social, recreational, and technical skill.

A professor of education and a layman, so far as industry and industrial arts were concerned, he envisioned the educative potential
in industrial arts, defined its nature, established its purpose, selected
its subject matter, and identified its outcomes. The clarity of
Bonser's vision was nothing short of amazing, and it continues to
be so. The full impact of his interpretation on industrial arts has
probably not been felt. Many leaders in the profession immediately
accepted his concept and began to extoll its virtues. Bawden, in
Leaders in Industrial Education, made an appropriate summary of
Bonser's industrial arts:

> If any one factor more than another was responsible for the
> extent and the quality of Dr. Bonser's influence on the trend of
> events, it was undoubtedly the crystalization of his ideas into a
> popular "definition" of industrial arts. The definition was happily
> worded, and stirred the imagination of those who were capable of
> comprehending its implications. With the accompanying interpreta-
> tion it also created the impression of being based upon sound rea-
> soning and thorough knowledge of the child and of the school.
>
>   .   .   .   .
>
> This definition was more widely and authoriatatively quoted than
> any other in the history of the movement . . . (11, pp. 37-38).

The new term *industrial arts*, although invented by Richards and
given meaning and status by Bonser, was popularized by many leaders

in manual training and manual arts. Among these were Charles A. Bennett, Bradley Polytechnic Institute, editor of the *Industrial Education Magazine*; Robert W. Selvidge, University of Missouri; Frank M. Leavitt, University of Chicago; Ira W. Griffiths, University of Wisconsin; Emanuel E. Ericson, State Teachers College, Santa Barbara, California; and William E. Warner, The Ohio State University. Bennett concluded his study of industrial arts with the following:

> While the term "industrial arts" was first used to designate work that developed as a reaction against the formalized courses inherited from Froebel, the term has become so popular in the United States of America that it is coming to include all instruction in handicrafts for general education purposes, whether formalized or not. Its meaning is essentially the same as the term "manual arts," though its connotations are different. In the term industrial arts, the "industrial" is emphasized; while, in manual arts, the "arts" is historically the distinctive word and, in the term manual training, "manual" is the important word (*15*, p. 455).

INDUSTRIAL EMPHASIS IN INDUSTRIAL ARTS. Bonser seemingly saw industrial arts as a study of what would be currently termed *manufacturing*. The changing of materials into useful products was to be done by hand and with hand tools. This no doubt reflected his concern for the elementary school. Since his pronouncement, industry has grown to much more than just manufacturing, however, and were he writing today, he might be willing to include such categories as transportation and communications in industrial arts, especially for the higher levels of the school. He might also advocate the use of machine tools in the light of the increasing influences of industry and technology on society.

The concept of industrial arts continued to unfold as other leaders attempted to place it at all levels of the public school. In this evolvement industrial arts became increasingly industrial, with attention given to the machine processing of materials. It came to include a variety of American industries, and this breadth became the point at issue in a professional controversy which is still unresolved: breadth of experience versus depth of experience.

William E. Warner in his *Reconstruction of Industrial Arts Courses* wrote of two epoch-making articles by Dean James E. Russell, in 1909, and Dr. F. G. Bonser, in 1911, and added these observations:

As a first result of the analyses made by Doctors Russell and Bonser and later experimentation carried out under the direction of Dr. Bonser, there was established the present conception of Industrial Arts for public school work. This conception is known as *The Industrial-Social Theory*, or *The Russell-Bonser Plan*. It was established and tried out by Dr. Bonser in 1910 in the Speyer School, demonstration and experimental school of Teachers College, Columbia University. The first published course of study on this basis of organization was included in *The Speyer School Curriculum* published in 1913.

As a second result, there was created a new type of shop known as a *general* or *composite* industrial shop or laboratory. This type of shop was designed because it more nearly answered the needs and demands of the new theory of organization. . . . Laboratories containing from two to ten activities are most common today . . . (71, pp. 7-8).

The objectives of the junior high school industrial arts were stated by Warner (71, p. 10) in a manner consistent with the national trends of the nineteen-twenties. He stated that the primary purpose was "developmental experience through manipulative and other activities introductory to the world's industrial work." Warner listed the following as secondary aims:

1. Exploratory or finding studies for the detection or discovery of interest and aptitudes.
2. General guidance values through broad occupational contracts and studies.
3. Consumers' or utilizers' knowledges and appreciations; the better choice and use of industrial products.
4. Household mechanics or the development of "handy man" abilities.
5. Avocational activities of adolescent youth in the pursuit of hobbies, and in the construction of things to possess either permanently or temporarily.
6. Vocational purposes in the definite preparation for a future occupation (applicable to from 0 to 15 per cent of the average junior high school group).
7. Correlation with other studies and interests both in and out of school.
8. The forming of *social* habits, development of social values (moral, civic, etc.) possible in every activity of junior high school, but particularly in the industrial arts because of the socialized setting possible (71, p. 10).

THE DILEMMA. When the Bonser concept was added to those of manual training and manual arts, confusion resulted. The Bonser plan both clarified and clouded the issues involved. Later proponents of manual training, with their attachment to and respect for technical-manipulative skill, adopted the work of the tradesman as their subject matter. By means of trade analyses the competences were isolated and then trained for. However, mechanization of industrial processes rapidly outmoded hand processes and changed the trades-man into a machine operator. During this conversion, manual train-ing slowly lost its place as legitimate educational shopwork. While these changes were taking place, manual arts—with its emphasis on the project—was in a position to make a smooth shift from hand to machine processes. However, many attached greatest values to hand processes, and, as a result, a breach developed within manual arts: the advocates of hand processes versus the advocates of machine, or industrial, processes. Several inconsistencies developed throughout the years. They became increasingly annoying to teachers and leaders in these fields, especially when the Bonser concept was injected into the thinking. The early manual training concept of training the mind by training the hand was challenged by newer concepts in psychology, which minimized the intellectual contributions of manual training and, theoretically at least, reduced it to purely manipulative activity. To be consistent, manual arts had to be manual; but many insisted on making manual arts industrial while others emphasized the arts aspect over the manual. The question was also raised by exponents of the new educational psychology of whether these forms of school-work were genuinely general education. They considered some man-ual training skills vocational and, as such, not legitimately a part of general education.

A TERMINOLOGICAL INVESTIGATION. Throughout the twenties, as shop-work in the schools became increasingly common, the distinctions between manual training, manual arts, and industrial arts became increasingly less sharp. The terms were used interchangeably, and other terms such as *practical arts, industrial education,* and *industrial training* were added as synonyms. The original concepts of manual training, manual arts, and industrial arts had been fairly clearly defined, but in usage they became crossed and mixed to such an extent that the individual missions were obscured. For decades after-ward, traces of this confusion existed in the profession—and perhaps still do.

The first evidence of organized research carried on by the industrial arts profession appeared in 1933, in a bulletin of the Western Arts Association entitled *The Terminological Investigation*. One of the most significant findings is in the paragraph entitled "Comparative Study of First Uses" that follows (88, p. 12):

The *Investigation* had not progressed far when it became evident that the reasons why people first used certain professional terms might serve to clear the situation. It was further conceived that there might be a possible relationship between the meanings back of these terms as they were first used, all of which would bear scrutiny and comparison. Accordingly, the present analysis is submitted for inspection as one approach to the scientific study of terms. The research techniques involved are historical and comparative.

MANUAL TRAINING	MANUAL ARTS	INDUSTRIAL ARTS
Inception: 1876	1896	1910
Influence: Della Voss, Runkle, Woodward	Bennett, Salomon, Griffith	Bonser, Dewey, Bigelow
Skill: Artisan basis, tool mastery	Craft basis, "Technics"	Individual basis, "Development"
Methods: Dictated exercises	Assignment of *useful artistic* projects	Projects and individual creativity
Content largely: Work in wood; *Mechanical* drawing	*Arts:* Graphic, Plastic, Textile, Mechanic, Bookmaking	Any representation of modern industry conditioned by stated objectives
End functioning: In itself	Avocational, nice to have done, development of appreciation for the Crafts	Exploration, Development of Personal-social Traits, Guidance, Consumer Education
Basis of Truth: Authority	Authority and Custom	Scientific evidence and Criteria
Centers in *Teacher*	Centers in *Project*	Centers in *Pupil*
Unit-Shop	Unit or General shop	LABORATORY OF INDUSTRIES or Unit-shop

This comparative interpretation has become a guide to differentiation between these concepts. Here industrial arts becomes distinctly unique by comparison. It has a quality of professionalism and educative maturity lacking in manual training and manual arts.

The Terminological Investigation, in the attempt to resolve the dilemma, defined industrial arts.

INDUSTRIAL ARTS is one of the *Practical Arts*, a form of general or non-vocational education, which provides learners with experiences, understandings, and appreciations of materials, tools, processes, products, and of the vocational conditions and requirements incident generally to the manufacturing and mechanical industries. The results are achieved through design and ·construction of useful products in laboratories or shops, appropriately staffed and equipped, *supplemented by* readings, investigations, discussions, films, visits, reports, and similar activities characteristic of youthful interests and aptitudes in things industrial.

The subject of *Industrial Arts* belongs peculiarly within junior and senior high school areas for such purposes as exploration, guidance, the development of avocational and vocational interests and aptitudes, specific manual abilities, desirable personal-social traits growing out of industrial experiences, ability to choose and use industrial products wisely, all coupled with the aesthetic relationships involved. In general, its purposes are *educationally social* rather than *vocationally economic*, although in the senior high school it may increasingly emphasize vocational objectives in a non-legal sense, for certain students.

Industrial Arts includes such industrial representations as drawing and design, metal work, wood work, textiles, printing, ceramics, automotives, foods, electricity, and similar units, either as separate offerings or in various combinations common to the "General Shop" or LABORATORY OF INDUSTRIES.

The term *laboratory* is more appropriate when the offering is provided upon an experimental or developmental basis, as is commonly done in the junior high school; and the term *shop* may be more appropriate where the work is carried on rather upon the production or economic basis, as may be done in the senior high school.

The term Industrial Arts is generally displacing the historical but narrower term *Manual Training*; and in common usage it has substantially the same significance as the term *Manual Arts*; although *Industrial Arts* emphasizes in addition the all-round arts of industry rather than just manipulative or "manual" aspects of artistic construction implied in the term *Manual Arts* (88, p. 27).

This definition has become an historic interpretation which has influenced the development of industrial arts programs since 1933. It appears to have been the first such professional pronouncement to follow Bonser's famous definition.

THE OHIO PROSPECTUS. A year after *The Terminological Investigation*, a most significant document appeared. Sponsored by the Ohio Education Association and the Ohio State Department of Education, it was entitled *A Prospectus for Industrial Arts in Ohio* (73). The *Prospectus* was a report of a study made by the State Committee on Coordination and Development of Industrial Arts Professional Interests in Ohio. Based on the interpretation of industrial arts established in *The Terminological Investigation* and the outcomes seen by Bonser, the *Prospectus* projected a concept far beyond that of manual training and of manual arts. The concept was marked by a concern and provision for the study of industries. Industry was considered as the basic source of subject matter for the curriculum. Of interest is that the word *technology* does not appear in the *Prospectus*, even though the proposal moved in that direction. One paragraph described the mission of industrial arts:

> The public school must provide an opportunity for young and old not only to become acquainted with changing industrial processes and the social-economic problems resulting, but to include a wide range of experiences particularly in the material changes which have and do occur. This is so evident if people are to participate intelligently in programs dealing with the social control of the industrial structure. The individual pupil needs to have actual contact with a wide range of industry. This will come not only through the performance provided him in a school's LABORATORY OF INDUSTRIES, but through planned visits and investigations to motivate further study in Industrial Arts and its related subjects of the problems involving capital and labor, conditions of employment and unemployment, transportation, advertising, salesmanship, the quality and use of materials and products, all in addition to many other related problems (73, p. 29).

The concepts expressed in the definitions of industrial arts in *The Terminological Investigation* and in the *Prospectus* were essentially the same, except that the former stated that industrial arts belongs peculiarly within the junior and senior high school while the latter views the program as encompassing all age and school levels. According to the *Prospectus*, an adequate program of industrial arts included a diversity of subject-matter units.

> . . . . While at least ten types of Industrial Arts subject matter are possible and common, only five because of time and space, have been presented and discussed in this chapter. These have been included: Planning, including drawing; Communication, including electricity; Metals; Textiles, including clothing and weaving; Transportation, including automotives, ships, and aeronautics; and Wood. Others include: Graphic Arts—Bonser referred to it as

Records—including paper making and letter press, intaglio, and planographic printing, all in addition to bookbinding; Ceramics, including pottery, concrete, and glass; Personnel, which refers to the pupil or operative side of Industrial Arts laboratories and involves problems common to all school "shops"; Foods; and then certain important, though minor units as: Leathercrafts, Jewelry, and the like (73, p. 93).

Accompanying the *Prospectus* in Ohio, during the thirties several exemplary public school industrial arts programs were installed. These programs, based on the concept projected in the *Prospectus*, served as pilot models for industrial arts in the state and influenced curriculum and laboratory planning nationally. Visitors even came from foreign countries to study this Ohio experiment.

A FEDERAL INTERPRETATION. Three years after the *Prospectus*, a United States Office of Education bulletin appeared entitled *Industrial Arts, Its Interpretation in American Schools (81)*. The bulletin was devoted to objectives, curriculum, administration, and supervision of industrial arts in the elementary school, the junior high school, and the senior high school, as well as in programs for adults, in higher education, and other extensions. The curriculum concept of industrial arts presented in the *Prospectus* was that used in the bulletin. The latter proposed implementation for the former.

THE NEW CURRICULUM. During World War II and the immediately ensuing years, the industrial arts movement was slowed for lack of teachers; but in 1947, at the first postwar meeting of the American Industrial Arts Association in Columbus, Ohio a new concept in curriculum—called the *New Industrial Arts Curriculum (7)*—was presented. The curriculum was to serve three functions: consumption, production, and recreation on the elementary, secondary, collegiate, and adult levels. The proposed curriculum content included areas of power, transportation, communication, construction, and manufacturing (with both manual and industrial emphasis), plus a division called *personnel*. This new curriculum was the joint effort of a group of doctoral students and W. E. Warner at The Ohio State University. It was too far ahead of the times to gain general acceptance, but like all advance thinking it has had its impact on the profession.

THE EPSILON PI TAU PLAN. A curriculum for industrial arts derived from an analysis of contemporary industry and reflective of technology was proposed in a dissertation by this author in 1957. Titled *Technology and Industrial Arts (62)*, it was first reproduced at the University of Illinois. Its subsequent publishing was assumed by Epsilon Pi Tau, the international honor society of industrial arts and industrial-vocational education. The proposal was marked by an expanded concept of the curriculum but with a definite purpose, calling for an industrialization and intellectualization of industrial arts. Three bases were offered for curriculum development: (1) the study of industries as industries, (2) the analyses of the functions of industrial arts as sources of subject matter, and (3) the derivation and analyses of curricular components as units of subject matter. The proposal was given entity as a plan by some of its supporters during the 1959 Virginia Industrial Arts Association conference.

THE MINNESOTA PLAN. A proposal for a redirecting of industrial arts teacher education appeared in 1958 as the *Minnesota Plan (54)*. It grew out of an industrial-education faculty study at the University of Minnesota. The proposal specified three broad areas within industrial arts teacher education: general education, professional education, and industrial arts subject-matter preparation. The latter includes three "cores of experience": the science-mathematics, the technological (tools and materials), and the design. A unique feature of the plan is the timing of the instruction within the cores. Intercore related courses are taken simultaneously for a maximum of integrative effect. The subject-matter program itself is largely a rearrangement with changed emphasis, so that the new structure has the appearance of being very substantially engineered. The proposal should be considered as one of the significant contributions to teacher-education curriculum development in the second half of the century.

THE WASHINGTON CONFERENCE. On June 20 and 21, 1960 the United States Office of Education—through Marshall L. Schmitt, Specialist for Industrial Arts—convened a conference for the identification and study of major problems and issues facing the industrial arts profession. Sixteen members—representing public schools, teacher education, city and state supervision, and major national organizations, with personnel from the Office as resource people and with the Specialist as Chairman—considered the following questions:

1. What is the place of industrial arts in American culture?
2. What objectives should be emphasized in industrial arts?
3. What guidelines should be followed in determining curriculum content for industrial arts?
4. What implications are there in Soviet polytechnic education for industrial arts?
5. What is the relationship of industrial arts to other school curriculum subject fields?
6. What changes are needed in industrial arts to meet the needs of the gifted and the slow learner?
7. What curriculum changes need to be made in industrial arts to best reflect technology and the needs of the students?
8. What competencies are needed by the industrial arts teacher to meet the challenge of the future?

The findings of the conference appeared in February, 1962, as a report entitled *Improving Industrial Arts Teaching (82)*. The title calls to mind the Federal bulletin of 1937 *Industrial Arts, Its Interpretation in American Schools (81)*. A comparison of the two reports shows that the underlying concepts and assumptions are closer than might be expected even with the quarter-century interval. Several of the questions studied are curricular in nature, which supports the contention that the number one problem in industrial arts today is the curriculum.

LEARNING BY DOING. By the time of the inception of industrial arts in 1910 and Richard's proposal to change the name of manual training, John Dewey was well along in his experimental program at the University of Chicago's elementary school. There he demonstrated a type of common school education modified by changes originating in a society being transformed by increasing industrialization. He considered the impact of the Industrial Revolution on American culture so significant as to necessitate a complete reformation of the elementary school. His book *School and Society (38)* explained his point of view. Dewey felt that modern industrialization, with its applications of science and mechanization, offered as intellectual an opportunity for learning as that found in the regular school studies. He recommended that the industrial occupations of weaving, sewing, cooking, and carpentry be studied in the elementary school and that the child be encouraged to explore among them. From this exploration with tools and materials drawn from these occupations would come knowledge essential to an effective participation in an industrial society.

Dewey's concepts of interest, experience, and problem-solving in the learning process were described in his *Democracy and Education* of 1916 *(37)*. Interest was seen as an energizer and an activator to learning, as well as being essential to actual learning. Learning was considered to be an experiential process. Popularization of Dewey's thesis of learning through experiencing reduced it to the familiar *learning-by-doing* slogan. This slogan was adopted by industrial arts educators as appropriate justification for activity—for the *doing*—in industrial arts. But what these educators did not sense here was that this concept was sound only within its proper context. For example, they overlooked Dewey's assumption that thinking begins with a problem. Habitually, the industrial arts teacher solved the problems in the project before he gave it to the student in order to assure its successful construction, without error. With this procedure, he, perhaps unknowingly, was removing *thinking* from the student's experience; what was left was merely *activity*—which Dewey hardly would have accepted as the essence of experience. More consistent with Dewey's proposal would have been to emphasize learning by experiencing with thinking at the core.

THE LABORATORY OF INDUSTRIES.   Given Bonser's social-economic philosophy of industrial arts, Ira W. Griffith's innovation, the general shop, and Dewey's plan for cultural education through a study of industrial occupations, it remained for William E. Warner to pull them all together. This he did in his proposal for a "laboratory of industries." He conceived a facility which would offer a broad cultural education by means of student exploration among the materials, processes, products, and occupations of industry. The laboratory itself was to be equipped for such exploration and was intended to provide a broadened experience. His proposal expanded the technical bases for industrial arts far beyond that of mere processing; in so doing, it collided with the stone wall of tradition. The impact, however, was sufficient to crack the wall. The *laboratory of industries* concept has come to be one of the major forces in the redirection of industrial arts that began in the late twenties and is still in progress.

THE AIMS OF EDUCATION.   In 1929, a mathematician-turned-philosopher—Alfred North Whitehead—brought together a number of his speeches in a volume called *The Aims of Education* (91). Somehow this work (and especially its fourth chapter, "Technical Education and its Relation to Science and Literature") escaped industrial arts educators, even though it spoke boldly and clearly to them. He accepted the thesis that the ideal state was one in which work is play and play is life (91, p. 53). From this he constructed a philosophy for technical education. His contention, "The curse that has been laid on humanity in fable and in fact, is, that by the sweat of its brow shall it live . . ." (91, p. 53), lends support to the postulate that the primary purpose of technology is to release man from drudgery. Whitehead proposed a national system of education comprised of three curricula: the literary, the scientific, and the technical —with a homogeneity achieved through their integration. His interpretation of technical education as being liberal is an invitation to leaders in industrial arts. The challenge is to conceive of a technical education that is truly liberating and at the same time a liberal education that is technical. It must work both ways. An industrial arts curriculum designed to be liberal would increase the acceptability of industrial arts on all levels.

TRADE TRAINING AND THE CURRICULUM. Well into the twentieth century, manual training, manual arts, and even the early industrial arts depended for teachers largely on tradesmen, even though as early as 1893, professional courses for teachers' manual training were offered at Columbia Teachers College. Necessarily, such teachers drew heavily on their own repertory of skills and knowledge for the content of their teaching. The teaching methods were designed to transmit this knowledge. Such instruction became highly formalized and mechanized, with graded exercises involving hand tools and their usage. During World War I the critical demand for naval tonnage for shipping supplies to our Allies brought about a new system of training aimed at producing skilled workers in the shipyards. Dr. Robert Selvidge of the University of Missouri drew on this method of training in his plan for systematizing instruction in industrial arts. A trade was separated into the many operations in which the tradesman was expected to be proficient. These were arranged in order from easy to difficult, and appropriate exercises and demonstrations were included in the instruction. Supplementing these units of operation were topics of information, which were intended to provide the facts of science related to the operations. Out of the plan grew the system of teaching by means of *instruction sheets* popularized by Dr. Selvidge. When applied to industrial arts the subject matter in any course was analyzed, categorized, and graded. *Operation sheets* explained procedures for using tools and some machine processes. *Job sheets* explained how to perform certain jobs or tasks, such as applying an oil finish and cutting a mortise and tenon joint. *Related information sheets* provided cognate knowledge—which might be scientific, cultural, historical, consumer, or other type as the teacher saw fit. The *project sheet* contained the drawings and the step-by-step procedure for completing a particular project. These were used in a graded sequence, and with a more liberal teacher the student might be permitted to choose from a selection of projects at any one level of difficulty.

Instruction sheets, while neither subject matter nor curriculum, were of such a nature as to identify, select, and organize subject matter. The selective process necessary in the preparation of the sheets enabled teachers literally to package the subject matter, file it, and distribute it as needed. The student was involved only as he mastered the technical processes and information and executed the projects. Perfect sheets were those which enabled the student to proceed independently without error. Consequently, problems for the student were minimized if not eliminated. Dewey would likely have insisted that student thinking, too, was eliminated. However, the technique greatly influenced the industrial arts curriculum. Once the sheets were prepared, the curriculum had been reduced to "fundamentals." If the student could read and follow instructions, he could succeed in the course. Whether he experienced a maximum of growth respective to his potential is still debated.

FORCES WHICH SHAPE THE CURRICULUM IN INDUSTRIAL ARTS. When one looks at industrial arts in retrospect, as we have been doing, the many forces at work shaping the curriculum become apparent. The changing economic, social, political, and cultural aspects of living effect changes in the education of any society. The origins of the forces at work in industrial arts are varied, their impacts are many, but the directions of their pressures seem to be arranged radially toward a common center. Perhaps this latter tendency produces the overall condition of statics so noticeable in our subject matter. A child squeezes an inflated toy balloon between his fingers. Pressed at one point it bulges at another, but still it retains the same capacity. We who are concerned with curriculum development in the sense that we see it as being more properly a *dynamic* than a static mass must be aware of the forces at work on it today. Perhaps they may be redirected, or even grouped, so that the total effect will be a forwarding action on the body of subject matter, thus overcoming its present static condition. Several of the forces now working on the industrial arts curriculum are identified in the following discussion. Can you add others?

THE POWER OF PRECEDENT. In any society, precedent in mores, standards, customs, and laws is justification for their perpetuation. They become traditional—a part of that society's culture. Industrial arts started as woodworking, mechanical drawing, and metalworking. This combination set a precedent and has become the national curriculum pattern. This is not to say that this combination was poorly chosen, or that it is weak. However, the history of technology demonstrates that knowledge in the fields of woods, drawing, and metals has increased many times beyond that of fifty years ago and that this knowledge has since then become intensely scientific and technical. When what we teach and do in today's industrial arts remains essentially the same as at the beginning, we know the power of precedent.

THE COMMUNITY. A common practice in industrial arts development has been to tailor programs to fit communities. This has usually meant that local industry was strongly reflected. If, for example, toolmaking was the major local industry, the program would be stronger in metals than in other areas. Likewise, when the community was rural, farm shop-type activities were emphasized. This influence is expressed here in the past tense because it is less common now than formerly and will likely become even less so as industrial diversification and decentralization proceed across the nation and as one community becomes technologically similar to another.

TEACHER EDUCATION. It has become a cliché that a teacher teaches as he was taught; and we may add that he probably teaches *what* he has been taught. Students graduating from one university are conditioned to carry on a program with certain characteristics; those from another have concepts and purposes at variance. Such differences appear rather clearly in curricular expression when the students enter teaching and when they enroll in graduate classes in another institution. Some difference of opinion has existed on the responsibility of the teachers college in curriculum leadership, but we feel the teachers college should properly be a major source of new ideas.

At present some teacher-education programs seemingly narrow student visions while concentrating on technical mastery. Others, in a spirit of liberalism, equip students with first-level appreciations marked by breadth of vision with little penetration beneath the surface. At what point does industrial arts teacher education become the center of curriculum confusion?

EDUCATIONAL PHILOSOPHY. Educational philosophy, the purpose of which is to provide direction and meaning for education, properly influences the curriculum. Bonser's concept of "impulses to expression or action" was proposed as a guide for the implementation of his system of industrial arts. Dewey's concern for the scientific method in education was implemented by a methodology for teaching founded on his doctrines of interest and experience. His influence on the industrial arts curriculum has probably been less than his influence on its teaching procedures. Those in industrial arts usually settled for the *learning-by-doing slogan*. Had they probed his philosophy deeply enough to find its key concepts for education, they might have been moved to vast curriculum changes.

The curriculum for industrial arts was first set on a base of absolutism and permanence. Then we felt secure with the Dewey slogan. But Dewey's philosophy had little place for absolutism; it was tempered by a recognition of fallibility.

INDUSTRIAL DEVELOPMENTS. New industrial materials, processes, and products influence the industrial arts curriculum as they provide constantly changing subject matter for study. The new processes find their way into the curriculum—usually after reduction to the handcraft level—and they tend to remain on this level. This tendency discourages an enriched curriculum responsive to new developments.

Why do we commonly include in our subject matter only those processes capable of handcraft-level demonstration? Why should we not study the processes as industry uses them? A serious-minded student of industrial arts will give these questions careful study.

THE PROFESSIONAL ASSOCIATION. The voice of the industrial arts profession is its associations—local, state, national, and honorary. Through these bodies, standards are set up which affect the entire profession. Such standards take many forms. They may appear as curriculum guides, status studies, or statements of position on issues. They may also be programs for conferences. These conferences concern problems and issues which the leadership assumes to be significant and timely. The matters with which a conference deals are indicative of the vision of its leadership. The individual teacher usually assumes them to be of major importance, whereas they may be of minor significance compared to the truly critical problems and issues facing the profession.

Curriculum is currently the number one issue for industrial arts. Agreement exists that the curriculum typically includes woodwork, mechanical drawing, and metalwork. Diversity begins when the curriculum is extended beyond these. It continues when the nature of the three original subject-matter areas is opened to a rethinking.

TEACHER INTERESTS. The personal interests of the industrial arts teacher commonly find their way into his subject-matter program. Many activities not directly related to woodwork, mechanical drawing, and metalwork have thus become a part of the curriculum. When well received, they frequently become permanent. This has happened, for example, in the case of photography, model-airplane building, construction of soap box derby racers, model-automobile design, and probably others. When the teacher as an individual has widely developed interests, this breadth shows itself in his program. And likewise, when his interests are narrow and confined, he is less likely to encourage his students to go beyond them.

STUDENT INTERESTS. Student interests beyond the regular course of study may also find their way into the curriculum. Many instances are known of students requesting to study certain fields with which the instructor was unfamiliar. Given encouragement, however, they—and their teacher—have gotten into the study of radio, hi-fi equipment, aeronautics, weaving, photography, and other such fields. Some of these catch on and become part of the program.

THE SCHOOL ADMINISTRATION. Within any one school system the policies of the administration and the degree to which it understands the purpose of industrial arts both affect the curriculum. When industrial arts is a required course, its content tends to be different from that featured when it is an elective. When formal courses of study are required, the subject-matter program tends to be unlike that in which the teacher is left to do as he thinks best. Administration support for industrial arts results in one curriculum; indifference, another. And, the disparity may often be in degree as well as in range of subjects.

THE TRADES. The influence of certain technical trades, for example, cabinetmaking, tinsmithing, and metals machining, is still strong in industrial arts even though curricular concentration is supposed to be on industries. The analyses of trades as sources of subject matter for industrial arts was most popular in the nineteen-thirties, but even today trades influence course construction. From such analyses tool operations were derived. They served as the fundamentals for teaching and for learning. And these, too, may still be found in use. The trade skill objective—technical mastery of processes—is still given as the major purpose and value of today's industrial arts by many industrial arts educators.

HOBBIES. Hobbies currently popular in a community easily enter the industrial arts program there. Witness leathercraft, the making of terrazzo-tile tables, lapidary, and such. Interest in do-it-yourself activities is a strong pressure for extending the program. With proper promotion, the teacher can make do-it-yourself instruction a legitimate part of the curriculum.

RESEARCH. The great source of new subject matter for industrial arts is properly tapped by research. This source comprises industrial research and development itself, as well as new materials, processes, products, energies, occupations, industries, systems, and concepts. We in industrial arts rarely utilize research findings for curriculum development. But when we do—as in content or resource researches— the real potential in subject matter is revealed. Perhaps if the numerous other influences shaping the curriculum were less influential, we would be forced to employ research more often. Only through extensive research can we know what is the right curriculum for industrial arts.

CONFLICTING CONCEPTS AFFECTING THE CURRICULUM. Industrial arts through the years has been beset by its full share of conflicting concepts. Some such conflicts may never be resolved; others are incapable of solution. Others would rather quickly disappear with objective analysis. So long as these controversies do beset us, however, they will divide industrial arts educators, and curriculum development will be hampered accordingly.

The issue of industrial arts as general education versus industrial arts as mere trade-competence training, while supposedly settled on one hand, is fully alive on the other. Of interest is that we in industrial arts usually consider industrial arts as a part of general education but at the same time we tend to measure pupil and teacher achievement in a school situation by evidence of technical mastery in the project. Such a measure often has its own yardstick in the competence of the related trade. The question is whether the general education value of industrial arts can be measured by achievement in technical processes.

Unity versus diversity is a perpetual issue in any field, never completely solved by philosopher or practitioner. Because the industrial arts curriculum typically contains woodworking, mechanical drawing, and metalworking, there would appear to be much unity among industrial arts educators as to curriculum content. But this is deceiving. With some thirty-eight thousand teachers, we probably have thirty-eight thousand different programs and directions. In exercising his freedom, the teacher does what he thinks is best—and typically has considerable freedom in carrying on his program. School administrators complain that industrial arts teachers from different teachers colleges require different facilities to teach the same course. The chances are that in these cases it is not the same course—only the same label. Statements of objectives by industrial arts educators include so many heterogeneous notions that their diversity of opinion is obvious. Many feel the need for a national program of industrial arts, such as seems to be the trend in other subject-matter fields. But others insist on the right of autonomy for both local program and teacher. Perhaps industrial arts educators need enough unity to make order out of their diversity.

Richards' early plea for making manual training industrial training now seems to have made good sense. Apparently the transition was never complete because the issue of handcraft emphasis versus industrial emphasis is still a lively one. This involves the sub-issue of the hand tool versus the machine. Most of us insist that hand-tool instruction precede that of machines; few have dared to reverse it. And yet we know that a youngster can often gain greater control of a material by means of a machine than he can with a hand tool. We know from experience that a hand tool is often more difficult to master for a particular operation than its machine counterpart. Compare the coping saw and the jig saw, the hand drill and the drill press. When we study technology we find that its primary purpose is the release of man from drudgery, but we still give college credit for hours of hand sanding. Our inconsistencies make us vulnerable. Too great a concern with maximum student growth and development per unit of time spent in industrial arts may tend to cloud the issue. The student should use the *best* process to achieve his goal —*best* relative to the nature of the task, to his maturity, to the quality standards being sought, and to the time available.

The question of depth versus breadth is well illustrated in the issue of the *general shop* versus the *unit shop*. This has produced a cleavage among industrial arts teachers that often produces sparks. Somehow the general shop became associated with the concept of breadth of understanding and the unit shop with depth and mastery of process. With study and reflection, however, we would likely discover that neither breadth nor depth alone is the essence of industrial arts. Nor is a compromise necessary. Both are desired within the same individual. We might also discover that the greater the penetration in depth of a study the greater becomes its breadth, the broader its implications, and the wider its applications. When one desires breadth of understanding, he cannot stop at a speaking acquaintance with the vocabulary of the field. When he wishes to penetrate in depth, he makes full use of his peripheral vision at the same time. Behind this issue of depth is a greater question that, when answered, will resolve the former: What should industrial arts be doing for the boys and girls of America because they are Americans? The search for the answer to this should include study of the description of the "gifted generalists" in the Rockefeller Report (66, p. 11).

The liberal and the conservative are always with us in any area of human living and thinking. Youth is most often considered liberal and age conservative. In industrial arts, the more liberal teacher has tended to ally himself with an expanding curriculum and the conservative with a circumscribed curriculum. The former is often the advocate of the general shop and laboratory of industries and the latter the unit shop. Peacemakers have attempted to smooth these troubled waters with the addition of a compromise—the general unit shop. The conservative and the liberal are not easily identified, however. The reason is that most of us are not wholly one or the other. Conservative and liberal concepts are easier to distinguish. For example, the former in curriculum would be expected to embrace absolutism, the latter, fallibility in the selection of course fundamentals. Absolutism suggests a finality in curriculum content and a freezing of the fundamentals. "Fallibilism" presumes that finality and absolutes are relative to the moment, that change is imminent, and that there is always a better way.

The question of perfectionism also frequently divides industrial arts educators. This is not a matter of discounting excellence; it is rather that two different standards are involved. One standard takes its measure from perfection in process, such as is possessed by the master craftsman. The other makes excellence relative to the student.

The role of the project and its nature have diverse and conflicting interpretations. Some see the project as a means, others as an end. Some insist that it provide for a full and free expression of the student through materials. Others believe that the project should be an integration of specified processes in a graded sequence.

Whatever the issues, they seem to be limitless in number as well as impact. You could draw up courses of study consistent with the thinking on each side of those issues discussed here. If these outlines were compared, the influences of the concepts in shaping the content would be apparent. The student should become aware of these issues and the others facing the profession. He should attempt to understand all sides before he takes a stand and be prepared to change his views as new facts are uncovered.

THE FIELD TODAY. The first half-century of industrial arts has been an interesting one. Conceived in a spark of idealism and illumined with the light of philosophy, industrial arts contained the potential for development into a system of fundamental education for all boys, girls, and adults. But strangely, it chose to restrict itself in curriculum and to serve but a small part of the school population. It may be argued that this was not of the industrial arts' making; yet the fact remains that the field of arts has had full responsibility for its own growth and development—and still has.

Bonser and Dewey gave both substance and support to a type of industrial arts that probably would have gained a rather full acceptance as general education among educators in general. Oddly enough, however, a vigorous opposition arose from within the ranks. The proponents of manual training tugged at the curriculum from one direction, those in manual arts from another, and the trades analyses group from a third—all like puppies attacking a pantleg. The *Terminological Investigation (88)* was a timely effort aimed at a clarification of terminology and concept.

Interesting, too, is the seemingly characteristic resistance of industrial arts to the influences of new concepts in purpose and curriculum. But immunity to change has not been complete; consequently, here and there throughout the country bright spots have appeared. They serve as sources of light generated by imaginative, inspired leaders. The current but scattered efforts at introducing the research and development concept is such a source.

Educators are currently asking a question that is becoming the challenge to the rethinking of industrial arts: "Is there no more to industrial arts than just making things?" Such a simple question should seemingly have a simple yes or no answer. And if industrial arts is to grow in influence and importance, it has no choice in its reply. The discussion which follows in the remainder of this study is based on an affirmative answer—that there *is* more to industrial arts than just making things—and is an attempt to illustrate this contention.

TO DISCUSS, TO DEBATE, TO DECIDE

1. What was the essential difference between *manual training* and *manual arts?*
2. Is there a place for either one, or both, today?
3. Why did Richards suggest a change in label? Would a change be advantageous today?
4. In Bonser's definition of industrial arts, what did he mean by the term *occupations?*
5. Why was Bonser's concept of industrial arts widely accepted for the elementary school, but not beyond that?
6. Industrial arts has frequently been in a dilemma. What is the nature of and the possible solution for its present dilemma?
7. In the comparison of *manual training, manual arts,* and *industrial arts* in *The Terminological Investigation,* the item "basis of truth" appears. How do you interpret this?

8. What differences might appear in two industrial arts programs as a result of centering one in the teacher and the other in the pupil?
9. Of what value should a professional honor society be to industrial arts?
10. What competences are needed by the industrial arts teacher to meet the challenges of the future? Can he meet them alone?

(Above) An old clock factory. Such a factory demonstrated the highest development of hand, precision metal working before the Industrial Revolution provided machine tools. (Courtesy: The DoAll Company.)

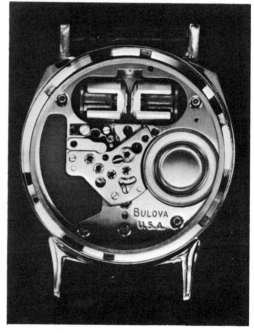

(Right) The interior of a new type of wrist watch. Man's time awareness has been evident for centuries. The clock was his first efficient mechanism to measure time. Originally made of wood, then of iron, then of brass, the clock eventually led to the pocket watch and then to the wrist watch. The watch shown includes an electronic circuit and a tiny power cell which produce a precise frequency standard. The familiar balance wheel and springs have been eliminated. (Courtesy: Bulova Watch Company.)

II

Technology: America's Primary Resource

What is technology? . . .

One approach to the subject is to look at technology as having an outer and an inner aspect. To illustrate: Modern technology may be perceived as an environment within which we live, made up of external and tangible things which we modify from time to time and which modify us. . . . Modern technology can also be viewed internally. In this sense it consists of skills of body and brain, of technical and administrative procedures, and of mental processes, both conscious and unconscious, some of them associated with value judgments which relate man's outer world to his inner one. . . .

—Charles R. Walker, Modern Technology and Civilization.
(Copyright 1962. McGraw-Hill Book Company, Inc.)

Technology may well be considered contemporary America's primary resource. Billions of people around the world consider it so—especially those in the underdeveloped countries who desire more of the material things to release them from drudgery, to free them from hunger, poverty, disease and ignorance, and to give them dignity in the eyes of the remaining two-fifths of the world's people. Technology is a primary resource because it serves primary needs. Technology in America feeds, clothes, houses, transports, informs, entertains us. It educates us, keeps us healthy and secure, gives us leisure and means to enjoy it. In this abundance we have reached the world's highest level of living; and at this height, we are probably the world's most envied nation. In fewer than five hundred years technology has become the American way of life and the great American resource. To understand our own culture, we must understand technology because it is our culture. To understand what has made America great, we must search technology. To understand what will keep America great, we must again study technology.

Man for a million years has been a tool user. But only in the last ten thousand of this million has he developed his tools beyond stone eoliths. During the last hundred centuries he has developed his tool usage to the point that he now can sit and watch a machine, a complex tool, do all of the work or even watch an entire factory tirelessly producing its products automatically. But this all began with hand tools and man's desire to gain power and control for himself. From the Old Stone Age to the New Stone Age, to the Bronze Age, and then the Iron Age, through the rise and fall of Greece, the Renaissance, and then on into the Industrial Revolution, man has moved in this hundred centuries. Since the Industrial Revolution of the last century, the Ages of Mechanization, Industrialization, Power, Electricity, and the Atom have succeeded each other; and now we have entered the Age of Space. During the first half of the present century alone, we have carried industrialization through the stages of mass production and automatic machines into an era of automation.

TECHNOLOGY: AN INTERPRETATION

The term technology, because of the looseness with which it is commonly used, requires a rather careful interpretation. The origin of the term is in the Greek word *techne* meaning art or skill. This combines with the Greek *logia* meaning study. Out of this comes the dictionary definition of technology as the science of the industrial arts. Here industrial arts refers to the arts of industry in the general sense and not to that phase of general education which we know as industrial arts. The arts of industry refer to arts, skills, crafts, technics, and knowledge as employed in industry.

The definition used by Dewhurst and the Twentieth Century Fund states:

> As technology consists of accumulated knowledges, techniques and skills, and their application in creating useful goods and services, the ultimate fruits of a country's technology are found in the standard of living its people are able to enjoy (39, p. 834).

In this sense technology is America's resource because it provides man's physical and material needs. Technology, too, is the primary resource because it is built on the utilization of man's primary aptitudes, his creative imagination, and his tool-using dexterity.

We shall let this interpretation of technology suffice as a guide to the study of the subject. A more complete summary is found at the close of the chapter.

TECHNOLOGY: MAN AND MATERIALS. Man and materials make technology. A study of technology provides for an understanding of the role of man among materials. Technology is the record of man's achievements in materials. It began when he first discovered that he could extend his power and increase his authority by using something beyond himself. A stone or a club in his hand lifted him above the animal because he then could more effectively subdue it.

Technology is the record of man's control over nature. When he first learned to ride a floating log, he extended his horizons. When he hollowed the log, he increased its transportative possibilities. When he built a ship, he was lured into the open seas; when he devised the magnetic compass, he could sail where he chose with the assurance that he could find his way back. The damming of a stream eventually led to control of flood waters and later to hydro-electric power, which gave him increased means of control over nature.

Technology is the record of man's ability to create his own environment. With it he built cities connected by rail and road. His airplane drew the world so close together that he now can literally leap from continent to continent. He places lakes where he chooses, plants forests about them, and burrows miles beneath the earth. Today within our own boundaries a primeval environment is rare indeed. And the Dutch have even built a country out of the sea.

But man also has a genius for creating great problems for himself. This talent grows as he develops his technology. With materials he can conquer distance and time on land, under the sea, and in space. He can eliminate plagues and poverty. But, along with such mastery, he has arranged the means for his own complete destruction. When you and I stand off to observe him, it appears that man does not understand the potential of materials any more than he knows the potential of himself. Let us study the technology, as a human creation, and through this achieve not only an intelligent usage of things, but gain a greater understanding of the human.

TECHNOLOGY: THE PROVIDER. Technology in its role of primary resource becomes at once the great provider for every American. Originating in man with his intellectual and tool-using aptitudes in combination with the resources of nature, technology is a man-made resource. With it man provides his physical-material needs for living as well as a good share of his luxuries.

In the United States our technology provides us with the greatest variety of goods known to any nation and in such abundance that we cannot consume them all. Even though some three-fifths of the world's people live under thatched roofs, not so in our country where technology is ready to provide modern housing for every family. Rare indeed would be a family which weaves the fabrics and tailors its own clothing today. But supplying these basic needs for human existence is only one service of technology. In any nation communication and transportation are primary socializing agencies. The enlightenment and humanizing of its people is only possible as technology provides the means: the printed word in books, newspapers, and periodicals; the telephone service which can reach the city, village, and home; the radio which reaches beyond the printed and spoken word; and the magic of television which finds its way around the world by Telstar. With the intricate network of streets and highways and automobiles being produced at the rate of some nine million per year, Americans have become the most mobile of people. Each year air travel moves us farther and faster. Our railroad systems, trucking lines, and pipe lines move bulk commodities from city to village and coast to coast on continuous schedule. Effective communications and transportation have become basic requisites for the democratic way of life. Adequate means for sharing and comparing of ideas and for social interaction bring understanding and appreciation. In these days of intercontinental missiles, effective communications and transportation can mean the difference between understanding and misunderstanding, between survival and annihilation.

Technology is a major means to individual as well as to national security. It makes possible accurate diagnosis of disease and provides treatment and cures. It has lengthened American man's span of life to double that in many of the lesser developed countries. It has increased the efficiency of military, police, and traffic protection and safety, whether on land, sea, or air.

Technology even helps itself make all of the foregoing possible. It provides the tools, the machines, the factories, and the necessary servicing for the production of its material goods. It conceives of and produces the facilities necessary to supply the foods, clothing, housing, communications, transportation, and security and places them here and there over the country to be most easily available. To meet increasing demands for goods and services, it provides its own research facilities in the quest for better methods to make better products faster and cheaper. Technology provides the materials it uses to produce its products and services, as well as its facilities. The search for natural materials goes on around the world while the search for man-made materials proceeds in the laboratories. American synthetics have quickly found their ways throughout the world and remote, indeed, is the village which does not know of nylon. Today the conversion of natural materials into new and more usable forms is a tremendous industry in itself. In all of this production, technology provides work and income for some seventy million people in the United States. And for these people and their dependents, technology makes available, too, the tremendous selection of goods and services which it produces.

Within this pattern, man finds work, not merely for the sake of work, but for the sake of income with which he consumes the resources which he has produced. In our society the worker is free to choose his work, but his choice is dependent upon the bounds of technology. To assure the material things needed in living and the income by which to avail himself of them, he demands the opportunity to work. Most of his work opportunities are found in such categories as manufacturing, power, communications, transportation, construction, research and development, management, and services. These categories include approximately 60 per cent of the total civilian employment in the United States. Changing technology changes the nature of the job and accounts for the fact that on the average the worker changes his job and often his occupation four or more times during his work life. The old adage that to eat, man must work is as true today as it originally was even though the nature of the self-sufficiency has changed.

Technology thus provides materials, tools, machines, industries, jobs, products, and dollars in a cycle that is both economic and social in its nature. It involves the lives of every American so intricately and completely that it has, indeed, become an American way of life. Ours is a technological culture, a material culture in which the effective combinations of man's natural intellectual capacities have been teamed with the materials supplied him by a most generous nature. We have demonstrated and developed a level of human living that has become the goal for the rest of humanity.

TECHNOLOGY: THE LIBERATOR. Technology is in the process of freeing man from drudgery, from poverty, from disease, from danger, from fear, from ignorance, and from isolation. It began with purpose. In the beginning man had only his muscles to provide the power he needed to gain control over materials and his environment. Although developing nations still depend upon muscles for power, we in the United States turn almost entirely to technology for our power. Human and animal muscle supply only about 5 per cent of the power consumed in American industry; mechanical means furnish the 95 per cent. However, as late as 1850 men and animals furnished some 75 per cent, and mechanical means, the rest.

As the great liberator technology functions as inventor, creator, designer, engineer, producer, builder, operator, and servicer. This is technology in its physical form. To understand technology we must however, look beyond its physical nature. The results of its productivity all come into focus in its role as the builder of civilizations. When man first became a tool-user, with a rock tied to a stick for a handle, civilization took root, and throughout known history civilizations have reached high levels whenever the peoples concentrated on their technology. History also tells us that these civilizations fell because the people failed not only to understand the phenomenon they had created but to use it wisely. This happened in Egypt, in Greece, and in Rome. In today's world those nations with the highest standards of living are those with the greatest industrial development. Standard of living here refers to the general level of living of a people, its level of freedom from drudgery and material enslavement. Thus history of civilization becomes a record of technological development. The Renaissance in Europe awakened a widsespread concern for technology as men rather suddenly and simultaneously in many countries sought to free themselves from centuries of ignorance and poverty. Increased wealth lay in commerce with other nations; but commerce depended on a thriving technology and from the thirteenth century on we note the world-wide explorations and searchings for new markets and new lands as men gained courage and confidence in science and in a developing technology.

Very few of today's industrial processes could be carried on with muscle power. With the aid of mechanical forms of power, man has been able to use machines to master materials. This mastery over machines has so developed that we now have machines to master machines. Electronic systems provide a precision control of automated processing which activates, regulates, corrects, and discriminates. Specifications can be fed into automated systems and out of them come completed assemblies, and we can reasonably expect that the next step will be the automatic production of entire complex units, such as the automobile. Man liberated himself from drudgery by using his brain. Today he is rapidly freeing himself from work and for leisure, the right use of which is a national problem.

Technology, in the process of elevating the standard of living, frees man from poverty as it provides him with gainful employment and income with which to purchase the material things he needs in his living. In the primitive society man, working long hours with inefficient production, could produce only enough food, for example, to supply his own needs. After he began to use tools, he could produce an excess and thus have some to barter or sell. The advancing technology has increased production and with greater production, the worker earns greater pay. Fifty years ago the national average hourly wage in industry was approximately twenty-five cents; today it is more than ten times as much, with little sign of it leveling off.

And while the average wage rate was rising, the average workweek was becoming shorter, leaving unprecedented leisure time.

From clay tablet to hand-lettered manuscript to the printed page represents several thousands of years in man's attempts to free himself from ignorance. Guttenberg's production of books by means of movable type, which was timed with the Renaissance and with the Reformation, undoubtedly hastened the Industrial Revolution. With the printed page knowledge could be recorded and made available for mass consumption. When books were lettered by hand, only the rich could afford them; and the same would be true today. Printing increased the demand for literacy. In these very times one of the strongest desires of millions of people in the developing countries is the ability to read and write in their own language. And even today there are millions of people in countries where tribal dialects have not yet been reduced to writing. The world-renowned missionary to millions, Frank Laubach, with his each-one-teach-one international program of literacy is now calling for printing presses and American graphic arts techniques to supply the reading materials for these millions as the next step in the process of their enlightment. Literacy thus opens the door to human growth and development on a national scale, but only technology has the key to unlock it. Once literate, people are ready for a concentrated development of their total technology. National programs of education are demanded. As the three-fifths of the globe's people learn about us in the United States and about people in other countries with well developed technologies, they, too, want this freedom from poverty and these material privileges. Radio has already reached into sections of the world where newspapers and books have not yet found their ways. And there it is informing people about local, national, and international events and issues which sets them to thinking about themselves and their own living. They are beginning to wonder and to want—to wonder how other people can live so well and to want the same.

As technology has enabled man to gain control over nature, it has released him from fear and superstition. Natural phenomena once bewildering and frightening can now be explained away, or bridled, or rendered harmless. The fear of the unknown in distance has been all but removed by developments in transportation. Medicines have replaced witchcraft and sorcery; from the feared lightning, man has learned to make electricity a servant. Now he looks forward to departure from this planet into space where once all was mystery. Man's technology extends his curiosity and increases his confidence. He now searches out mysteries to study and to conquer.

The United States took some four centuries to raise its technology to its present phenomenal level—phenomenal as compared to that in the developing countries—but these people will not wait that long. Technology has informed them of a better life, and technology must supply it. Our technology is capable of reproducing itself in other lands, and these people know it. These millions hope to achieve the level of human dignity they have heard about. This can come only through a liberation from poverty, ignorance, and drudgery. People in early cultures spent most of their time and energy in getting food, clothing, and housing, and otherwise protecting themselves, thus insuring a perpetuation of the race in a subsistence economy. Such time as may have been left over was used to exercise the mystic rituals and customs of the tribe and thus appease unhappy gods. When a simple technology gave them control, however limited, over their environment and fate, men were moved to question, to propose, to try out even better ideas. The man in today's highly technological civilization who is freed from drudgery, ignorance, fears, and lower levels of enslavement is in a sense being re-created himself because of the very technology he created. His technology creates the physical liberation which begets a cultural liberation as man becomes free to, and moved to, seek a fuller utilization and realization of his native capacities. As he thus finds greater meaning and value in living, he is moved to even greater imagination in things technological. And these greater things will provide even greater liberation as he learns to live well with them.

TECHNOLOGY: THE RE-CREATOR. Technology is the great provider of leisure for the American. The trend in the reduction of the length of the workweek shows that while twenty years ago some 67 per cent of the hourly employees had a five-day week, today about 95 per cent do. Put another way, a worker in 1900 in the United States worked sixty hours per week and after sixty years of the century his successors work thirty-eight. This means that today he works slightly more than half as long to earn a living as he did at the start of the century. It could be that by the year 2000 he may work only half as long as he did in 1900. Technology is fast lifting White-head's curse of living only by the sweat of one's brow.

But technology has not rested with this leisure. It has busied itself with the production of means for man to consume his leisure time. With its characteristic resourcefulness, not only is technology providing thousands of products and services for leisure time use, but it has also created new things to appeal to new leisure time interests. It is creating hobbies as it provides the equipment for pursuing them. And all of the industries supplying the goods and equipment for recreational purposes provide at the same time work for millions of people. In man's work and in his play technology has a major role, and today the purpose of work can be considered leisure.

TECHNOLOGY: THE INTEGRATOR. Technology brings about a oneness wherever it goes. Each industrial product is an integration of materials and parts drawn from different sources, different companies, and different countries. It demonstrates an effective combining of materials, processes, skills, and intellect. Every industry demonstrates a high level of integration within itself through the coordination of all facilities and personnel. Watching the final assembly of an automobile is an experience in integration. The proper chassis, body, wheels, the type of tire, the horsepower of the engine, all fit the specifications and illustrate technological predestination.

Technology is bringing the world together with its media of transportation and mass communication. A country, no matter how remote, which does not have facilities to accommodate commercial airplanes is exceptional. And no matter on what airline one may travel, he can be sure of essentially the same standards of efficiency as he finds in his home country. Air terminals today are international crossroads where people from many world cultures cross paths in the process of world integration. Radio communications, as already discussed, spread information over the entire globe simultaneously with its origin. Television facilities, too, are appearing throughout the world. Television simulcasts in our country are no longer uncommon, but rather expected. Telstar and intercontinental viewing is now a reality. Nationwide direct-dialing telephone service makes the voice of a distant friend but seconds away. The uniformity in technological services wherever one goes suggests an integration too. Automobile service stations in any country will satisfactorily lubricate the vehicle and provide needed supplies, for instance. The word electronics is a part of an international vocabulary even though many national and tribal languages have no word for it.

Technology then, acts as a great unifier in bringing parts of the world together, just as it brings automobile parts together into the whole. The interchange of materials, products, techniques, and ideas made possible and desirable by technology effects a universal oneness; and at the same time, enables nations, industries, and people to demonstrate a uniqueness as they search for solutions to the same or similar problems and come up with better ideas. Technology too, has contributed to a oneness in goals, individual, community, and national. Our goal of a network of superhighways over the nation, when achieved, will tie us all closer together. A community's goal of an efficient transportation system for itself effects an integration from the planning stage through the actual utilization of the service. The oneness in the human goals for freedom from drudgery and freedom for a finer living is another example.

TECHNOLOGY: THE CREATOR OF WEALTH. Change in the form of materials is for the purpose of increasing their values; it is known as *value added* in economics. A ton of iron ore, for example, may be worth $10 per ton, but a ton of automobiles has a value of roughly $2000, and most of it is steel. Main springs for wrist watches, originating from iron ore, have a value of approximately $2,250,000 per ton. The value of the facilities alone for the manufacturing industries in this country is estimated at more than a hundred billion dollars. These facilities include property, buildings, and equipment, the latter two of which are wealth created by technology itself. Manufacturing alone contributes about one-third of the total national income.

TECHNOLOGY: THE LEVELER. Technology has become a great leveler, a great evener, as it reaches the point where it can satisfy the material needs of all people. As products and services become available to all, socio-economic strata become less distinct, and the barriers between man and man lessen. At the same time that technology moves toward an abundant living for all, it levels by lifting. It lifts the level of living to increasingly higher standards.

TECHNOLOGY: THE PACIFIER. Technology can also be called a great pacifier because it appeases the pangs of hunger. It could appease these pains much more rapidly if its human masters were more human. Technology appeases a hunger for knowledge with its many media for human education. It provides means for the development and the utilization of human intellect and skills, and thus provides a way to satisfy a basic human urge for self-betterment. Technology seemingly serves as an international tranquilizer for conflicting tensions and drives to dominate. History may find that the intense concentration of science and technology on the development of super weapons for human annihilation has had a sobering, quieting, and possibly a maturing effect on those who sense the potential in such weapons. These products of technology may prove to have been portents of peace. Technology by providing for the needs and services of man can ease problems of discrimination, which cause national tensions in three-fifths of today's world. Each human is entitled to human dignity, and the first steps to realize this goal include the elimination of poverty and ignorance. Jobs, income, and a more abundant living can, for example, enable people to have shoes. Among the millions of unshod, shoes are symbols of equality.

TECHNOLOGY: THE ENERGIZER. Technology provides the energy and power by which man gains control over nature. It provides the power to activate itself. However, more importantly, it serves as an energizer of humans. The never ending search for better ideas, products, processes, and services activates the intellect. One idea suggests a better one; one achievement leads to a greater one. As invention stimulates thinking, thinking stimulates inventions. The search for the better involves more than an improved product, process, facility, or service already existing. It involves new concepts as better solutions to all problems or as solutions to new problems. New products involve new uses for existing materials or new materials. These materials require new processes and new machines or adaptations of existing processes. The pressure for greater production at lower costs, which is spurring the drive to automatic production, involves much more than making machines self-operating. Production design, for example, must be considered within the limits and possibilities of automation. Today's automobile engine has been produced with the assistance of automation. However, its present design and structure is such that it may not be economically feasible to produce it on a fully automatic basis. A new kind of power plant will eventually be designed for completely automatic production.

Adding all of these aspects of new and better ideas together results in a rather full involvement of men, materials, and machines, and this involvement in today's technology is in a state of continual change. During the first half of the century the rate of this change has been accelerating. For example, the industrial concept of planned obsolescence results in a continuous flow of new products and makes current models obsolete. This creates greater markets for the new and is more than a promotional scheme for increasing sales. It is a demonstration of a control of technology in which ever-improving products and services are conceived and created. The ultimate aim of this is to effect an increasingly finer living, not for the few but for every American, and hopefully for every human.

THE SPIRIT OF TECHNOLOGY. Behind all technological development is the power of the human excited by the spirit which tells him that there is a better way. Without this spark technological levels remain fixed and thinking, sterile. Among many peoples even today their technology is as it was centuries ago. This is apparent in their manufacturing, communications, transportation, dependence on muscle power, housing, tools, machines, implements, utensils, and all such components of technology. In such cases the challenge to the young is to acquire the skills of the elders who are the masters. It is not to excel, not to find better ways than the masters use. Low levels of technology create little need for education beyond that required by the young to fit into the cultural patterns of the village, and thus these people remain enslaved by mysteries and superstitions which higher levels of technology explain away. In an advancing technology the spirit holds that there is always a better way, and the challenge is to find it. Some may choose to ascribe this advancement to the motive for profit. However basic this may be, the native human desire to find better solutions is even more fundamental, and may it never cease.

The Stages of Technology

The evolution of technology in America can be described as being in ages, stages, or levels. Such periods as the Machine Age, Power

Age, Scientific Age, Air Age, Space Age, and Atomic Age are referred to so commonly as to make us wonder in just what age we are at any one time. The answer is not easy to find since we appear to be entering and leaving ages with increasing rapidity. However, the earlier stages are relatively easily identified especially as one studies the technologies in emerging nations. Three-fifths of the world's people still live at or below the agrarian level. Our present culture instead of evolving through the hunting and fishing stage, the agricultural stage, and then the industrial, as is the typical pattern in the development of civilizations, began as a transplant from Europe. Such industries, including agriculture, needed to supply the essentials for living were started immediately. Within the first half of the seventeenth century, besides the glass plant at Jamestown, shoe manufacturing was underway at Plymouth, shipbuilding had begun at Salem, and textiles were being woven at Rowley, Massachusetts. Commercial fishing, lumbering, and ironmaking also were underway. Following the Revolutionary War and the War of 1812, industrial development leaped forward as world markets, the settlement of the West, and the declining materials dependency on Europe created demand for American products. Within a few years a revolution in manufacturing methods and processes was beginning, and human ingenuity was called on to meet these demands for consumer products as well as to supply new industries. There were locomotives, steamboats, telephones, machine tools, and many other such products to supply which had not existed before. This revolution we know as the Industrial Revolution. It is today often termed the first such by those who see automation as the second complete change in industrial methods.

The chart Stages of American technology (see Fig. 2-1) shows the evolving of our technology, beginning with hand processing of materials, using muscle power. Within this progression an even more important revolution is the change in concepts of power, materials, processes, and work. The student of technology will want to investigate these changing concepts. They contain meanings, purposes, and principles fundamental to technical change.

THE CHANGING CONCEPT OF POWER. From the beginning man has been able to do work because of his physical structure. For thousands of years he used his bodily strength to provide his own transportation whether by foot or paddle. With a concept of power limited to that of muscle, either man or animal, the growth of technology was limited. This is evidenced in many of the emerging nations of today. When wind was harnessed to a windmill turning a rotor which in sequence drove a power take-off, man was at once elevated to something greater than a source of horsepower. This type of mechanical power from nature was used in America as early as 1640 by the Dutch in Manhattan. With the success of this harnessing, inventive minds looked farther. They saw falling water as a means to drive a rotor, a water wheel. But wind and water, powerful as they may be, are not available in every place at all times. Soon their limitations were reached, and new uses for mechanical power were devised. Now the best use for the power in falling water is the hydro-electric plant, but its first applications in manufacturing were in textile thread factories. American cotton goods were manufactured with power looms driven by water wheels at Waltham, Massachusetts in 1810. Such power sources were stationary rather than portable, and transmission of the energy over great distances from the source was not feasible. The utilization, however, promoted the breakthrough to higher levels of creativity and inventiveness.

Newcomen's atmospheric engine in 1705 which followed Papin's similar development in 1689 and the use of a gunpowder-powered engine in 1680 suggested possibilities for self-contained power plants of a heat-engine type. James Watts' perfection of an external combustion engine, a steam engine, in 1769 was the next step the role of technology played in releasing man from muscular labor. Refinements and adaptations to the steam engine made it a source of portable power propelling carriages, ships, trains, and tractors. When Nicholas Otto in Germany made the first successful internal combustion engine in 1864, he demonstrated the application of different scientific and technical principles than were employed in the steam engine a century earlier. But beyond this he opened the door to a more extensive use of power than he dreamed. In the century since the introduction of the Otto engine, based on what is now known as the Otto-cycle, the internal combustion engine powered by petroleum has spread to every continent, driving trucks, aircraft, boats, tractors, electric power plants, rice mills, and the like. Further than this, it has become so much an accepted source of power that we use it as a plaything in children's toys.

Electricity, generated by water power or steam, increased power

1607 First permanent colony in America, Jamestown, Va.
1608 First factory in America; glassplant, Jamestown, Va.

PERIOD	STAGE	POWER	MATERIAL	PROCESS	WORK
1608	Handcraft	Muscle: man, animal	Wood, iron, bronze, clay, glass	Hand, hand tool	The craftsman makes the complete product
1800	Machine	Wind, water, stationary external and internal combustion engines, stationary electric motor	Steel, alloys, aluminum	Machine tool	The craftsman specializes in jobs, operations; inventor
1900	Power	Portable internal combustion engine		Mechanization, mass production	The craftsman becomes a machine operator
1915	Production	Portable electric motor		Assembly line, automatic machines; electric, hydraulic, pneumatic controls	Assembly man, engineer
1940	Research		Synthetics, plastics, man-made elements		Scientist, researcher
1952	Automation	Miniaturization	High refractory metals, ceramics, plastics	Electronic controls	Human engineering, technician, servicing
1960	Nuclear-space	Atomic, solar	New materials	Automated factories	The technician and worker specialize

Fig. 2-1. Stages of American technology

consciousness especially when it was made available to whole cities. Water power was used to drive such a generator at Appleton, Wisconsin in 1882, and in the same year Thomas Edison put a central electric power station into operation in New York City. With George Westinghouse's contribution of alternating current, America entered an Electric Age. Today portable electric motors, demonstrating the concept of miniaturization, along with the internal combustion engine are found in practically every American product where the widest stretch of the imagination presumes an application. The ability of industry to make power machines so tiny as to fit in a wrist watch shows the heights of our power techniques. Energy from the sun and from the atom in the form of heat converted to electricity and that from atomic reaction is used to furnish super-heated steam to drive turbines.

In this power progress one finds an advancing science and technology. From an original dependence on human muscle to the direct utilization of forces in nature, to the release of energy in combustible natural materials, and then to the utilization of solar and atomic sources in three and one-half centuries is remarkable indeed. Of course, the beginning settlers in America came with concepts, techniques, processes, skills, and sometimes tools acquired in other countries, which gave us an early advantage. But even so, within the same period of time no other country has become completely power conscious. Even today's toys introduce our children to applications and concepts of power.

As this power progression demonstrates an increasing technological creativeness with each level of achievement, it suggests at the same time an increasing intellectual power of the human. Surely a greater intellect is required to conceive of means to exploit the atom than to bend one's back to lift a load. The ability to sense power in falling water and wind and the creative imagination to use it suggests an extending of intellectual horizons as man looked beyond his own muscles or those in his beast. At today's stage in power development we now attempt to see beyond present experimentation and wonder what the ultimate may be. Certainly we are closer now than we have been.

How a people conceive of power is a good index of their understanding of nature. It may likewise be a good index of their national intellectual development. As power frees man from drudgery, it energizes his imagination, elevating his goals and ambitions and changing his philosophy of living. An increase in knowledge has accompanied the expanded concepts and applications of power. Through trial-and-error experimentation wind machines became successful and demonstrated a certain level of mechanical comprehension. The water wheel itself probably required no greater ingenuity to perfect, but in both cases the utilization of the available power challenged the intellect. Problems, such as changing the direction of the power and converting it to reciprocating motion, must have taxed the resourcefulness of those early inventors, but the experiments added to an accumulating body of scientific and engineering knowledge. The internal combustion engine required special fuel, and improvements in the machine required improved fuels. Petroleum chemistry is now a body of knowledge. This engine when first installed in a box kite ushered in the science of aeronautics.

The discovery of electricity sparked a fuller development of technology than would have been possible with mechanical power and its accompanying level of intellect. J. F. Reintjes (3, p. 4) in speaking of the intellectual bases of automation points out that today's technology has a broader base than that of the eighteenth and nineteenth centuries. It now grows out of advancement and knowledge in such scientific fields as mathematics, physics, chemistry, and electronics. The earlier technology was geared largely to mechanical innovations. Experience with power forms beyond the muscular called on an intensive study of nature whether the power was derived from wind or from the atom. Understanding nature has led to an increase in its control by man. Man's progress in technical power dramatizes his release from the animal level, but more than that it demonstrates his greater power: intellectual and creative. Here then is the great change in the concept of power.

CHANGING CONCEPTS IN MATERIALS. Nature provided early man with readily available materials in usable form. A branch or root of a tree served as a weapon; a bone, shell, or rock, as a cutting tool. But before he could use the wood in a log, he had to devise more efficient tools. The dependence on finding natural materials suitable for use without processing was possible so long as his material needs were simple. The discovery of fire and its effects increased the usefulness of certain materials, clay for example. Its hardening by exposure to heat made it immeasurably more usable. The use of materials in their natural forms served technology rather adequately until the Machine Age, which demanded better materials than wood for the machines themselves. Glass, fired clays, cast iron, paper, ink, leather, and textiles were being used before the colonization of America. Some of these, glass for instance, may be considered more man-made than others. So long as the technology was at the crafts level, these materials, plus wood, which was most commonly used, served the purposes. But as new ideas for products, tools, and machines were discovered and new processes were developed, better materials were necessary. Steel made possible a level of technology not attainable with cast iron. Aluminum was found to be better than iron or steel in many applications.

The Industrial Revolution, which changed the means for controlling materials in production, would not have occurred except for an attitude of experiment, which provided a stimulus to find new truths. The concept of experiment as means to discovery of truth in nature found a widespread acceptance in the seventeenth century as the scientists of the day put to use the technological developments in existence: telescope, clock, watch, thermometer, microscope, magnetic compass, air pump, melting furnace, refined chemicals, and others. The experimental attitude and method were employed with increasing intensity as an advancing technology both demanded and facilitated it. At about the turn of the present century the professional chemist and the mechanical engineer came into their own in industry. Until their arrival the inventor was the source of innovation. Technical scientific research began to produce new materials. Metallic alloys, plastics, synthethics, manufactured materials, man-made elements, all are common in today's industrial materials. The concept of experiment has led to the development of the newest major industry: research and development, also called the industry of discovery.

CHANGING CONCEPTS OF PROCESS. The first use of the wheel is thought not to have been for transportation but as a revolving flat rock on which to fashion moist clay. This simple machine even though powered by hand enabled the potter to increase his production. When he discovered how to use a bisque mold, not only did he increase production, but he did it with a uniformity of product. When he discovered that firing his ware in a hole in the side of a bank produced a harder material and that it was more economical than firing in the open, he became rather fully engaged in an implementation of a machine concept.

Thousands of years, however, were required before the craftsman, the producer of consumer goods who often was his own toolmaker, accepted machine processes. During the nineteenth century as the Industrial Revolution gathered momentum and extended its influence throughout all of industry, acceptance of the machine and machine processes was by no means complete. Resistance by craftsmen who saw the mechanized process as competing with hand skills was to be expected. Even so, as products increased in complexity and variety, the craftsmen was hard put to "manu-factor" them. To train for the all-around versatility which had been the mark of the master craftsmen required more time than apprentices were willing to invest. To expect one man to have complete versatility was beyond reason. Specialization in hand processes was the only solution. The greater this specialization for the individual worker the more nearly machine-like he functioned, and as he increased his rate of production, the more his operations were simplified. At this point, the craftsmen themselves conceived of mechanisms capable of duplicating hand motions and processes. The transition from hand to machine processes occurring near the end of the 19th century is an interesting study. Today's antiques produced during that period show product design reflecting the craftsman's touch compromised by mechanized accommodation. The pride of the living room in that day was the hard coal heater, an intentionally ostentatious masterpiece of founding. It gave the molder his great opportunity to demonstrate control over iron. Here was a process, sand molding, with which the molder-craftsman could defy the machine, and he did it rather successfully for another half-century. The architecture of the period, often labeled Victorian because of its ornateness, was in reality a great final demonstration by the carpenter, turner, cabinetmaker, gilder, carver, and other masters of hand processes. Each was challenged to show his command of materials. When assembled the total effect was often one of excess, but at the same time the quality of the individual efforts may have been superb.

As machine processing was able to demonstrate that it could successfully duplicate hand processing, which was its early challenge in manufacturing, its next goal was to out-produce and underprice its competition. Today we know that mechanical processing is necessary to obtain quality and quantity at the lowest cost. Further, we know that only by automatic processing can we have certain types of products, such as gasoline, lubricants, and electricity. In the quantities and qualities required they are available only when produced through automation.

The economics of the times make increasing automation necessary. It is justified as the only means by which the masses of Americans can enjoy the products of industry. But the changing concepts of processes with which we are concerned do not necessarily originate in laws and principles of economics. Hand processing in its pure form required muscle power, for example, the village blacksmith. Hand-tool processes, too, were powered by muscle but required an additional mastery, that of the tool. When tools were combined with mechanical power, the craftsman could perform the same operations much faster, and often with greater accuracy, as in the drilling of holes. This not only saved time but permitted him to master new processes and materials and to produce new products. He was freed to think and work on a higher level, to gain an even greater mastery.

When his higher thinking had developed a machine that could convert a material into a part, he had in a sense de-skilled the process. The operator was only required to feed the machine. High skill level was involved in the design, development, manufacture, and servicing of the machine, rather than in its utilization. Mechanization of process required mass production of machine parts. In these quantities the problem of assembly was solved by the so-called assembly line, which Henry Ford first demonstrated in building automobiles from piles of parts.

Materials processing by automatic machines was a first step to the automatic factory and automation. This suggests the idea of levels of automaticity. The lower levels required an operator to manipulate controls, push buttons, insert material, remove parts. With development the operation was de-skilled to the point of merely pushing buttons, waiting for the completion of the cycle, and then pushing buttons again. The more the work was de-skilled, the easier it became to displace the operator until in automation the concept of a machine activating and regulating itself as well as evaluating its work and correcting its processing, all as it produces parts or even assemblies of parts, became an actuality. Automatic processing developed from manual controls to those mechanical, hydraulic, electric, pneumatic, and finally electronic. At present the latter appears to be the ultimate as the master control; in operation it involves the others. The issue at the heart of changing concepts of processes remains as the hand versus the machine. In out-and-out competition machine processing has won. It now seeks to produce products bearing the nature and feeling of hand crafting. This implies the weakness of the machine: it cannot create. If hand processing is to retain its identity, it must remain pure. This will require that the craftsman express his ideas without the assistance of machines. The temptation to do it easier or faster by machine is difficult to resist, but if hand crafting is to continue to exist and flourish, it must produce that which the machine cannot. This requires a unique kind of intellectual effort which can think in terms of hands and hand tools.

THE CHANGING CONCEPT OF WORK. Consumer goods in the early American colonies were produced by craftsmen who emigrated from Europe with their skills, knowledge, and sometimes with the aid of a bit of craftiness, their tools. The cabinetmakers, carpenters, potters, cobblers, glassworkers, and others plied their trades and took in apprentices as a means to increase production. The master craftsman was able to devise and construct the entire product, which often meant that he also manufactured the necessary materials used. With such versatility required of the craftsman, the supply of qualified apprentices was limited and the training period lengthy. The rapidly increasing population with its growing demand for products and the restrictions on the emigration of skilled workers from England added up to a breakdown in the craftsman manufacturing system. An apprentice could be trained in a relatively short time to become expert in one or two processes. The master then could organize his production so that his men specialized in particular processes or jobs, and thereby he increased his production. It was but a short step to the invention or adoption of machine-tools to facilitate the processing. The more the worker utilized such devices, the more he became a machine operator, a job classification in today's industry. While machines and their operators could produce parts, assembly was essentially a hand operation. Well into the twentieth century the assembly man in a factory assembly line commonly spent his work day installing bolts and nuts, or screws to hold parts together.

The mechanical engineer with his knowledge of materials and, mechanisms began to simplify production work during the forepart of the present century. Other engineers: industrial, electrical, structural, plant, and such soon appeared. All were concerned with increasing efficiency and cutting costs. The concept of work simplification came into clear focus as these experts continued to study the technical problems. Scientists and professional researchers joined the industrial organization in the interim between the two World Wars. Since then, annual expenditures for industrial research have grown to approximately fifteen billion dollars with most of the searching thus far concentrated on the technical. When machines were perfected that were capable of greater production than the operator could manage, when the operator could no longer keep up, machines were designed to operate machines.

Much study and experiment was involved in what was originally called time and motion study in the effort to reduce human inefficiency in the operation of machines. But it was eventually found that the human does not readily become machine-like in his work. Outside factors influence his performance, such as noise, poor lighting, personal problems, health, and conflicts with supervision. A new science appeared during World War II called industrial psychology, and sometimes termed human engineering. This was evidence of a growing awareness of the need to study the human as well as the machine. One problem inherent in the emphasis on mechanization and automatization has proved especially vexing: worker boredom. His job had been so simplified and so de-skilled that it became difficult for him to remain alert. Absenteeism, accidents, and labor problems increased. Several approaches to solutions have been tried. Job enlargement, a concept based on increasing worker competence and responsibility in his job, has been found successful. Devising machines to take over hazardous operations is common practice. Background music, rest periods, recreation programs, and the like are also employed.

As industry becomes automated, in the sense of continuous automatic production, the machine operator is no longer needed. In his place is a highly skilled, intelligent technician whose job it is to operate the system and to keep it in operation with proper servicing.

The job responsibility has increased, as have the qualifications for it. But the goal of work simplification, set by the early craftsman who divided the work skills among his men, still remains in industry. The recent attention to creativity in industry with brainstorming and suggestion rewards suggests a new approach to simplification of work: drawing ideas from the workers themselves rather than relying on efficiency engineers. Work simplification eventually leads to work elimination because the process of simplification depends on eliminating.

In our day we can see rather clearly the realization of the original goal of technology: the freeing of man from drudgery. Man has devised machines which do this effectively. But the concept of drudgery has changed too. Once it was backbreaking, animal-level labor; now it is monotony, hazard, menial activity. Even the service occupations, the fastest growing job classification today, are being given the simplification treatment. Faulty parts are identified by electronic equipment; replacement procedures are standardized. We have now reached a point in technological development where the very purpose of work is being questioned. Once it was necessary to existence; once it was considered moral and spiritual. Now it seems to presume a different end: leisure. To one who has lived for the past half-century it must seem farcical to say that the purpose of work is leisure. But the gradual decrease in the workweek since 1900 with no leveling off in sight has brought more leisure than we have known and than we know what to do with. Work may still be good for the soul, but we may increasingly have to find this catharsis in leisure. Technology has freed man from drudgery, but what has it freed him for? This he must answer.

Technology and Industry

The relationship of technology and industry may at times seem so close that they appear to be one and the same. The philosophical interpretation of technology already developed may suggest the relationship of means and end. Industry can be thought of as the means to today's technology, as the producer, the creator of the technology. In our search for meaning, we suggested that technology be considered as the control which man has developed over his material, physical environment. At this point we should examine the relationship between technology and industry with the above concept as our basic tenet. We can assume that technology is man's systematized control over his physical, material environment. The extreme breadth and generalness involved in this tenet, however, require further examination before the concept of technology is focused with sufficient clarity to isolate its elements for study, as is necessary in the search for industrial arts subject matter which follows later. Earlier in this chapter, technology was defined as the study or science of the industrial arts. Now study is defined as careful examination, investigation, inquiry, research in order to determine the facts. And a science is defined as systematized knowledge derived from study, observation, experiment, and test. A broad interpretation of industry considers it as the system of enterprises for the development, production, and utilization of material goods and services by which a people gain control over their physical environment. Through rather logical deduction, then, technology becomes the science of industry. As such it becomes the systematized knowledge derived from study, experiment, research, development, design, invention, and construction with materials, processes, products, and energies. Put another way, technology can be considered as the field of systematized knowledge derived from the study of the nature, the principles and practices, the products, the services, and the energies provided and employed by industry. Consequently, we study industry to learn about technology, its techniques, skills, processes, products, services, and occupations. We find meaning and significance in technology as we study the contributions of industry to man's control over his physical environment and to the ends to which he uses this control.

TECHNOLOGY AND SCIENCE. Technology began when man learned to walk erect and he could put his hands to new use. He found an added power through his facility for manipulating materials, and with his hands he freed himself from the level of an animal existence. He discovered how to use grasses and reeds to make containers and how to waterproof them with moist clay, and how to make protective clothing. With his hand-fashioned weapons he could survive greater dangers. Technology and hands started the civilizing process. With the use of hands came a humanizing of the human. Science as an institution came along thousands of years after the beginning of technology; its appearance is placed in the sixteenth century. (See chart Evolution of American industry, Fig. 3-1, pp. 64-65). By that time technology was on its way. Printing had been mechanized; water and wind had been harnessed for power; and ships and compasses were taking men around the world and home again. Porcelains and glass had been perfected and the spinning wheel was making thread from cotton, wool, and silk fibers. The craft guilds were supplying consumer goods while artisans and craftsmen were building palaces, cathedrals, and canals. With the materials, tools, and technics of technology man now had the means to experiment and to test. He had the motivation to search and to invent. Technology gave inquiring minds something to wonder about and to wonder with. By the sixteenth century philosophers had already had centuries in which to disclose the meaning and purpose of man's material achievements. Jesus Christ had introduced a new religious concept, and the Christian church had had fifteen centuries of history. All of this was a good base on which to build a science and an attitude of science.

In the United States the rise of engineering is placed at the close of the last century and the beginning of the present. The industrial revolution was well under way when the professional engineer replaced the inventor. World War I brought out the chemical engineer and the chemist. Since then engineering has become an integral part of industry, integrating science and technology. By mid-twentieth century the rise of industrial research was well under way. Today industrial dependence on research is rapidly becoming complete, not only for the discovery and development of knowledge. The latter is known as pure or basic research. Today science is teamed with technology in an effort to gain an increased control of man's environment and to extend the range of his environment. Technology furnishes science with tools, materials, and machines with which to do its exploring. Science uses existing technology as a stepping stone to a higher development. The science of today becomes the technology of tomorrow.

TECHNOLOGY: MEANS OR END? To this point our analysis of technology reveals its rather extended virtuosity. But just as the hammer is used to build a cathedral so it can be used to destroy it. Implements of construction can serve equally well as tools of destruction. Fire melts, cures, welds, sterilizes, creates, and it also consumes. Atomic energy can demolish whole cities at the same time that it has the capacity to drive power plants furnishing electricity to hospitals ministering to the victims. Technology is capable of good and of evil; in itself it is neither. Created by man, technology is used by man as he directs. Whether it is used wisely or stupidly, that is his decision. At this moment in history statesmen, sociologists, economists, scientists, industrialists, educators, clergy, and the layman himself are all faced with this decision. Materialism is considered by some as synonomous with communism and as such becomes sinister and wicked. The purpose of this study is not to advance materialism or even to discuss it. It is rather to appeal for an intensive study of the material culture and the technology, and of the role of the individual in it. Such a study should enable us to use the technology rather than to abuse it. The primary role of the technology is seen as man's means to liberating his fellow man from the shackles of poverty, ignorance, drudgery, sickness, superstition, danger, fear, and in so doing freeing him for living on a higher plane. Let us consider technology as this great means devised by man; it is his great tool. If it becomes the great end, it may result in just that.

TECHNOLOGY: A SUMMARY INTERPRETATION

Technology, functioning in its many roles of provider, civilizer, emancipator, integrator, leveler, pacifier, and energizer, becomes at once the great benefactor. Conceived in man's creative imagination, the highest level of his intellect, and carried out with his native tool-using aptitudes and an abundance of materials and energies, technology seems to follow the plan of a great Creator. His purpose for this human involvement must have been to demonstrate to man himself his own natural potential as a creator since He made man in His own image. He must also have seen this technology as a human expression of concern for man's neighbors because of its potential for elevating, dignifying, and ennobling human life. Technology moves toward the complete elimination of all the physical enslavement of man in order to free him for a higher living and to permit him to develop and to use his still unknown, unused talents. So long as man must slave away his life to maintain a subsistence, his full potential must go unused—a waste of precious talent. Technology, as it is taken into all the world, humanizes man, both giver and receiver. It is the great civilizer, for it brings man out of the savage state and elevates him to heights of human excellence and achievement. Here in our country technology has become our way of life. We depend on it for products and services, for income and wealth. We stand on it to reach higher and to see farther. Technology shapes our culture. It is our control over our physical environment without which cultures and civilizations die.

When we are able to understand the full meaning of technology, we will likely see it as the great benefactor. Until that time, we may look upon it with suspicion and distrust. The conflicts between labor and management, dramatized by strikes, commonly result in claims of victory. These suggest to all the world that management is imperialistic and that organized labor is humanitarian. The worker caught in this conflict may see his job only as a means to his own income, and the more income the better. He may see his employer as an opponent. If he felt that he were part of a master plan directed to the elevation of all men through technological development and in the process was being elevated himself, he would likely see his employer as a partner.

There are those who look down on work with hands, tools, machines, and materials as beneath the dignity of the truly educated, cultured, and liberated. Perhaps they are trying to maintain an intellectual aristocracy in the pattern of ancient Greece. When they gain a full understanding of the American culture, as they may now assume to understand the early Greek, they will likely see technology as conceived in and as fully dependent on the highest order of the human intellect. So long as they hold technology and industry as evil monsters that, while they provide the necessities of living, consume the spiritual and intellectual potential of man, they see only his remains, a living automaton dwelling on materialism. Technology can be more than material; it can be man seeking to achieve the highest level of human excellence. It can be man reaching for the summit in human ennoblement, and in his very efforts utilizing his native resources and finding his liberation as he is able to see meaning and purpose in living.

The full power and potential of technology will only be known when it is used for the elevation of man. The full power of American technology may never be known unless it is allowed to serve all of the world. When this is permitted, the full meaning of technology will likely become apparent; and it will indeed have become America's primary resource that calls for the full utilization of man's primary aptitudes: his creative imagination, his reason, his problem-solving facility, his tool-using talents, and his capacity for concern about his neighbor. In summary, technology may be identified by the following:

1. As the result of the interaction of man, mind, materials, and energies.
2. As man creating his own environment, from subsistence to elevation.
3. As man controlling nature: security through control of natural forces.
4. As man expressing supreme purpose: man with gifts for ideation, reason, problem-solving, creating, and construction within an environment of materials and energies for a freeing of all man from enslavement.
5. As man's control over his destiny on earth and in space.

Finally, when one needs a concise term to use as a synonym, technology can be defined as the material culture.

TO DISCUSS, TO DEBATE, TO DECIDE

1. What does the statement "Technology is America's primary resource" mean?
2. Why should an American be expected to understand the technology?
3. Why has technology in the United States reached higher levels of development than in other countries?
4. What relationships exist between technological development and standard of living in a country?
5. Can industrial arts make any significant contribution to strengthening our country in the technological duel with Russia?
6. Explain the philosophy of materialism. In which country, the United States or Russia, is it presently finding the greater expression and receiving the more emphasis? Is there anything good to be found in materialism?
7. What elements of our own technology would be most immediately adaptable and useful in a primitive society?
8. Discuss the spirit of technology. What does it mean for a teacher carrying on a traditional, conservative program?
9. What relationships exist between science, industry, and technology?
10. What other "great civilizers" are at work today besides technology?

(Above) A home "manu-factory." The colonial home was the producing center for many materials and consumer goods. Here the women are shown combing, spinning, weaving, and sewing. While home industries are no longer common in the United States, they are essential to industrialization in countries such as Japan, the Philippines, Thailand, and others. (Courtesy: The DaAll Company.)

(Right) Automobile body stampings are produced from coils of steel sheet fed into batteries of presses. Today's metal forming practices are so different from those of the early blacksmith that the latter doubtfully could ever dream of their possibility. Today's factory is likewise different from the home factory of colonial America. (Courtesy: Ford Motor Company.)

III

American Industry:
A Perspective

When, in 1620, the Pilgrim Fathers stepped from the "May-flower" onto Plymouth Rock, the most precious physical possession they unloaded was the collection of one hundred and two tools, implements, and utensils with which they were to start life anew in the New World.

—John W. Oliver, *History of American Technology.*
(Copyright 1956. The Ronald Press Company.)

In a search of the technology for industrial arts subject matter the first step is to look at industry itself. The perspective to follow attempts to do that. It lays a background in the early development of industry. Then it adds details which bring the development up to the present with attention to automatic production and automation. The picture is completed with a set of implications for industrial arts drawn from the study of industry.

AMERICAN INDUSTRY:
HISTORY AND DEVELOPMENT

The full story of American industry begins with man, not with the nation. Before Columbus' discovery of America the wheel, watch, clock, paper, printing, needle compass, sailing ship, spinning wheel, water wheel, windmill, potter's wheel, air pump, gun powder, and copper, bronze, and iron smelting had been invented or discovered and reasonably well perfected. When primitive man first used a stick or a rock to assist him in making a kill or in preparing his food, he multiplied his strength, improved his accuracy, and increased his production. As *Civilization Through Tools* (95, p. 5) points out: "Man's history began with a change in the pelvic bones permitting standing and walking erect, thus freeing the hands to use as a tool." The study points out further that human hands are:

> . . . amazingly adaptable and variable tools. Grasping instruments that can seize, hold, press or pull with muscles supplying the energy. It was tools, held in the hands, for pounding, throwing, scraping, drilling, and cutting that gave humans their superiority and began to multiply their strength (95, p. 5).

Through thousands of years man has gradually acquired a facility with hand tools, then with machine tools, and then with machines, each of which has released him from a lower level of enslavement until today through the phenomenon of automation, it appears that he shall be finally freed from a drudgery which has shackled him since he first discovered that to eat he must work.

The chart (Fig. 3-1) Evolution of American industry, chronicles significant events and developments from the beginning of American industry. This chart in a sense shows stages of technological development as does the chart in Fig. 2-1, Stages of American technology. However, the intent here is to show a progression in the evolution of industry. As shown in Fig. 2-1, the seven stages of technology are based on key technological developments which touched off waves of progress and concomitant changing concepts of power, materials, processes, and work.

THE PERIOD OF COLONIZATION. Industry in Colonial America depended on materials, tools, and know-how acquired and developed in Europe, particularly England. It had its beginning in a transplanting of culture. All of the power developments, machines, manufactured materials, and the rest in the first level of the chart, Fig. 3-1, were in use in Europe by the time that American colonization began. This meant that seeds of the machine concept were included in the transplant even though few if any machines were actually brought to America.

DOMESTIC PRODUCTION. Industry had its origin in the home. In primitive agrarian cultures the home was the center of production for food, clothing, housing, tools, and weapons. Through the centuries tools, techniques, and skills improved until more of some products were produced than were consumed in the home, and some were left over for barter or sale. Customers spurred productiveness and inventiveness. Eventually some homes became factories that employed members of the family. Home industry was common in early European industrial history and was necessary in Colonial America to provide the material needs of the new country. Home "manufactories," the next level of industrialization, took over the manufacture of products or parts of products, especially in textiles and clothing. The industrialist contracted with the family for the production in the home. Processing was largely by hand.

FACTORY MANUFACTURE. Craftsmen's guilds, as a part of the industrialization movement, flourished in Europe long before the discovery of America. Early development of the new country was dependent on the skills and tools of emigrating craftsmen. The rapidly increasing demand for products with the arrival of increasing numbers of settlers and the strong desire to become materially self-sufficient in order to hasten the break in dependence on the mother country required greater production than was possible with handcraft processes. As early as 1608 young America had a factory, a glass plant at Jamestown, Virginia.

The system of home manufactories was common in New England and served until steam-powered manufacturing plants took over. The home factories were then no longer sufficiently profitable or productive. What had been largely woman's work was taken over by factory machines, the operation of which was so simple that children were employed for the purpose. The fly shuttle was used here as early as 1788, but not until after about 1810 did weaving become a factory process when the first cotton goods were made at Waltham, Massachusetts. The increase in the use of industrial factories for all types of production brought about a decline in the guild system.

FROM FACTORY MANUFACTURE TO MECHANIZATION AND ELECTRIFICATION

Steam power adapted to the manufacturing industries in the early nineteenth century is considered to have set in motion the movement

DATES	PERIOD	POWER DEVELOPMENTS	MACHINES	MANUFACTURED MATERIALS	PROCESSES	CONSUMERS PRODUCTS
To 1700	Colonization (industrial development at this stage largely European)	Muscle, windmill, water wheel, treadmill, belt drive, gear drive	Potters wheel, spinning wheel, water wheel, watch, clock, printing press, mortar and pestle, loom, windmill, wood lathe	Cotton, silk and wool thread, cloth, glass, glazes, bronze, cast iron, paper, ink, lumber, leather	Spinning, weaving, dying, glass blowing, casting, forging, enameling, printing, clay firing, paper making, glazing, leather tanning, wood turning	Peasant type, with emphasis on the utilitarian; royal type, with emphasis on the aesthetic
1700 to 1750	Domestic production	Line shaft transmission	Spinning jenny, power spinning wheel, metal lathe, metal planer	Malleable iron, plaster of Paris, charcoal	Iron pudding, slip casting	Unit production, enter: retailing
1750 to 1800	Factory	Steam engine, compressed air	Power harness loom, leather splitter, Fourdrinier, grain reapers	Coke, natural cement, machine-made paper, machine-made cloth	Metals machining, power weaving, Fourdrinier paper making, interchangeability	The craftsman an entrepreneur
1800 to 1850	Industrial manufacture	Water turbine, paddle wheel	Bessemer converter, hydraulic presses, machine forge, A.C. generator, jigs, fixtures	Steel, house paint, celluloid, chemicals	Bessemer steel, open-hearth steel, mechanical refrigeration, chrome tanning, Leather splitting, hydraulic pressing, jig forming	American production sufficient to supply American needs
1850 to 1900	Mechanical power	Internal combustion engine, steam turbine, Diesel engine, screw prop., portable power with manual controls	Spinerette, veneer lathe, conveyors	Rayon, safety glass, synthetic lacquer, glass fiber, nylon, plastics, plywood, hardboard, aluminum	Glass sheet drawing, electric refrigeration, synthetization, assembly line, continuous production	Quantity production, Chain stores, mail order retail, ready-made clothing
1900 to 1950	Mechanization and electrification	Small electric motor, farm tractors, hydraulic power, jet power, electronic controls	Automatic machines, automatic systems, automatic sections, automatic factories	Age of synthetic materials; natural materials as sources of chemicals	New processes originate with organized research; adaptation of basic processes to synthetics	Models, trade-ins, standard parts, guarantees, quality standards, synthetics, appliances
1950	Automation	Chemical-physical, solar, cybernetics	"Recreation machines"	New material—as combinations of natural and/or synthetic, additional chemical elements	New processes for new materials; simplification of common processes	Synthetics replace natural materials, refinement, redesign for automatic production

DATES	PERIOD	OCCUPATIONAL ASPECTS	MANUFACTURING INDUSTRIES	TRANSPORTATION	COMMUNICATIONS
To 1700	Colonization (industrial development at this stage largely European)	The family system with each member contributing; royal craftsmen as designers and builders	Paper mill, lumber mill, glass plant, meat packing plant, shoe making, ship building	Oxcart, wagon, leather shoes, commercial sailing ships	Movable type, book publishing, postal system
1700 to 1750	Domestic production	Household crafts, home "manufactories"	Sugar refining, coal mining	Stage coach, schooner	
1750 to 1800	Factory	Craftsman as designer and builder; apprenticeship as preparation	Cotton, silk, wool, thread factories	Conestoga wagon, balloon flight, macadam roads	First magazine
1800 to 1850	Industrial manufacture	Division of labor, craftsmen narrowing fields	Textile mills, rubber goods, farm machinery, clothing, tools, machines, leather goods, nails	Cumberland Turnpike, Erie Canal, railroad, steam ships, horse-drawn streetcar, water mains, Welland Canal, natural gas lines	Modern postal system
1850 to 1900	Mechanical power	Labor specialization, child labor laws, A.F. of L., U.S. Dept. of Labor, enter: tradesman, enter: engineer	Automobile, copper, zinc, oil refining, powerplants, food processing, paints, chemicals, skyscraper building	Pullman cars, oil pipeline, Suez Canal, transcontinental railroad, electric streetcar, pneumatic tire, world flight, auto	Rural free delivery, typewriter, telephone, cable, switchboard, recorded sound, linotype, movie
1900 to 1950	Mechanization and electrification	De-skilled labor, worker becomes machine operator	Rolling mill, toys, recreation, research, rayon, nylon, plastics	Airplane, airship, C.A.A., Panama Canal, rockets, paving, conveyors	Radio, television, parcel post, air mail, movie theaters, sound movies
1950	Automation	Job enlargement, enter: the technician, "Man masters machine," scientists become philosophers	Industries automated and decentralized, "Second Industrial Revolution"	Space travel, automatic controls	Direct dial telephone, simultaneous world television

Fig. 3-1. Evolution of American industry.

65

toward industrial mechanization, known historically as the Industrial Revolution. With mechanical power, production was increased and labor costs lessened because unskilled labor could man the machines. Throughout the nineteenth century the struggle between the craftsman and the machine was fought, sometimes with fury. The craftsman struggled for survival in the battle of production only to be overwhelmed by the same kind of inventive power which had originally made him a craftsman. The climax in the struggle, which saw mechanization displace hand methods in industrial production, can be considered to have occurred with the appearance of the small, portable electric motor shortly before the end of the century. This power unit was as influential in the complete mechanization of production as was the invention of barbed wire in the settlement of the West. With it machine controls became more precise, complex line shafting became unnecessary, plant layout became more flexible, and machines could be set up as individual production units.

Continuing improvement in mechanization brought an increasing production and a substantial change in the nature of worker skill. Further refinement in production processes and product design enabled machines to do even more work, until the worker, now a machine operator, had only to manipulate a lever, or push a button as he inserted and removed parts. For a period during the first half of the present century, further increase in production through further simplification of mechanization seemed relatively impossible. The only other possibility was the operator himself. Consequently, the efficiency expert with his time and motion studies looked for ways of eliminating, simplifying, and speeding up the worker's movements in operating the machine. Soon he had the worker at the peak of his speed, and yet the machine was not producing as rapidly as it could. In some industries the emphasis was placed on keeping worker morale high to assure peak performance; in others, production was increased by adding machines and operators as production units. But if human limits were production limits, only one solution to the problem of increasing production remained: the development of machines to pull the levers and press the buttons in place of the operator. Thus the era of automation. Wassily Leontief, writing for the September, 1952 issue of *Scientific American* which was later included in the Scientific American book *Automatic Control*, describes the impact of automatic control as follows:

Looking back, one can see that 1910 marked the real turning point in this country's economic and social development. That was the year when the last wave of immigration reached its crest;. the year, also, when our rural population began to decline in absolute terms. Between 1890 and 1910 our national input of human labor had shot up from 28.3 million standard man-years to 42.5 million. Then in 1909 the model-T Ford began to roll off the first continuous production line. This great shift to mass production by machine was immediately reflected in shorter hours. In the next decade our manpower input increased by only one million man-years, and after 1920 it leveled off and remained almost constant until the early 1940s. Even at the peak of the recent war effort our total labor input, with an enormously larger population, was only 10 per cent greater than in 1910. Automatization will accelerate the operation of forces which have already shaped the development of this country for nearly half a century (70, pp. 78-79).

The year 1910 is not located in the chart, Fig. 3-1, but the nature of the industrial picture in the block 1900-1950 shows that industrial activity was growing in intensity. Many of the key technological discoveries and inventions appeared in the early part of the century; for example, the airplane, automobile, vacuum tube, farm tractor, and continuous production. Of interest also is that the concept of industrial arts appeared at about this time.

Automation

Throughout the industrial history of America a basic drive has persisted: to produce more, to make it better, to make it cheaper. When the early craftsman began to produce more than his own family consumed, he had some to sell. His productiveness as well as his inventiveness was spurred, and he soon had customers. The pressure of increased demand found him unable to keep up, so he hired other craftsmen and secured apprentices. In this progression the product became increasingly complex. New ideas called for new processes and better materials with the result that the craft itself became increasingly complicated. Soon the same craftsman could no longer produce the entire article. Dividing the production between two or more craftsmen temporarily solved the problem. The greater the complexity of and the demand for the product, the greater became the division of labor and the less the all-round skill of the craftsman.

Accompanying this increase in specialization of work came a continuing refinement of essential tools and invention of new tools to suit new processes and materials. But hand tools were too slow. Ingenuity combined mechanisms with tools to make machine tools, which lessened work and speeded production. The awl was coupled to a rack and pinion and driven by a crank, making work more convenient. Within this evolution of tools and machines and the attendant search for sources of power to replace muscle, automation was conceived. For immediate purposes at this point, automation is considered to be completely automatic production. To understand the concept better, one should study the nature and purpose of the tool and the machine in the evolution of civilization. One should recall early attempts at finding sources of mechanical power to replace muscles, which set in motion the first Industrial Revolution. One should visit American industries, large and small, to see ingenious devices which today produce for man the things he uses in living. In all of this, one will sense the drive to automation in the pressure for greater, more economical production.

Lewis Mumford constructs a background for automation in his *Technics and Civilization:*

> Machines have developed out of a complex of non-organic agents for converting energy, for performing work, for enlarging the mechanical or sensory capacities of the human body, or for reducing to a mensurable order and regularity the processes of life. The automaton is the last step in the process that began with the use of one part or another of the human body as a tool. . . .

He adds:

> The essential distinction between a machine and a tool lies in the degree of independence in the operation from the skill and motive power of the operator: the tool lends itself to manipulation, the machine to automatic action. . . . The difference between tools and machines lies primarily in the degree of automatism they have reached. . . .

Completing the background, Mumford states:

> Moreover, between the tool and the machine there stands another class of objects, the machine tool; here, in the lathe or the drill, one has the accuracy of the finest machine coupled with the skilled attendance of the workman. When one adds to this mechanical complex an external source of power, the line of division becomes even more difficult to establish. . . . (56, pp. 9-10).

Mumford places the automaton as the final stage in a process of the evolution of the tool. One imagines a huge building devoid of humans but full of automatons in robot-like fashion, pressing buttons, pulling levers, and transferring parts as the ultimate in production mechanization. Other early writers on the subject, too, seemed to envision essentially the same, since the logical successor to the human workman was the mechanical man. In the decades since, interpretations of automatic production have changed and are continuing to change as earlier solutions to problems are found wanting, and as new inventions and discoveries make possible new applications of mechanical and electronic principles and systems.

AUTOMATION DEFINED. Current definitions and descriptions of automation have apparent unanimity and rarely involve the automaton and the robot; but enough diversity exists to make these definitions difficult for the layman to comprehend. There seem to be "brands" of automation, for example, the Ford plan, involving the automatic transfer of parts from one processing station to the next. This has become known as the Detroit plan. There is the mechanical approach to automaticity, and there is the electronic, as championed by Norbert Wiener in his *The Human Use of Human Beings* (93).

Peter F. Drucker in his *America's Next Twenty Years* describes the three basic principles of automation as follows:

> There are three basic principles which make up the logic of Automation. Wherever the three are actually used there is genuine Automation even if there are no automatic machines, no electronic controls or computers, no "mechanical brains." Unless they are understood and consciously applied, Automation will not work.
> The first of these is the principle of *economic activity as a process*. In early industry, as typified by the job shop, the integrating principle of work was skill. In Henry Ford's concept of mass production the organizing principle was the product. In Automation, however, the entire activity of the business is a whole entity which must be harmoniously integrated to perform at all.
> A process knows neither beginning nor end. It may have stages but it does not divide into parts as such. From the ultimate consumer back to the first supplier of raw materials it has to be seamless, so-to-speak, yet at the same time conform to the second principle: that of *pattern, order, or form* behind the seemingly random and unpredictable flux of economic phenomena. . . . (*41*, p. 9).

According to Drucker this structure of forms includes patterns for events of all kinds. For example, automation requires a patterned rate and distribution of orders; styling and fashion changes must be capable of analysis for purposes of prediction. He continues:

> Finally Automation has a principle of *self-regulating control* which derives from its nature as process. As every true process must, it contains the means of its own regulation and correction. It must be able to maintain the equilibrium between ends and means, output and effort. And it must be able ahead of time to set standards of acceptable performance, which it then can use as pretests and as governors. . . .
>
> In these basic principles, Automation is little more than a projection into the economic sphere of philosophical beliefs that have become dominant in the past fifty years. . . .
>
> It is of course not necessary for a business manager to know anything about the philosophical foundations of Automation, let alone to be a scientist or philosopher himself. It is not even necessary for the experts in Automation within a business to know these things. But it is absolutely necessary for both the business man and his Automation specialists to understand clearly that Automation is not a box of tricks or a bagful of gadgets. Automation is a methodology, with all the strengths and limitations that the term implies (41, pp. 9-10).

OBJECTIVES OF AUTOMATION. In laymen's words, the objective of automation is to make machines run machines. This objective, simply put, involves several goals: (1) to reduce the manual effort required in production; (2) to free man's efforts for a higher level of work which the machine cannot do, or which invention is not able to make it do; (3) to meet the increasing demand for products which mechanized production alone cannot meet; and (4) to lower the costs of products so that, with consequent increase in purchasing power, more people can buy them. Examination of these objectives shows a striking similarity to those of American industry in any period of its development.

STEPS TO AUTOMATION. Industrial management seemingly does not consider automation a revolutionary process; it is rather, evolutionary. But over a period of time its effects will likely have proved revolutionary. It can be considered to have begun when primitive man first used a rock as a hammer, and it will culminate with the automatic factory. Walter Polakov (63, pp. 36-37) in discussing the Age of Power tells of an early attempt in a German textile plant to increase the production of thread. One spinner was given two spinning wheels to operate using both hands and both feet. He reports that the pressure placed on the worker made it impossible for the worker to divide his attention between the machines and still coordinate his movements.

When Richard Arkwright adapted a power drive to James Hargreave's spinning jenny, some of the pressure on the worker described by Polakov was relieved. For the first time, then, whole factories were set up around a single manufacturing process, the spinning of thread by water power. Such factories still required many workers but the production per worker was multiplied by the use of mechanical power.

The first creditable example of automation in America was in 1784 near Philadelphia. There a miller named Oliver Evans built and operated an automatic factory. It was a water-powered mill in which, in a continuous process, grain was ground into flour and sacked by machine. Such incidents are not uncommon in the early history of industry; they are industry in development.

The evolutionary development of automation accompanies the evolution of the technology, the development of industry, and the perfection of tools and machines. Specifically it follows these steps: the hand, the hand tool, the machine tool, the production machine, the semi-automatic machine, the automatic machine, the fully automatic production unit, the fully automatic system, the fully automatic section, and finally, the automatic factory. Today American industry's development as a whole is probably at the stage of the semi-automatic machine; it is moving rapidly up the scale toward automatic production. How rapidly it progresses depends on many factors: economic, social, and political. In the process as many writers put it, the United States appears to be in its second Industrial Revolution.

The first stage in the development of automation as a new process was the automatic handling of materials, possible on a conveyor line. Some writers include the "disassembly" of hogs on overhead trolley-type conveyors in the meat-packing industry in the early part of the century as the first example of this level of automation (42).

The second stage was the processing of materials by automatic handling. This processing was first an assembly-type as when in 1914 Henry Ford had workers pull Model-T chasses along the floor be tween other workers and piles of parts.

In the third stage both automatic processing of materials, as in parts manufacture, and sub-assembly accompany the automatic handling on conveyor lines. When this is combined with automatic controls systems, which begin with specifications furnished by tape, card, or film, and activate, regulate, correct, inspect, discriminate, and in a sense, supervise the entire production, the highest level of today's automation is reached.

AUTOMATION AND ELECTRONICS. In the days of a mechanized industry control of quality and production was largely in the hands of the machine operator. In automation, control is centered in the machine itself. Early attempts at the integration of process and controls were mechanical in nature, and because of limited speeds of response through mechanisms and hydraulics, production was little greater than when the machines were man-operated. The development of the vacuum tube and the realization of its potential applications introduced the possibilities of electrical and electronic controls that are responsive at the speed of light. Today automation and electronics are inseparable.

The more human-like automatic controls become, the more electronic they are. In fact, the more that is discovered about the workings of the human brain and nervous system, the greater becomes the potential in electronic controls. W. Grey Walter, Director of the Burden Neurological Institute in London, writing for *Scientific American* on "An Imitation of Life" (70, p. 124) states: ". . . it was not until the electronic age that serious efforts were made to imitate and even to surpass the complex performance of the nervous system."

Cybernetics

The transmission of communications within an automatic machine, and to and from this machine, is the key to automatic production. Such communications activate immediate controls of processes and direct the operation of the machine. To this complexity of communications and controls Norbert Wiener has given the name *cybernetics* (92, p. 15). He derived it from the Greek word *kubertetes* or steersman. A goal in the design of an automatic machine is the perfection of controls so that the machine is self-controlling, self-correcting and even capable of discrimination. These are qualities characteristically human.

The imaginative mind which first visualized the completely automatic machine may have gotten its idea from a study of a man at work. It could have pictured two men, one calling out the directions and the other making the respective responses. With the aid of the senses of sight, hearing, smell, touch, and possibly taste, in addition to the purely manipulative skill of the respondent, the team could function precisely, productively, and methodically.

Electronics in automation supplies the human attributes and facilities which the machine does not possess. It calls out the instructions in the required order, activates the required processes in proper sequences, analyzes its product in terms of the pre-established specifications, makes the immediate necessary corrections, makes the required discriminations, and delivers the product exactly as prescribed in the quantities called for at the designated time.

The Computer

The device which does the "thinking" in automatic production is the computer. Sometimes called the electronic brain, the *digital* computer is used for accounting. It remembers, calculates, discriminates, tabulates, and furnishes solutions at fantastic speeds of one to ten million cycles per second. The *analogy* computer works with the measurement of physical quantities and converts information from a physical analogy, diagram, translating scale, position, or even color into directions.

FEEDBACK. Wiener describes the operation of the automatic machine as though the parts of the machine must speak to each other in an appropriate language, without speaking or listening to any person except in the initial and terminal stages of the process. In this conversation (92, p. 151) cognizance must be taken of what the machine has already said. This is feedback. It is commonly illustrated with the governor, which James Watt invented to control his steam engine. This governor, incidentally, is now considered to have been a significantly greater technological contribution than the steam engine itself. The governor is pre-set for a maximum engine speed. When the engine begins to turn too fast, the centrifugally activated balls fly upward and simultaneously move a lever which begins to shut off the supply of steam. Likewise as the engine speed drops under the load, the balls fall and the mechanism calls for more steam by opening the valve. In this process of self-regulation the tendency of the engine to increase its speed is simultaneous with the tendency to decrease it, and the tendency to decrease it is accompanied by the tendency to increase the speed. This line of communication between governor and fuel supply is feedback, which in the modern automatic machine operates many controls besides that of speed. It is used to control the movements of cutting tools, speed and accuracy of the processing, uniformity of color, size, and such. Wiener gives credit for the production potential in automatic processing to the electronic vacuum tube. Before it was included in control systems, the electromechanical systems had already reached their relatively low limits of speed.

HYDRAULICS AND PNEUMATICS. Automation has developed largely around electronic controls under the assumption that this type of controls represented the ultimate. However, new developments with hydraulic and pneumatic systems have shown the way to even simpler and more economical control methods. For many applications both fluids and air can be made to respond rapidly enough to effect the desired control.

THE AUTOMATIC FACTORY. Because automation is an evolving process, we must keep in mind that the automatic factory is the end product rather than the beginning of automation. This opinion is commonly expressed in the literature, but at the same time many doubt that complete automatization is possible. Differences of opinion on the possibility of the automatic factory may arise because American industry has not yet had enough experience with automatization to be able to draw well-grounded conclusions. Some current examples of automated factories have been in existence so long as to seem commonplace. The local electrical power plant typifies automation quite accurately. The home heating system, with the thermostat taking the place of the electronic computer, becomes completely automatic when the source of electric power is included in the system. When the thermostat calls for more heat, an electric spark ignites the fuel which is furnished simultaneously by an electric motor-driven injector. Instantaneously with the call by the thermostat, the closing of the electrical circuit calls upon the powerplant generator to deliver the necessary current. If this heating system were the only current consumer in the system, the generator would be idle until called upon to furnish the power to activate it. Electricity is not stored in the powerplant or in the transmission lines; it is consumed as made. Oil refineries have gradually become automatic through necessity. Today's petroleum products could not be produced by means of hand controls even if labor were available. The chemical processes involved could not be carried on without the precision of automatic controls.

IMPLICATIONS OF AUTOMATION. The social and economic impact of the current industrial revolution has already produced fundamental changes in some basic cultural concepts, for example, that of work. The virtues in work have been sung for centuries; it has even had its moral and spiritual values in the growth and development of the individual. Philosophers, theologians, and educators have tried to associate work with dignity until it has, in fancy at least, taken on a power which gives it therapeutic value. But now comes automation with its purpose to eliminate work, to free men from labor. The great revolution may well then be in the cultural, the social, and the economic rather than in the industrial areas. Automation will free the worker from muscular work and from the deadening, repetitive work in mechanized production. It will cut down the length of the work day and increase the leisure day. It will require a high level of intellectual competence from the worker. As it makes more and better products increasingly more available to more people, it will raise the material level of living. Automation will not make a finer living; it will only make a finer living possible for all people. In the process of achieving this finer living, man must find himself in the technological scene. The new industrial arts wants to help him.

After a study of the evolution of American industry, one becomes aware of several conditions which typify the nature and role of today's industry within the technological culture. Automation now brings them into sharp focus. These are:

1. The nature of industrial production
2. The nature of the job
3. A current concept of work
4. The role of research
5. The new leisure
6. A material culture.

THE NATURE OF INDUSTRIAL PRODUCTION

If technology is defined as the science of industrial arts and manufacture, its present level of development is considered to be at its highest, to date. Today's technology is marked by the integration of science and mechanization, which produces the phenomenon of automation. In earlier discussions on the development of industry and the changing nature of the job, the evolution of industrial production was pictured as a lengthy and slow process. From the beginning of the present century, however, the rate of change has been accelerating, and this acceleration is likely to continue. Obviously hand-operated industry could not provide today's material needs, either in quantity or in quality. We cannot go back to the earlier production methods as is suggested now and then by the exponents of the "good old days." The nation's health standards would fall from their present heights, its automobiles could not run on that kind of gasoline, its people could not have synthetic fabrics. The more one studies about today's technology, the more apparent it becomes that an increasingly high standard of living is only possible by means of an increasingly productive industry. Dewhurst makes a point of this in *America's Needs and Resources*:

> Resistance to the introduction of laborsaving machinery is understandable, for it sometimes results in personal tragedy to the workers who are displaced. Over the long run, however, it is *only through technological disemployment* that material progress is possible. If all the men operating canal boats in 1830, and livery stables in 1900, and other dying industries, had stayed in the business, and their sons had followed them, railroad travel would still be a luxury that few people could afford and the private automobile a plaything of the idle rich. If the capital, labor, and entrepreneurial talent released by technological progress had failed to enter and create new industries, we would have been unable to raise our standard of living by producing more of existing goods and a fabulous variety of new, better and cheaper products (39, p. 909).

Only one direction seems available for production process change to go—to the automated. The literature of a few years ago commonly pointed out that automation would be possible only in large industries where great quantities would be produced. Small mechanized industries would still be needed to produce those items in lesser demand, those subject to frequent model changes. This opinion is noticeably less frequent today. The change is undoubtedly due to experience with automatic production and to the growing conviction in industry that what man can conceive, he can produce. The search for means to make processes increasingly automatic would be relatively simple if it were but a matter of finding *better ways* to change the form of materials. Simultaneous with this searching is the continual quest for *new and better products* to lure the consumer into spending. The new model makes the previous one obsolete. And the continual development of new or improved materials calls for *new production processes* different from those already developed. Altogether, these three areas of discovery produce a changing industry that has no time to spend in perfecting the old, either in method or product. It must continue to change to survive, and this change brings improvement in production.

THE NATURE OF THE JOB. Man's search through the centuries has included the quest for means and ways, first, to make his labor easier and lighter, then to make it simpler and faster, and now finally, to eliminate it completely. The history of the job is a record of a demand for products and for faster methods for making them available. The nature of the job performed by the production worker has changed along with the development of the technology; and to meet the continuing demand for greater production, changing the job becomes both means and end. The industrial job has passed through several levels of development to the present time: the home craftsman, professional craftsman, tradesman, machine operator, technician.

THE HOME CRAFTSMAN. From the time that man first realized that he could devise improved means for doing the same job, he has been challenged to make the job an easier one. A stick tied to a rock for a handle gave him an increased power over the rock alone, whether he used it to grind his grain or to kill. His labor was made lighter and yet more productive. From then to the period of industrialization in the evolving civilization the home craftsman continued to discover and to invent techniques and tools to make his work easier and more accurate and his production more abundant as he went about providing food, clothing, housing, tools, utensils, and protection for his family. Home industry flourished until more productive forms of industrialization were able to provide a people with their necessities for living.

THE PROFESSIONAL CRAFTSMAN. The home craftsman disappeared and reappeared as the professional craftsman who made his living by producing more than he needed and selling the surplus. In turn he bought those products from others which he could not feasibly produce but which he needed to complete his living. With an increasing demand for his products, owing to the growth in population and the desire of people for things which they did not or could not make for themselves, the professional craftsman had to have help. A logical solution was to apprentice boys to the master craftsman. The system of apprenticeship served until it too could no longer keep up with the demands for products. The professional craftsman was versatile among materials. He invented processes for producing them, devised tools for shaping them, and designed products to utilize them. Being an entrepreneur, he also marketed his production. But even with all of his technical ingenuity, his production continued to fall behind the demand. It became more difficult to find boys willing to serve the lengthy apprenticeships, and the master increasingly had to employ his apprentices at those jobs which they could do well, without concern for their well-rounded training.

THE TRADESMAN. When the apprentice system gradually broke under the pressures of production, the trade, a narrower area of technical skills essential to production, evolved. The work of the master metals craftsman, for example, was divided among a number of the tradesmen: blacksmith, tinsmith, coppersmith, silversmith, and the like. Likewise, the work of the woods craftsman became specialized in the turner, the joiner, the cooper, the cabinetmaker, the wheelwright, the patternmaker, and others who came to be known as tradesmen. The respective job became less complex and less demanding of the worker, for experience demonstrated that the way to increase production was to decrease the breadth of skills needed by any one man.

THE MACHINE OPERATOR. As machines found growing acceptance in the industrialization of production, greater numbers of workers were required to operate them. With Eli Whitney's introduction of the technique of interchangeable parts in 1798, machine manufacture became the key to increased production at lower costs. Industrial ingenuity continued to produce machines which gradually performed more of the processing of the products until the machine operator was required only to feed and to activate his charge. At the extreme development of such mechanization the operator could be trained within a few hours or even minutes to perform the few operations. He needed to do little thinking and was required to have little if any technical skill.

AUTOMATION AND THE JOB. Management, labor unions, workers, and government are concerned about the future of industry as production becomes more and more automatic. Labor's initial reaction to the labor-saving machine was one of apprehension, fear of losing jobs. Early history records numerous incidents in which the inventors of such machines and their machines were violently treated. An automated industry operates with fewer workers than a mechanized one. That is the plan. Consequently, many workers assumed that automation abolishes jobs and puts people out of work. The evolution of American industry has been, from the beginning, a process of devising machines and systems of mechanization to reduce the amount of labor required. This process has caused a displacement of workers, but over the years, it has effected an increase in employment. The greatest increase currently is in the service industries—those which service the products and keep them in operation. The process of industrialization has changed employment patterns: jobs become obsolete, new ones are created, industries disappear, new ones spring up. One great problem now facing the nation includes that of shifting workers within an industry, transferring workers from one industry to another, and retraining workers for new jobs so that employment is essentially continuous and so that the transition can result in an upgrading of the worker.

Within the past few years several major industries have eliminated numbers of jobs in the process of modernizing and consolidating. At the same time they have offered to finance the retraining of the displaced workers for new jobs. One unexpected result has been the nearly complete rejection of the opportunity to learn new lines of work. This reaction is puzzling because one expects that workers would be eager to learn new skills in order to qualify for better jobs. It does point out the strength of attachment of the worker for his job even though it is not often of the type in which he can feel the degree of responsibility and pride inherent in the work of the tradesman and once even characteristic of work in the factory. But one thing is certain. Today's workers in almost every field will have to expect that jobs will become obsolete just as products do and perhaps even sooner than expected, and that changing jobs and retraining for new ones is already a part of the pattern of work in American industry. No longer can he as a young man find a job in industry and look forward to holding it for a lifetime of work as once was possible.

At this very moment the conversion of industrial processing to automation in the factory as well as in the office is proceeding at a greater rate than earlier predicted. Pertinent literature of as little as five years ago did not anticipate this rate of acceleration. When a manufacturer retools or replaces equipment, he is forced to go more automatic. The opening of the world free trade market is giving unexpected impetus to the conversion. Another reason for the increasing automation is that the term itself is now being used to include any automatic processing whether it involves the previously mentioned facility for feedback or not. The term is becoming more flexible and inclusive, but it still is specific enough that its application and its effects are easily recognizable.

THE TECHNICIAN. In an era of automation the worker assumes a new role, that of the technician. Almost axiomatic is that this worker will need a comparatively high level of technical competency, as well as of personal qualities, if he can be assigned the control of a piece of equipment which may cost upwards of a hundred thousand dollars, and which must be kept in continuous production to pay for itself and return a profit to the owners. Continuous production is an automated industry's goal as well as its method. The following is a series of characteristics of the technician's job condensed from the literature:

1. The job is new. It had not commonly existed earlier.
2. The job is classed as highly skilled, in contrast to that of the machine operator.
3. The job entails far more worker responsibility.
4. The job is not "automatic" as it was for the machine operator
5. The job has been enlarged rather than reduced.
6. The job is salaried.

7. The job requires greater worker intelligence.
8. The job requires technical competency, but of a type unlike that of the craftsman.
9. The job requires a high level of technical knowledge.
10. The job requires emotional stability and maturity.
11. The job offers promotional possibilities, advancement into larger automated units, systems, and sections.
12. The job probably consumes less time than it did for the machine operator, and it offers better pay.

Any of these marks of the technician's job may be subject to change as automatic production experience is gained, but at the present time they do describe the qualifications of this new worker. At least one question is obvious: where will industry get workers with such qualifications? To this there appears to be one answer—training, retraining, and education.

The Concept of Work

One of the amazing changes accompanying the trend toward automatic production is that of the attitude toward work. From the time of recorded history until the impact of the Industrial Revolution was felt, man had to spend as much, or more, time in work as he did in leisure in order to supply himself and his family with the things needed in living. Dewhurst (39, p. 40) gives the following estimated employment figures on man-hours per week for the past one hundred years:

1850—69.8	1910—55.1
1860—68.0	1920—49.7
1870—65.4	1930—45.9
1880—64.0	1940—44.0
1890—61.9	1950—40.0
1900—60.2	1960—37.5

As the number of hours worked per week has decreased throughout the past century, the standard of living has continued to improve. Paradoxically, the less man works, the better he lives. This is, of course, not altogether true, but for purposes of noting technological change, the fact remains.

Manual labor has been included for its moral and spiritual values as an essential in the daily living of certain religious groups from the time of Christ. Early educational reformers, in rebellion against abstract learning, reasoned that manual work was educative and established experimental schools to prove it. With all of the dignity that work may have possessed through the centuries, man himself has carried on an incessant search for the means to lessen it. Among those cultures which have devised tools and machines to do work, the people have come to enjoy the highest standards of living. Current literature on automation makes frequent references to a consequence: the freeing of man from labor, the releasing of man from a level of enslavement to a level in which his full talents may be employed for intellectual, cultural, and spiritual growth: a literal re-creation.

The changing concept of work involves a change not only in the amount of work but in its nature, also. If industrial work were still largely muscular in nature, a shortening of the workweek to present levels would, of course, be favored by workers. Earning the same amount of money with less labor has its appeal. However, the evolutionary change from muscular to routine and then to technical work in automation may be as socially significant as the accompanying decrease in the length of the work day. The fact that the industrial worker may be employed for his brains rather than his brawn heralds a revolution.

The nature of skill is also changing as industry goes automatic. Muscular work required a low level of skill; machine operation required no muscular work and little manual skill. In automation skill takes on an intellectual quality as the ability to discriminate and make quick accurate decisions becomes essential to keeping the machines in operation. To those workers who build pilot model machines, craftsmanship, as evidenced in manipulative skill in tool and machine operation, is needed. For servicing, the ability to diagnose trouble and replace parts becomes the technical qualification. Thus the all-round versatility of the early craftsman, including his manipulative skills, his inventiveness, and his design ability, is no longer typical of the worker's qualifications for competence in the new industry.

THE ROLE OF RESEARCH. Industrial research at the beginning of this century was virtually unknown. Not until about 1900 did the professional engineer become essential to industrial development; World

War I produced the first great demand for the chemist. During the period from 1850 to 1900 (see chart, Fig. 3-1), the mechanic who devised machines became the engineer. Since World War I research has become an increasingly essential element in industrial evolution. Until the entrance of the professional, technical researcher, the inventor supplied the new ideas in the form of new products, new processes, and new machines. He conceived of new applications of the accepted scientific principles and laws, using such materials as nature furnished.

The development of industrial research has been geared to the development of science. James B. Conant, in discussing the development of science as an institution in the United States, points out that (27, pp. 16-17) while the scientist in the nineteenth century was concerned with discovering nature's laws, the inventor was taking advantage of these discoveries for practical ends. The scientist seemingly looked down upon the inventor, and the inventor was contemptuous of the scientist. The status of the scientist is further described by Conant:

> . . . science was not an outcast in this country, but even as late as 1917 it was primarily the inventor, not the scientist, who was looked to by the general public as being the prime mover of technology; he was the man who had changed our habits and made possible our new comforts; in other words, the inventor had conquered nature and put it to man's use (27, p. 20).

According to Conant during the period between the two World Wars science was firmly established as an integral partner in technological development in this country. Then the atomic bomb demonstrated that the scientists had become inventors. The status of the scientist was changed:

> . . . The scientist was no longer thought of as a man in an ivory tower, gradually unravelling the secrets of nature for his own spiritual satisfaction, but as a miracle-worker who like Watt or Edison before him could bring about tremendous transformations of man's relation to his material surroundings.
> The changed status of the scientist, to my mind, is one of the major significant developments of the last decade . . . (27, p. 21).

The role of research in today's industry may be likened to that of miracle working, in which a miracle may be defined as an act or happening that goes beyond what is known concerning the laws in the material or physical sphere. The search is on for new knowledge as well as for better products, simpler processes, and means to greater production at lower costs. Industrial research is becoming the source of new ideas; it is America's newest industry; it is the industry of discovery; it is the industry which creates new industries. Industrial research is also essential to industrial survival in a free economy.

THE NEW LEISURE. When man had to work twelve hours a day, as he did a hundred years ago, to earn a living, he had about four waking hours left after his eight hours of sleep. Some of this was consumed in eating and some in necessary work at home. Consequently, he had no problem of leisure because he had no leisure, or at least not enough of it to make a problem. Today he has more leisure time than work time, and the trend is toward even more leisure. What to do with one's leisure is now of concern if for no other reason than its abundance. This leisure now is a characteristic of a technological society; it becomes a problem of discretionary time (see 45, pp. 62-63). The following appears in the Introduction to *Automatic Control:*

> . . . Mechanization has multiplied our output per man-hour by two in each generation for the past hundred years. Providing our capacity for social invention is equal to the task of securing a rational distribution of purchasing power, automatic control can continue to relieve men and women of unhealthy, unpleasant or unworthy work and gives them increased material well-being and leisure (70, p. X).

This statement prompts the question, does well-being accompany leisure? The answer is, of course, conditional, but the problem of finding this well-being in and through leisure may well become far more involved, and in its solutions, far more complex than the problems in any system of automatic control. If we assume that what one does in his leisure is fully as influential in achieving this well-being as what he does in his work day, then the intelligent use of leisure becomes more than an individual problem. It becomes a family problem, a community problem, a school problem, even a state and a national problem because of the numbers of people involved. Wisely used, this abundance of leisure can produce that abundant living envisioned by the philosopher. There can be time to do those things which draw out the full potential of man as envisioned by his Creator.

Just as industrialization is making increased leisure available, so leisure will make increased industrialization necessary. Industry will be called on to provide those products used in leisure-living: more books than ever before, more sports equipment, more musical instruments, more cameras, more facilities for travel, and such. For the great many who will find their re-creation through work at home, more tools, more machine tools, more paints, and more building materials will be needed. All of this will be accompanied by greater demands for instruction, addressed to the schools as well as to established recreation agencies. This is the miracle of American industrial genius: to produce more products, pay greater wages, provide more leisure, and furnish more means for the utilization of leisure, all at the same time that less work is necessary.

A MATERIAL CULTURE. We fix 1910 as the year in which an agrarian culture in the United States gave way to the industrial; for the first time in its history, more people earned their living in industry than in agriculture. Since then America's culture has become increasingly technological, including its agriculture. The material culture is one aspect of the total culture: that which has been shaped by technological invention, discovery, creativeness, production, and consumption with material. The story of man's material culture begins with the development of tools. Civilization Through Tools (95, p. 7) states: "The story that these tools tell is a source of inspiration. It marks the abandonment of tradition and, in its place, the use of human forethought, imagination, and individual concept as the way to progress." Man's material culture is the sum total of what he knows and does with materials. America's achievement of the world's highest standard of living is a result of its scientific, industrial, and technological progress.

Most likely man, especially in America, is not yet fully competent to use wisely the products of industrialization. The concept of materialism has fired many a philosopher to condemn, or at least to question, the ceaseless drive to even greater industrialization. Of interest, however, is that many of the great scientists, inventors, engineers, mathematicians, and economists of the century have themselves become philosophical about man's technological development. This is an indication that industrialization is coming of age, that a maturation is taking place through which the great technologists are searching for meaning and values for living in the industrial culture which they have helped to produce. Ernest Nagel, writing for the September, 1952 issue of *Scientific American*, which was later published in *Automatic Control*, expresses a point of view which is becoming increasingly easy to document:

> There is next the fear that an automatic technology will impoverish the quality of human life, robbing it of opportunities for individual creation, for pride of workmanship and for sensitive qualitative discrimination. This fear is often associated with a condemnation of "materialism" and with a demand for a return to the "spiritual" values of earlier civilization. All the available evidence shows, however, that great cultural achievements are attained only by societies in which at least part of the population possesses considerable worldly substance. There is a good empirical basis for the belief that automatic control, by increasing the material well-being of a greater fraction of mankind, will release fresh energies for the cultivation and flowering of human excellence . . . (70, pp. 7-8).

Nagel then suggests an inspiring vision of the future of goodness.

> There has been no diminution in opportunities for creative, scientific activity, for there are more things still to be discovered than are dreamt of in many a discouraged philosophy. And there is no ground for supposing that the course of events will be essentially different in other areas of human activity. Why should the wide adoption of automatic control and its associated qualitative methods induce a general insensitivity to qualitative distinctions? It is precisely measurement that makes evident the distinctions between qualities, and it is by measurement that man has frequently refined his discriminations and gained for them a wider acceptance . . . (70, p. 8).

America's standard of living is tied to its industrial growth and development. This is not to say that progress in materials produces an equal progress in the quality of living; there is a social lag. Man's ingenuity with materials and machines has thus far outstripped his ingenuity for good living. This condition has prompted reformers to plead for a slowing of technological progress until man himself catches up. The great question facing man is: how can he assimilate the continual changes in living effected by technology so that his culture may reach increasingly high levels at a more rapid rate? He is not yet wise enough to know how, but he is in the process of discovering. The answer may not lie solely in man himself, in his nature, or in his purpose in being; it may lie in the machine. Arnold

Tustin made this penetrating observation for the Sept., 1952 issue of *Scientific American,* which was later published in *Automatic Control:*

> Man is far from understanding himself, but it may turn out that his understanding of automatic control is one small further step toward that end (70, p. 23).

There is an assumption that may provide a reasonable peace of mind: the better man understands the material world that he now has, the more wisely he is able to use it, and the more likely he is to see that its best is yet to come. Man knows that he is better off with the technology than without it, but to use it so that he can draw ever closer to the goodness that he is capable of, remains from this time on the challenge to him as an individual and to all of his great socializing agencies. This is the position of industrial arts in education: to understand technology we must study it.

THE NEW AUTOMATION. In the few years since John Diebold coined the term automation (40) industry has made extensive production changes through an increase in automation, which was to be expected. But such uses for automation have suggested even greater ones. Where once its application was largely to manufacturing, today it is everywhere—in communications, transportation, business, medicine, education, and even in the home. The next decade will see some startling developments which even now suggest that a revolution in automation is underway.

The new automation, as employed in the projection of satellites into orbit under complete self-control, stirs the imagination. If it is possible to develop automatic transportation into space and back, it must be possible to develop automatic transportation on the ground. Sooner or later one will be able to program a cross-country vacation trip on the computer of his automobile. He will be able to sit back and enjoy the trip as his automatic chauffeur and navigator take over complete control and responsibility, except for footing the bills, of course. Such applications are seen in the fabulous new field of heuristics (from the Greek, meaning invention, discovery) in which it will be possible to program the machine for certain objectives. The machine will then take over, making any necessary adaptations, corrections, and detours to achieve the objective.

The limitations to the future of the new automation lie only in the imagination. It is more than ever true that what mind can conceive, man can construct. But it all adds up to the fact, and this has been brought out before in this discussion, that the great revolution in all of technology is not technical but intellectual. Man now has intellectual tools and machines to do his work. The great effect of this revolution will be cultural rather than technological and industrial. It requires a higher level of intellect to conceive of and to produce such innovations than it did to produce the hand hammer and saw. It requires a higher level of the intellect to understand them, something for which we must try in industrial arts. Let this then set us thinking as we search for a new industrial arts. We will find it only when we make fullest use of our own imaginations and it will be, when we find it, first of all, intellectual.

Technological Lag in Industrial Arts

American technology is marked by change. In technologically underdeveloped countries indigenous materials, processes, products, services, occupations, and industries tend to change slowly. When change is greatest, it often comes from adopting foreign technology rather than from an evolution of its own. Standards of perfection are perpetuated from generation to generation; the goal of the young is to reach this level of skill. In the United States the goal is to exceed and to excel. Technological achievements of one generation are but stepping stones to greater progress in the next. Throughout the Crafts Age of technology (see chart, Fig. 2-2), which began at about the fifteenth century and ended with the patenting of the steam engine in 1769, change was rapid as compared to that of the preceding centuries of recorded history. The most used material of the Age was wood; the processes were with hand tools; the power was provided by muscle. The development of the machine, the steam engine, to provide dependable mechanical power opened the door to a greater technology, to the Machine Age or the Age of Mechanization. Improved mechanical power made the dynamo possible. With it the Age of Power moved in rapidly, and technology continued to change at an accelerating rate.

We know that woodworking is typical of today's industrial arts, that hand-tool processing is the accepted pattern. With wood, then, as the material and hand tools, muscle-powered for the processing, today's industrial arts fits technologically into the Crafts Age. Such a placing may not be altogether proper, but it may be more so than we care to admit. If industrial arts is to reflect today's technology, it must necessarily change and keep changing. Technical fundamentals of the Crafts Age are not likely to be those for the Scientific Age. Some may argue that industrial arts cannot keep pace with technology and industry. If keeping pace means duplicating in the classroom what industry does and has, this position is undoubtedly true. Provision for the highly specialized equipment and controls is beyond feasibility. However, keeping pace may have other meanings.

We can reflect the spirit of technology, the attitude and application of search and research, the inventiveness, the creativity, the experimenting and developing, the problem-solving, all of which are a part of, and fundamental to, an advancing technology. We can study the nature and purposes, the organization and management of contemporary industry. We can experiment with the basic processes for converting materials. Even the technological environment of the student can go beyond the confines of the school into industry. We can also get students involved in truly liberating technical projects that demand full concentration and occupation and tax their youthful ingenuity. We can teach for the maximum growth and development of the student within an environment of ideas, materials, machines and energies. Reflecting technology involves selecting the elements which are the keys to change and growth. These will become our fundamentals. Our practice of building programs largely around materials processing probably accounts for the technological lag in industrial arts. The search for subject matter in later chapters reveals a wealth of subject matter that goes far beyond materials and processes. By using this more comprehensive subject matter, we can close the technological gap.

AMERICAN INDUSTRY
IMPLICATIONS FOR INDUSTRIAL ARTS

If industrial arts derives subject matter from industry, we must also accept that the nature of that subject matter is in a state of continual change and that subject matter accepted as proper at the turn of the century may be now outmoded. Automation itself may make a new look at the industrial arts curriculum necessary. The following implications are drawn from the preceding study of American industry and point directly to industrial arts:

1. Machine production, in contrast to the handcraft, typifies industry more than ever in contemporary industry. Consequently, machine experiences should typify industrial arts.
2. As industrial production is taken over by machines, the industrial arts laboratory should include essential machine equipment of a diversified type, including production centers whereby means of progressive processing and conveyor transfer, a reasonably representative industrial atmosphere, can prevail.
3. As industry demands increasing technical competences in the worker, industrial arts must also become more technical and scientific.
4. As industry requires increased technical competences, educational-vocational-industrial orientation and guidance become more than ever a real responsibility of industrial arts.
5. The changing concept of work being effected through automation should be reflected in industrial arts. Pupil experiences must be made increasingly real and meaningful to effect the maximum growth and development by drawing out and strengthening a variety of talents and interests. This process should more adequately prepare the individual for vocational choice, whether on the secondary or the collegiate levels. Emphasis must be put on the student doing things the "easy" way rather than on the "hard" way.
6. With industry attaching increased importance to engineering, inventing, creating, designing, researching, planning, and the like, it is axiomatic that industrial arts should do likewise in the laboratory. With intellectual competence becoming a basic qualification for work in industry, it would seem appropriate to make industrial arts more intellectual also.
7. Because of the changing qualifications of the industrial worker, increased emphasis should be placed on the need for youth to complete its secondary schooling. The inherent holding power of industrial arts should be used fully.
8. The design of industrial arts projects should typically reflect the industrial design concept of integration of materials, process, structure, construction, and function rather than the craftsman-artist concept.
9. The success of automation depends on technical, scientific understandings of machine principles, mechanisms, materials, processes, systems, circuits, and such. Consequently, industrial arts must contribute directly to such understandings.
10. Automated systems are typified by precision of process and control. Here is additional reason for emphasis on precision in student work and thought. Qualitative standards, beginning

with the work of the scientist in the development of automatic machines, must necessarily have been high to make automation possible.

11. The manufacture and service of automatic machines demands extreme accuracy and technical competence by the worker. Emphasis should be placed on tool and machine skills in industrial arts in order that aptitudes herein may be discovered, developed, and directed. Excellence in thinking correlates with excellence in material expression.

12. In an age of automation, with the attendant increase in leisure time, the recreation function of industrial arts should be re-examined and emphasized.

13. The need for technicians, engineers, inventors, designers, and scientists will likely become increasingly great as industry moves into automation. Consequently, industrial arts should provide technical education throughout its entire school program, of a sort which guides youngsters through experiences which point out aptitudes for and stimulate interests in things technical and scientific. The handcraft activities are not likely to be adequate.

14. Contemporary industry is continually searching for better ideas. Automation itself was conceived in imagination. Similarly, in industrial arts the student must be continually encouraged and motivated to discover and develop better ideas and simpler methods. He must be permitted and encouraged to experiment, invent, and devise.

15. The key characteristic of American industry is its time-consciousness. Doing it faster has been the challenge since the beginning of industrialization. Perfection is relative to time and to now. In industrial arts efficiency in the use of student and teacher time must become of major concern. Project perfection must be relative to time and to now in the maturation of the student. Time is individual man's most precious asset; he has but a limited supply in which to achieve his potential.

16. The complexity of today's materials, tools, machines, processes, products, and occupations indicates man's continuing gain in mentality over his counterparts of the past. And if this is true, today's student is logically capable of greater intellectual and materials achievement than the student of the past. He must be capable of greater achievements than the projects drawn from a Crafts Age technology and handed down in current textbooks. The project in industrial arts reflective of today's technology must rightly be more complex than that of an

earlier level and must demand a fuller involvement of the student.

17. All of industrial change and technological development is proceeding with increasing rapidity. Quicker and quicker we get farther and farther from the past. Industrial arts in education cannot take its time to close the cultural lag with which it is identified. It is already obsolete except for that student whose intellectual development has been retarded.

18. New human capacities are becoming apparent with technological development. Man is demonstrating that dreams are no longer mere fantasy. They are instead goals to be reached in technological stride. We know exactly where the moon is and how to get there, but not so many years ago this was the height of impossibility. If it is not on the itinerary of tourists by the time the ink is dry on this page, it will be soon. We in industrial arts must take a new look at the human in our classes. His capacities far exceed the abilities we have commonly concentrated on developing.

19. Just as there are varying levels of human competence required in industry and just as there are varying degrees of human giftedness, there must be varying programs of industrial arts. One level of program cannot be all things to all students. Industrial arts can vary in level of intellect and creativity as well as by type of subject matter.

20. Automation was conceived in imagination. It is implemented by science and engineering as the highest level of what we may call the technological intellect. It is logical that its understanding, utilization, and control require as much intelligence. Industrial arts then must reach the student of superior mental capacity. But if it is to do so, it must be an education of that caliber. Technical skill and craftsmanship are no longer ends; they are means to greater achievement. If they become ends, they will be goals only for the less-than-normal.

TO DISCUSS, TO DEBATE, TO DECIDE

1. Can today's industrial arts fairly be placed at the level of the technology in the Crafts Age?
2. What has been the significance of a development such as Whitney's interchangeable parts?
3. What specific applications are made of electronic computers in modern industry? What did industry do before it had them?
4. Will tapes, cards, and other such devices eventually replace the shop drawing in industry?

5. What are the social implications of the changing nature of work?
6. What does the statement that the purpose of work is leisure mean?
7. How does the job of the craftsman differ from the technician in modern industry?
8. How can the rather recent and sudden interest in research among American industries be explained?
9. What qualifications would you expect of a worker whom you put in charge of a $100,000 automatic machine?
10. How could industrial arts contribute to an advancing of technology?

(Above) Boring cannon barrels in early America. The barrels, originally of bronze and later of iron, were cast hollow by means of a core. Boring and reaming were highly skilled operations. Note the boring tools under the bench. (Courtesy: The DoAll Company.)

(Right) A close-up view of a machining operation along a 63-station automatic machine tool line in an automobile engine plant. Here cylinder heads are being processed in a system known as the "Detroit" type of automation which employs transfer of the part from station to station. Cylinder boring is done similarly. It is thought that the cannon was the forerunner of the internal combustion engine. Can you see a relationship? (Courtesy: Ford Motor Company.)

IV

An Industries Analysis: The Classification of Subject Matter

. . . *alike for masters and for men a technical or technological education, which is to have any chance of satisfying the practical needs of the nation, must be conceived in a liberal spirit as a real intellectual enlightment in regard to principles applied and services rendered. In such an education geometry and poetry are as essential as turning laths.*

 —Alfred North Whitehead, *The Aims of Education.*
 (New York: The Macmillan Company, 1929.)

   A perspective of American industry should show its major dimensions. The following analyses of industry in breadth and depth attempt to do this. They show the general nature and extent of eight categories of industries: manufacturing, construction, power, transportation, electronics, research, services, and management. These groups are assumed to account for all American industry that would be essential for a curriculum study in industrial arts. These categories were determined, after considerable study and search of industrial literature and after numerous trial groupings, to be the best, simple yet inclusive, classification this writer could arrange.

One of the major problems in a classification of industries is to establish a simplified system of grouping with a maximum of consistency within each group and sufficient inclusiveness as to be representative. The primary source of industries listings for this study is the *Census of Manufacturers* (77, 78, 79) and the *Annual Survey of Manufacturers* (76), publications of the United States Department of Commerce, Bureau of the Census. The following statement, which has been of use in the classification for this study, appears in an explanation of the process of industries identification used in these publications:

> An industry consists of a group of establishments primarily engaged in the same line or similar lines of economic activity. In the manufacturing field, the line of activity is generally defined in terms of the products made or the processes of manufacture used. On this basis, there may theoretically be thousands of manufacturing industries corresponding to the different types of products and processes used in their manufacture. However, industries established in this manner would be too numerous to deal with and, further, would not generally satisfy the criteria considered essential in the creation of a good system of industry classification (77, p. 7).

The *1947 Census* (77, 78) groups some 450 individual manufacturing industries into 140 sub-groups and further, into 20 major industry groups with several sub-groups. The major industries are:

Food and kindred products
Tobacco manufacture
Textile mill products
Apparel and related products
Lumber and products, except furniture

Furniture and fixtures
Paper and allied products
Printing and publishing industries
Chemicals and allied products
Petroleum and coal products

Rubber products
Leather and leather products
Stone, clay, and glass products

Primary metals industries
Fabricated metals products

Machinery (except electrical)
Electrical machinery
Transportation equipment
Instruments and related products
Miscellaneous manufactures

The *1958 Census of Manufactures* employs essentially the same system of classification although the standard industrial classification was revised in 1957.

With the aid of this information, the classification of the manufacturing industries here was relatively simple and was done largely on the basis of materials categories: ceramics, chemicals, foods, leather, metals, paper, plastics, rubber, textiles, woods, plus graphic arts and tools and machines.

American industries are thought of as producing either goods or services, but to arrive at a classification, representative and inclusive, other categories must be included. The building industries, which may be considered as manufacturing in a sense, are accounted for in the *construction* industries. The supplying of energy for power used by industry, business, the home, and the individual is seen as a segment of industry and is classed as the *power* industries. The manufacture of transportation equipment is included in the Census classification, but transport systems utilizing the equipment are not. The *transportation* industries for this study include both aspects.

The category of *electronic* industries includes the manufacture of electrical machinery as listed by the Census Bureau as well as applications and utilization of this machinery, including electronic communications. The dependence of all industrial development on the electronics industry suggests its key position in the technology, and for that reason it is included as one of the eight categories.

The Census categories include research as integral with the industries, but owing to the trends in the establishment of research as an *industry to produce industries*, largely in the past two decades, and owing to its recognition by industry as being indispensable and strategic, special emphasis should be made of it here.

The management aspects of the manufacturing industries are presumably integral in the Census classifications. However, because as many or more persons are employed in the management, or the nonproductive end of industry, as are employed in the productive end, it is imperative that management be included as a category. The representativeness of industry would not be complete without it.

One of the most rapidly growing employment fields today in the United States is that of services (exclusive of domestic services which are declining in numbers employed). The reason for its expansion lies in the growth and development of the manufacturing industries. More work is being done by machines whether in industry itself or at home. These machines are becoming increasingly automatic and complex. The problem of maintenance, repair, and servicing is technical in its solution, which requires the assistance of specialists. The service occupations are a result of the demand to keep the machines and equipment operating. Because of their essential nature in technological living, these occupations are included in the category of services.

Analyses for Subject Matter

When one makes an analysis of two or more industries in search of structure, organization, systems and sequence of operation, personnel staffing, and such, he finds that they have much in common. In fact, there are patterns common to all industries and especially to analogous ones. Manufacturing industries, for example, employ materials, processes, products, power, machines, and people in whatever they produce. All industries have research, engineering, marketing, management, and maintenance divisions. We call such organic divisions *functional components*. Their identification and derivation result from analyses of industries such as may be pictured in charted organization and in materials handling sequences. It is not feasible to include here the total of such detailing, nor is it necessary. Fig. 4-1 shows an organization typical of the manufacturing industries. In the analyses of the manufacturing industries which follow, the entire outline structure and sequence is built around four groups of functional components: materials, processes, products, and people or occupations. Each of these is analyzed in a rather logical manner. The list of components that follows is representative but not necessarily inclusive.

In the other categories of industries individual patterns of analysis are necessary because of the differences between industries. However,

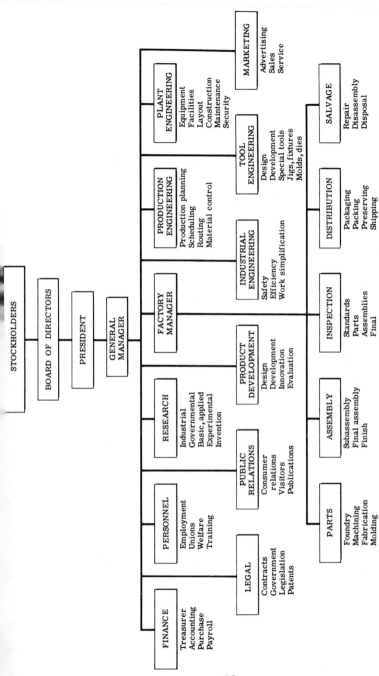

Fig. 4-1. Typical functional structure of manufacturing industries. The various functions may appear in other positions and relationships in specific industries. Such analyses of industries reveal origins of the functional components and the curricular components for industrial arts as appears in the Master List, see p. 195.

99

comparisons of all of the derivations show much in common. The frequency with which similar components appear suggests a fundamentalism among them. Because they are fundamental, they become legitimate subject matter for industrial arts, and in this role we will identify them as *curricular components* in Chapter VI.

THE MANUFACTURING INDUSTRIES

The Ceramics Industries

The first factory in America is said to have been a glass plant established at Jamestown, Virginia, in 1608. Brickmaking and the use of terra cotta antedate glass, however, by several thousands of years. Egyptian potters used the wheel as early as 4,000 B.C., and the Chinese were firing pottery thousands of years before this. The ceramics industries today include the manufacture of products from inorganic, nonmetallic minerals, using high temperature heat treatment. The products are unusually diverse as is evident in the accompanying outline analysis.

The clay products industries have only recently turned to automatic machines for production. Automatic jiggers now produce dinnerware; firing is done in continuous kilns; ware is glazed by automatic spray; but the automatic handling of ware between processing stations is not yet common. Flat glass and metal enameling and cement manufacture are already largely continuous and automatic. The recent developments in combining ceramic materials with plastics, minerals, and metals to produce new or better materials show that the golden age of ceramics is yet to come.

I. Basic Ceramic Materials

Clay	Cement	Plaster
Glass	Enamel	Synthetics
Glaze	Stone	

II. Typical Basic Processes

  A. Manual

Clay	*Glaze*	*Enamel*
Throwing	Brushing	Applying

Modeling	Dipping	Grinding
Wedging	Grinding	Screening
Welding	Spraying	

Glass	*Stone*	*Cement, Plaster*
Blowing	Cutting	Casting
Cutting	Faceting	Finishing
Grinding	Lapping	Mixing
Polishing	Polishing	Modeling

B. Mechanical

Clay	*Glaze*	*Enamel*
Blunging	Decorating	Decorating
Extruding	Grinding	Dipping
Jiggering	Mixing	Grinding
Pressing	Spraying	Spraying
Pugging		

Glass	*Stone*	*Cement, Plaster*
Blowing	Cutting	Casting
Grinding	Faceting	Finishing
Polishing	Grinding	Grinding
Pressing	Lapping	Mixing
Rolling	Polishing	Polishing

C. Chemical

Clay	*Glaze*	*Enamel*
Analyses	Analyses	Analyses
Compounding	Compounding	Compounding
Deflocculating	Test	Test

Glass	*Stone*	*Cement, Plaster*
Analyses	Analyses	Analyses
Compounding	Cleaning	Compounding
Etching	Etching	Etching
Silvering		Setting

D. Thermal

Clay	*Glaze*	*Enamel*
Calcining	Firing	Firing

| Drying | Fritting | Fritting |
| Firing | | |

Glass	Stone	Cement, Plaster
Annealing		Calcining
Forming		Drying
Melting		
Tempering		

III. Typical Products

A. Art Products

Clay	Glass	Enameled Metals
Jewelry	Jewelry	Jewelry
Pottery	Novelties	Murals
Sculpture	Synthetic jewels	Novelties

Stone	Cement, Plaster
Jewelry	Novelties
Monuments	Sculpture
Sculpture	

B. Household Products

Clay	Glass	Enameled Metals
Cooking ware	Cloth	Appliances
Dinnerware	Cooking ware	Pots, pans
Sanitary ware	Dinnerware	Sanitary ware
Tiles	Fixtures	
	Mirrors	

C. Industrial Products

Clay	Glass	Enameled Metals
Abrasives	Bottles	Cabinets
Insulation	Equipment	Containers
Insulators	Insulation	Equipment
Kilns, ovens	Insulators	Housings
Refactories	Jewels	Signs
Resistors	Lenses	
Transistors		

Stone	*Cement, Plaster*
Abrasives	Chemicals
Cutters	Wall board
Jewels	

D. Structural Products

Clay	*Glass*	*Enameled Metals*
Block	Block	Buildings
Brick	Doors	Houses
Liners	Panel	Panels
Pipe	Tile	Signs
Tile	Windows	

Stone	*Cement, Plaster*
Block	Portland cement
Terazzo	Cement block
Veneer	Gypsum plaster
	Wallboard

IV. Basic Occupations and Occupational Fields

A. Management

Administration	Finance	Records
Supervision	Legal	Sales
Personnel	Purchasing	Plant engr.

B. Technical, Scientific

Ceramic engr.	Mechanical engr.	Serviceman
Electrical engr.	Researcher	
Chemist	Tradesman	

C. Production

Caster	Glazer	Molder
Finisher	Inspector	Packer
Decorator	Kiln man	Jiggerman

D. Design, Development

Product designer	Artist	Modeler

V. Representative Functional Components

Design	Chemistry	Integration
Decoration	Materials	Manufacturing

Invention	Processes	Inspection
Research	Products	Evaluation
Engineering	Machines	Distribution
Measurement	Tools	Utilization
Safety	Production	Standards
	Management	

The Chemicals Industries

The chemicals industries are those which manufacture chemicals and chemical products in the following types of categories: industrial organic chemicals, industrial inorganic chemicals, drugs and medicines, soaps and related products, paints and allied products, gum and wood chemicals, and fertilizers. The petroleum industry is also included for this study. Chemicals manufacturing today is largely automated not only because the processing lends itself to that but because the nature of the chemicals and the processes require it. Many chemicals and chemical products in use today could not be produced other than automatically because of the precision control necessary and the hazards involved.

I. Basic Sources of Chemicals

   A. Organic

Animal	Fish	Vegetable

   B. Inorganic

Minerals	Petroleum	Water
Air		

II. Typical Basic Processes

   A. Manual

Application	Filtering	Separating
Blending	Grinding	

   B. Mechanical

Atomizing	Filtering	Weighing
Beating	Grinding	Pumping
Blending	Separating	Drilling

C. Thermal

Activating	Distilling	Fusing
Annealing	Evaporating	Melting
Boiling	Fritting	Sterilizing

D. Chemical

Analyzing	Compounding	Oxidizing
Anodizing	Deflocculating	Saturating
Bleaching	Dissolving	Sensitizing
Carbonizing	Etching	Slaking
Cleaning	Fermenting	Synthesis

E. Electrical

Charging	Filtering	Plating
Electrolysis	Fusing	Igniting

F. Nuclear

Heating	Radiation	Transmutation

III. Typical Basic Products

Adhesive	Glass	Photographic
Cements	Lubricants	Plastics
Dyes	Medicine	Rubber
Fuels	Paints	Solvents

IV. Basic Occupations and Occupational Fields

A. Management

Administration	Finance	Records
Supervision	Legal	Sales
Personnel	Purchasing	Plant engr.

B. Technical, Scientific

Chemists	Technicians	Tradesmen
Engineers	Inventors	

C. Production

Chemists	Engineers	Technicians

V. Representative Functional Components

Analyzing	Invention	Products
Chemistry	Management	Refining

Design	Manufacturing	Research
Development	Materials	Safety
Diagnosis	Measurement	Standards
Distribution	Mining	Testing
Evaluation	Processes	Utilization
Experiment	Production	

The Foods Industries

The foods industries for study in industrial arts are those involved in the industrialization and mechanization of food production and manufacturing as evidenced in industrialized agriculture, in the factory, and in appliances and utensils for foods preparation in the home, school, industry, and business. They do not include agriculture or the preparation of foods for eating.

The mechanization of agricultural production has been proceeding at an increasing rate. According to Dewhurst (39, p. 801), in 1910 only one tractor and fifty autos were produced, while in 1953 the production figures had increased to approximately four and one-half million of each. Today milking, for example, is largely done with mechanical milkers with the fluid piped directly into electrical coolers. The home kitchen of the near future is described as being so automatic that a wave of the hand will activate the built-in concealed appliances. All of such applications of the technology to foods are of concern in this category.

I. Areas of Industrialization

    A. Farm

	Construction	Equipment	Power
	Culture	Harvest	Transportation

    B. Factory

	Construction	Manufacturing	Preservation
	Distribution	Packaging	Transportation

    C. Home

	Appliances	Furniture	Refrigerating
	Dinnerware	Kitchen	Utensils

II. Basic Occupations and Occupational Fields

A. Management

Administration	Personnel	Records
Finance	Plant engr.	Sales
Legal	Purchasing	Supervision

B. Technical, Scientific

Agricultural engr.	Electronic engr.	Servicemen
Chemist	Mechanical engr.	Tradesmen
Electrical engr.	Researcher	

C. Production

Assemblers	Operators	Technicians
Finishers	Packers	Testers

D. Design, Development

Designer	Home economist	Inventor
Engineer		

III. Representative Functional Components

Appliances	Invention	Products
Chemistry	Machines	Research
Design	Management	Safety
Distribution	Manufacturing	Services
Engineering	Materials	Testing
Equipment	Measurement	Tools
Evaluation	Processes	Utilization
	Production	

The Graphic Arts Industries

The graphic arts industries include those involving the communicative processes: drawing, photography, printing, and publishing. These are representative of the basic graphic arts media: drawings, pictures, and the printed word.

Technical drawing in industry has been, and is, a slow, painstaking, precision-type work. But it is now being subjected to study for purposes of simplification, mechanization, and actual elimination. The recording of necessary information, as commonly found on the production drawing, on tape, card, and film for automated production suggests the possible end of the drawing, the blueprint, as a production tool. Photography, by contrast, is being explored for possibilities of greater application in industry. Combined with electronics, the applications appear to be unlimited. At present closed circuit television is being used, for example, to permit viewing of the processing of materials and parts at various stages in automated systems. Printing in its many forms has become increasingly automatic with the development of phenomenal press speeds and simplified processes.

GRAPHIC ARTS—DRAWING

I. Basic Types, Applications of Technical Drawing

Aircraft	Electrical	Mechanical
Architectural	Engineering	Design
Charts, graphs	Lofting	Sketching
Construction	Machine	Advertising

II. Typical Basic Processes

A. Manual

Layout	Rendering	Lettering
Detailing		

B. Mechanical

Enlarging	Printing	Transferring
Lettering	Projecting	

C. Electrical

Copying	Recording	Reproducing
Projecting	Enlarging	

D. Mathematical

Graphics	Forces	Geometry

III. Basic Occupations and Occupational Fields

Draftsmen	Tracers	Checkers
Illustrators	Letterers	Printers

IV. Representative Functional Components

Presentation	Lettering	Materials
Representations	Techniques	Tools
Interpretation	Standards	Equipment
Specifications	Types	Processes
Reproduction	Recording	Utilization

GRAPHIC ARTS—PHOTOGRAPHY

I. Basic Types, Application

A. Still

Candid	Industrial	Portrait
Commercial	News	Scientific

B. Movie

Commercial	Entertainment	News
Educational	Industrial	Personal

C. Scientific

Astronomical	Medical	Production
High-speed	Macroscopic	Radiography
Infra-red	Microscopic	X-ray

II. Basic Materials

Chemicals	Paper	Woods
Glass	Plastics	Adhesives
Metals	Rubber	Gelatin

III. Basic Processes

A. Manual

Composing	Operating	Retouching

B. Mechanical

Copying	Enlarging	Projecting

C. Chemical

Developing	Exposing	Sensitizing

D. Electrical

Lighting	Printing	Timing

E. Optical

Enlarging	Reducing	Condensing

F. Thermal

Drying	Reticulating	Mounting

IV. Basic Products

Films	Projections	Accessories
Movies	Slides	Equipment
Photographs	Supplies	Tools, machines

V. Basic Occupations and Occupational Fields

A. Management

Administration	Finance	Records
Supervision	Legal	Sales
Personnel	Purchasing	Plant engr.

B. Technical, Scientific

Chemists	Physicists	Engineers
Tradesmen	Technicians	Mathematicians

C. Production

Operators	Testers	Finishers
Assemblers	Packers	Photographers

D. Design, Development

Designer	Engineer	Inventor

E. Photography

Commercial	Industrial	Scientific
Cinematography	News	Portrait

VI. Representative Functional Components

Research	Materials	Accessories
Invention	Processes	Standards
Design	Products	Services

Engineering	Manufacturing	Utilization
Chemistry	Equipment	Management
Physics	Tools, machines	Legislation
Measurement	Operation	Evaluation
Production	Refining	
	Integration	

GRAPHIC ARTS—PRINTING

I. Basic Types

Relief	Planographic	Intaglio
Typewriter	Lithographic	Engraving
Letterpress	Stencil	Etching

II. Basic Materials

Chemicals	Metals	Plastics
Ink	Paper	Rubber

III. Typical Basic Processes

A. Manual

Block cutting	Etching	Typesetting
Duplicating	Platemaking	Stenciling
Engraving	Printing	

B. Mechanical

Duplicating	Platemaking	Typesetting
Engraving	Printing	Routing

C. Thermal

Cooking	Drying	Fusing
Activating	Embossing	Welding

D. Chemical

Developing	Etching	Inkmaking
Sensitizing		

E. Electrical

Exposing	Platemaking	Driving

IV. Basic Products

Advertising	Labels	Periodicals
Reproduction	Money	Materials
Decoration	News media	Equipment
Educational media	Records	Tools
Instructions	Books	Machines

V. Basic Occupations and Occupational Fields

A. Management

Administration	Finance	Records
Supervision	Legal	Sales
Personnel	Purchasing	Plant engr.

B. Technical, Scientific

Chemists	Inventors	Technicians
Mechanical engr.	Tradesmen	Servicemen

C. Production

Binders	Compositors	Operators
Engravers	Linotypists	Assemblers
Typesetters	Photographers	Inspectors

D. Design, Development

Artists	Designers	Inventors

E. Writing

Authors	Editors	Correspondents

VI. Representative Functional Components

Research	Utilization	Manufacturing
Invention	Equipment	Installation
Design	Tools	Distribution
Engineering	Editing	Services
Chemistry	Publishing	Standards
Materials	Composing	Accessories
Processes	Measurement	Testing
Products	Management	Machines
Safety		Refining

The Leather Industries

Analysis here of the leather industries includes the manufacture of leather and products from leather. Until the turn of the century leather manufacture was largely handwork, using essentially the same processes as had been used for hundreds of years. The discovery of chrome tanning was the turning point in the development of the industry. This process produced types, qualities, and colors of leather not previously possible. The first leather splitting machine was an American invention in 1809, as was the first shoe pegging machine in 1852.

I. Basic Types of Leathers

Calfskin	Goatskin	Steerhide
Cowhide	Sheepskin	Imitations
Horsehide	Reptile	Synthetics

II. Typical Basic Processes

A. Manual

Cutting	Sewing	Fabricating
Dyeing	Skiving	Unhairing
Decorating	Trimming	

B. Mechanical

Buffing	Sewing	Staking
Graining	Shaving	Toggling
Scudding	Splitting	Unhairing

C. Chemical

Bating	Tanning	Seasoning
Depilating	Preserving	Waterproofing

D. Thermal

Drying

III. Typical Basic Products

Accessories	Drive belts	Luggage
Cases	Footwear	Upholstery
Clothing	Harnesses	Books

IV. Basic Occupations and Occupational Fields

A. Management

Administration	Finance	Records
Supervision	Legal	Sales
Personnel	Purchasing	Plant engr.

B. Technical, Scientific

Chemists	Engineers	Inventors

C. Production

Cutters	Tanners	Stitchers

D. Design, Development

Fashion designer	Industrial designer	Engineer

V. Representative Functional Components

Research	Chemistry	Inspection
Invention	Materials	Fabrication
Design	Processes	Distribution
Development	Products	Utilization
Engineering	Management	Manufacturing
Measurement	Safety	Standards
Integration		
Production		

The Metals Industries

The metals industries cover the processing from mining through the manufacturing of metals and metals products. Within this group are such major metals producing industries as iron, steel, aluminum, copper, lead, and zinc. Metals products manufacture has almost no limits; machines are all largely of metals. Chemistry has recently been able to produce entirely new materials by chemically combining metallic elements with other materials, for example, cermets, combinations of ceramic materials and metals.

I. Metals as Materials

A. Typical Base Metals

Aluminum	Iron	Tin
Copper	Lead	Zinc

B. Typical Alloying Metals

Chromium	Manganese	Tungsten
Cobalt	Nickel	Vanadium

C. Metals as Energy Sources

Cobalt	Plutonium	Uranium

II. Typical Basic Processes

A. Manual

Bending	Filing	Riveting
Drilling	Forming	Sawing
Embossing	Planishing	Tapping

B. Mechanical

Broaching	Milling	Shaping
Drawing	Planning	Spinning
Drilling	Pressing	Stamping
Grinding	Rolling	Threading
Indexing	Sawing	Turning

C. Thermal

Alloying	Forging	Soldering
Brazing	Heat treating	Sweating
Enameling	Smelting	Welding
Molding	Annealing	

D. Chemical

Coloring	Oxidizing	Preserving
Etching	Plating	Sensitizing

E. Electrical

Charging	Induction	Plating
Conduction	Magnetizing	Welding

III. Typical Basic Products

A. Industrial

Controls	Hand tools	Metals
Conveyors	Machine tools	Machines

B. Power, Transportation

Aircraft	Industrial	Railways
Conveyors	Pipe line	Ships
Farm machines	Powerplants	Vehicles

C. Construction

Doors	Hardware	Roofing
Fasteners	Heating	Structure
Fixtures	Paneling	Windows
Furniture	Plumbing	Wiring

D. Household

Appliances	Furniture	Tools
Fixtures	Musical instr.	Utensils

E. Personal

Jewelry	Medical equipment	Currency

IV. Basic Occupations and Occupational Fields

A. Management

Administration	Finance	Records
Supervision	Legal	Sales
Personnel	Purchasing	Plant engr.
Planning		

B. Technical, Scientific

Chemists	Mechanics	Physicists
Draftsmen	Mechnical engr.	Researchers
Inventors	Mineralogists	Tool engr.
Technicians	Tradesmen	Servicemen

C. Production

Operators	Assemblers	Testers
Molders	Finishers	Miners
Machinists	Inspectors	Packers

D. Design, Development

Craftsmen	Draftsmen	Artists
Designers	Engineers	Modelers

V. Representative Functional Components

Research	Processes	Tools
Invention	Products	Machines
Design	Manufacturing	Utilization
Development	Operation	Distribution
Experiment	Finishing	Management
Materials	Fasteners	Mining
Structures	Production	Testing
Measurement	Safety	Refining
Integration		Standards

The Paper Industries

The importance of the paper industries to the American consumer is not so much in the paper he himself uses for communications as in the hundreds of his everyday products which are made of paper. The paper he consumes is largely in books, magazines, newspapers, boxes, towels, and such products. There are some five thousand kinds and grades of paper in use today. They are broadly classed as paper for writing and printing and papers for mechanical and structural uses in wrap, cartons, and building materials. Historians claim that the printing industry would have had a much earlier start had paper been perfected earlier.

I. Basic Raw Materials

   A. Wood Materials

Bast fibers	Wood fibers

   B. Nonwood Materials

Rags	Straw	Old paper
Cotton fibers		

II. Basic Types, Kinds of Paper

Box board	Ledger	Stationery
Book stock	Newsprint	Wall board
Card	Coated	Wrap

III. Basic Paper Products

Art materials	Household	Newspapers
Books	Insulation	Packaging
Drawing	Magazines	Plastics
Novelties	Photographic	Building

IV. Basic Processes

A. Manual

Cutting	Wrapping	Sealing
Folding		

B. Mechanical

Cutting	Fourdrinier	Packaging
Folding	Laminating	Pressing

C. Chemical

Bleaching	Coating	Waterproofing
Coloring	Preserving	

D. Thermal

Drying	Cooking

V. Basic Occupations and Occupational Fields

A. Management

Administration	Finance	Records
Supervision	Legal	Sales
Personnel	Purchasing	Plant engr.

B. Technical, Scientific

Chemists	Technicians	Servicemen
Mechanical engr.	Tradesmen	

C. Production

Operators	Cutters	Assemblers

D. Design, Development

Designer	Artist	Inventor

VI. Representative Functional Components

Research	Chemistry	Products
Invention	Measurement	Manufacturing
Design	Materials	Finishing
Development	Processes	Fourdrinier
Engineering	Evaluation	Packaging
Management	Safety	Standards
Production		Utilization

The Plastics Industries

The development of the plastics industries has been little short of phenomenal since World War II. Today this group of industries produces the plastics materials known as synthetics, as well as the products made from these materials. The first synthetic plastic was made in 1868 by John Wesley Hyatt of Albany, New York. Chemically it was cellulose nitrate and came to be called celluloid. The next major development was that of Bakelite in 1909. Since then fifty or more new plastics compounds have been developed and used commercially. The industry employs relatively few people, but with its highly mechanized and automated production, plastics products are so common today that one might assume that the materials had been in use as long as those with which they compete. The plastics industries include four distinct types of operations. These are: the production of the plastics materials; molding and extrusion to make molded products; the fabrication to manufacture products from sheet, rod and tube plastics; and lamination which impregnates other materials with plastics and produces sheet, rod, and tubes, and fabricated products.

I. Basic Types of Plastics

A. Thermosetting

Analine-formaldehyde	Phenol-formaldehyde	Polyesters
Phenol-furfurfal	Aminos	

B. Thermoplastic

Acetates	Nitrates	Vinyls
Acrylics	Polyethylene	Polystyrene
Casein		

II. Basic Processes

A. Manual

| Carving | Cementing | Grinding |
| Forming | Fabricating | Polishing |

B. Mechanical

| Casting | Fabricating | Laminating |
| Calendering | Cold molding | Pulp molding |

C. Thermal

Blowing	Drawing	Laminating
Compression mold	Extrusion	Post-forming
Contact mold	Injection	Pulp molding

D. Chemical

| Bonding | Manufacturing |

III. Basic Products

A. Industrial

Adhesives	Insulation	Tools
Bottles	Parts	Tubing
Chemicals	Paints	

B. Household

| Appliances | Furniture | Utensils |
| Novelties | Table tops | Toys |

C. Personal

| Clothing | Footwear | Pens |
| Jewelry | Novelties | Pencils |

D. Construction

| Adhesives | Flooring | Preservatives |
| Finishes | Paneling | Windows |

IV. Basic Occupations and Occupational Fields

    A. Management

Administration	Finance	Records
Supervision	Legal	Sales
Personnel	Purchasing	Plant engr.
Planning		

    B. Technical, Scientific

Chemists	Physicists	Tool- and die-
Engineers	Machinists	makers
Researchers	Welders	Pipefitters
		Servicemen

    C. Production

Assemblers	Operators	Packers

    D. Design, Development

Artists	Designers	Modelers

V. Representative Functional Components

Research	Materials	Management
Invention	Processes	Distribution
Design	Products	Service
Development	Manufacturing	Utilization
Experiment	Inspection	Integration
Engineering	Measurement	Safety
Chemistry	Analysis	
Production	Standards	

The Rubber Industries

The first rubber products manufacturing plant in the United States was the Roxbury India Rubber Company in Roxbury, Massachusetts, established in 1832. The early rubber products were less than satisfactory, however, because when exposed to heat, they became sticky and when exposed to cold, they became hard and brittle. Charles Goodyear's discovery of the process of vulcanization in 1839 eliminated these defects and opened the way to the development of the great rubber industry. World War II, with the attendant shortage of natural latex, prompted the perfection of synthetic latex which since that time has made possible the discovery of even more uses for rubber. At this writing, atomic radiation is past the experimental stage for curing automobile tires. Synthetic rubber and plastic are closely related, and the merging of these industries today is common.

I. Basic Types of Rubber

  A. Natural

Wild	Smoked sheet	Crepe

  B. Synthetic

GR-S	Buna-S	Neoprene
Butyl		

  C. Reclaim

II. Basic Processes

  A. Manual

Molding	Cutting	Assembling

  B. Mechanical

Mixing	Molding	Calendering
Cutting	Extruding	Plasticating
Beating		

  C. Chemical

Evaporating	Washing	Coloring
Coagulating	Reacting	Drying

  D. Thermal

Drying	Curing	Vulcanizing

III. Basic Products

  A. Industrial

Belting	Insulation	Sheeting
Tires	Tube	Accessories

  B. Power, Transportation

Insulation	Tubing	Flooring
Tires	Seals	Adhesives

C. Construction

Paints	Coatings	Flooring
Upholstery	Seals	Adhesives

D. Household

Adhesives	Utensils	Accessories
Upholstery	Insulation	Mats

E. Personal

Footwear	Sporting goods	Toys

IV. Basic Occupations and Occupational Fields

A. Management

Administration	Finance	Records
Supervision	Legal	Sales
Personnel	Purchasing	Plant engr.
Planning		

B. Technical, Scientific

Chemists	Engineers	Tool- and
Physicists	Draftsmen	diemakers
Researchers	Machinists	Patternmakers
		Maintenance

C. Production

Operators	Builders	Finishers
Millmen	Curers	Packers

D. Design, Development

Artists	Designers	Inventors

V. Representative Functional Components

Research	Measurement	Standards
Invention	Materials	Machines
Design	Processes	Equipment
Experiment	Products	Utilization
Development	Manufacturing	Controls
Engineering	Inspection	Management
Chemistry		Safety

The Textiles Industries

The textiles industries may be considered to have had their origin in the discovery of weaving—the interlacing of threads in an over-and-under pattern. Evidence exists that the Egyptians were weaving as early as 3,500 B.C. with spun cotton fibers. Many of the most significant inventions of the eighteenth century were in the fields of textiles production, particularly the production of threads for weaving. These included John Kay's fly shuttle in 1733, James Hargreave's spinning jenny in 1764, and Richard Arkwright's water frame in 1768. The beginning of American power-driven factories is said to have been Samuel Slater's cotton textile thread mill in Pawtuckett, Rhode Island, in 1790. This preceded by three years Eli Whitney's cotton gin. The introduction of synthetic cotton, called rayon, in this country in the early 1920's, started a revolution in the textiles industries. Today several different synthetic fibers are used in textile products that rival both wool and cotton.

I. Basic Raw Materials

    A. Plant Fibers

Bamboo	Cotton	Flax

    B. Animal Fibers

Hair	Silk	Wool

    C. Mineral Fibers

Asbestos	Glass	Metallic

    D. Snythetic Fibers

Cellulose	Nylon	Orlon

II. Typical Basic Processes

    A Manual

Braiding	Embroidery	Sewing
Carding	Knitting	Spinning
Dyeing	Printing	Weaving

B. Mechanical

Bolting	Cutting	Spinning
Braiding	Ginning	Warping
Carding	Knitting	Weaving
Decorating	Printing	Combing

C. Chemical

Bleaching	Dyeing	Sizing
Compounding	Finishing	

D. Thermal

Drying	Pressing	Laminating

III. Basic Products

A. Industrial

Belting	Insulation	Rope
Covering	Lamination	Upholstery

B. Construction

Acoustics	Insulation	Floor covering
Decoration	Rope	Wall covering

C. Household

Bedding	Ornaments	Upholstery
Draperies	Rugs	Wall covering

D. Personal

Clothing	Medical supplies	Ornament

IV. Basic Occupations and Occupational Fields

A. Management

Administration	Finance	Records
Supervision	Legal	Sales
Personnel	Purchasing	Plant engr.
Planning		

B. Technical, Scientific

Researchers	Physicists	Tradesmen
Chemists	Engineers	Servicemen

C. Production

Operators	Weavers	Assemblers

D. Design, Development

Artists	Designers	Inventors

V. Representative Functional Components

Research	Processes	Standards
Invention	Products	Operation
Design	Decorating	Tools
Experiment	Manufacturing	Machines
Development	Measurement	Testing
Engineering	Utilization	Inspection
Chemistry	Evaluation	Management
Materials	Production	

The Tools and Machines Industries

As industrialization progressed through the nineteenth century and into the twentieth, industries had increasing difficulty in designing and making their own production tools and machines. The manufacture of such items soon became an important industry. This type of production is reputed to be the most difficult to automatize because of the nature of the processes involved. The tools and machines category includes the production of all tools, machines, and equipment used in other manufacturing and service industries, and includes much more than the recognized machine-tool industry. Because of the nature of the production, the tools and machines industries depend largely on skilled craftsmen using machine tools for the construction of their products. Precision is essential, and much scientific study, experimentation, invention, and designing is required to develop new machines for new processes and for new materials.

I. Basic Categories

Hand tools	Production machines	Dies, jigs
Machine tools	Production systems	Conveyors

II. Basic Materials

Ceramics	Plastics	Textiles
Metals	Rubber	Woods

III. Basic Processes

(See Manufacturing Industries category for processes for respective materials.)

IV. Basic Occupations and Occupational Fields

A. Management

Administration	Finance	Records
Supervision	Legal	Sales
Personnel	Purchasing	Plant engr.

B. Technical, Scientific

Researchers	Mechanical engr.	Ceramics engr.
Chemists	Tool engr.	Electronics engr.
Physicists	Electrical engr.	Servicemen
Mathematicians	Machinists	Instrumentmakers

C. Production

Machinists	Assemblers	Welders
Operators	Molders	Electricians
Technicians	Coremakers	Patternmakers

D. Design, Development

Tool designers	Industrial designers	Inventors

V. Representative Functional Components

Research	Materials	Utilization
Invention	Processes	Mechanism
Design	Products	Controls
Experiment	Standards	Construction
Development	Systems	Structures
Representations	Circuits	Management
Models	Installation	
Integration	Production	
Manufacturing	Safety	

The Woods Industries

The woods industries for this study include lumbering and wood products manufacturing. In the early settlement of the country, trees provided only three or four types of materials, most of which were lumber and fuel. Today an estimated sixty per cent of the harvested tree goes into the manufacture of chemicals, and the prediction is that this proportion will increase. Much of the tree that was formerly discarded is now converted into cellulose, a basic ingredient in plastics. The many new uses for wood being developed demonstrate that the wood products industries are approaching their greatest period of development. This is in answer to the predictions of a few decades ago that wood would soon be replaced by other materials.

I. Common Commercial Woods

    A. Hardwoods

Oak	Birch	Cherry
Ash	Maple	Basswood
Elm	Walnut	Hickory

    B. Softwoods

White pines	Spruce	Cedar
Yellow pines	Fir	Balsam

    C. Foreign Woods

Mahogany	Grenadilla	Ebony
Teak	Rosewood	Satinwood

II. Basic Processes

    A. Manual

Carving	Fabricating	Planing
Forming	Filing	Sanding
Sawing	Fitting	Scraping
Boring	Joining	Decorating

    B. Mechanical

Sawing	Bending	Laminating
Planing	Shaping	Veneering

Boring	Sanding	Forming
Turning	Texturing	Mortising

C. Chemical

Distilling	Gluing	Preserving
Extracting	Dyeing	Dissolving
Finishing	Plasticizing	Fireproofing

D. Thermal

Drying	Burning	Etching
Steaming	Cooking	

III. Basic Wood Products

A. Lumber

   1. Industrial lumber

Containers	Machines	Toys
Furniture	Vehicles	Utensils
Musical instr.	Sports goods	Tools

   2. Construction lumber (for buildings)

Agricultural	Industrial	Public
Commercial	Transportation	Private
Governmental		

   3. Veneer, including plywood

Construction	Packaging	Decoration
Transportation	Compregnating	Miscellaneous

B. Woods as Chemicals

   1. Sawdust

Wood flour	Wood hydrolysis

   2. Pulpwood

Paper	Plastics

   3. Bolts, limbs, stumps, etc.

Extractives	Distillates

C. Miscellaneous

Fuel	Litter	Turpentine
Timber	Hardboard	Rosin

Ties	Drugs	Balsam
Oils	Dye	Bats
Teas	Insulation	Cooperage
Pipes	Foods	Matches

IV. Basic Occupations and Occupational Fields

   A. Management

Administration	Finance	Records
Supervision	Legal	Sales
Personnel	Purchasing	Plant engr.

   B. Technical, Scientific

Foresters	Botanists	Architects
Chemists	Engineers	Woodworkers

   C. Production

Lumber mfg.	Construction	Trades
Wood products	Chemicals	

   D. Design, Development

Artists	Designers	Inventors
Architects		

V. Representative Functional Components

Research	Tree farming	Management
Invention	Lumbering	Application
Design	Materials	Manufacturing
Development	Processes	Testing
Experiment	Products	Services
Chemistry	Tools	Integration
Measurement	Evaluation	Standards
Production	Machines	Utilization
	Safety	

THE CONSTRUCTION INDUSTRIES

The magnitude of the construction industries in this country is everywhere apparent today as one sees schools, hospitals, industrial plants, military installations, highways, expressways, shopping centers, and private housing being built wherever one goes. The use of mechanized processes, heavy equipment, and factory manufacture has made construction largely industrial in operation today in contrast to the handcraft building practices of a few years ago. Taken from the preliminary analysis of the construction industries, the *architectural elements* and the *construction elements* were drawn out and used here as the sources of the functional components. These were considered applicable to, and inherent in, the various types of construction: residential, community-civic, commercial, industrial, transportation, and governmental.

I. Architectural Elements as Functional Components

  A. Design

Aesthetics	Philosophies	Standards
History	Authorities	Periods

  B. Engineering

Architectural	Electrical	Air conditioning
Structural	Civil	Sanitation
Heating	Lighting	

  C. Materials

Ceramics	Plastics	Wood
Leather	Rubber	Paper
Metals	Textiles	Miscellaneous

  D. Planning

Functional	Financial	Legal controls
Community	Estimated	Contracts

  E. Presentations

Sketches	Picturial	Plumbing
Floor plans	Models	Electrical
Working drawing	Plats	Air conditioning
Detailing	Structural	Landscaping

  F. Specifications

Materials	Bids	Structures
Standards	Costs	Time
Equipment	Finishes	Quality

G. Standards

Structural	Quality	Lighting
Materials	Quantity	Electrical
Process	Professional	Heating
Application	Codes	Sanitary

H. Structures

| Wood | Brick | Block |
| Concrete | Tile | Metal |

I. Supervision

| Planning | Estimating | Construction |
| Design | Specifications | Equipment |

II. Construction Elements as Functional Components

A. Air Conditioning

| Controls | Deodorizing | Smoke control |
| Cooling | Filtering | Heating |

B. Carpentry

| Materials | Standards | Structures |
| Processes | Fastening | |

C. Communications

| Intercom. | Telephone | Tube |
| Television | Piped music | |

D. Decoration

Color	Flooring	Texturing
Draperies	Rugs	Wallpaper
Furniture	Painting	Accessories

E. Earth Moving

| Excavating | Filling | Grading |
| Ditching | | |

F. Electrical

| Conveyors | Heating | Power |
| Filtering | Lighting | Communications |

G. Flooring

| Design | Installation | Maintenance |
| Finishing | | |

H. Furnishings

Appliances	Draperies	Rugs
Dinnerware	Furniture	Upholstery

I. Heating

Controls	Installation	Types
Fuel	Maintenance	Services

J. Masonry

Applications	Finishing	Materials
Curing	Forms	Preparation

K. Lighting

Controls	Natural	Practice
Electrical	Principles	Wiring

L. Refrigeration

Air conditioning	Dehumidifying	Freezing

M. Roofing

Applications	Materials	Standards

N. Sanitation

Equipment	Sewage	Systems
Legislation	Services	Water

O. Structures

Applications	Materials	Strengths
Fastenings	Pre-fabrications	Types

P. Transportation

Bridges	Escalators	Streets
Elevators	Highway	Grade separations
Parking		

III. Basic Occupations and Occupational Fields

A. Management

Supervision	Finance	Records
Management	Legal	Sales
Personnel	Purchasing	Plant engr.

B. Technical, Scientific

Architects	Operators	Draftsmen
Engineers	Technicians	Craftsmen
Contractors	Inventors	Researchers

THE POWER INDUSTRIES

Machines without power are useless. In a study of technology one discovers the amazing rapidity of conversion from hand process to mechanization in American industry. This conversion was possible to the extent that better sources of power than muscles were developed. The total work output in the United States from all sources, including wind, water, minerals, fuels, and wood fuel, in 1850 is estimated as 10.3 billion horsepower hours. This increased to some 78 billion by 1900 and 675 by 1950, according to Dewhurst (39, p. 908). Today the shift to mineral, including coal and petroleum, sources of energy for power is nearly complete. However, power from atomic energy is now the hope in certain sections of our country, as well as in many foreign countries.

I. Powerplants

    A. Internal Combustion

        1. Types

Reciprocation	Rocket	Jet
Turbine		

        2. Principles

Operation	Mechanical	Cooling
Controls	Lubrication	Muffling
Carburetion	Thermal	

        3. Components

Battery	Rod	Muffler
Block	Crank	Piston
Blower	Distributor	Radiator
Camshaft	Injector	Spark plug
Carburetor	Impeller	Supercharger
Controls	Magneto	Valve
Flywheel	Pump	Miscellaneous

        4. Fuels

Distillate	Gasoline	L-P
Gas	Kerosine	

5. Engineering Standards

Combustion	Efficiency	Clearances
Compression	Materials	Torque

6. Applications

Transportation	Agricultural	Recreational
Industrial	Domestic	Scientific

B. External Combustion

1. Types

Cylinder	Turbine

2. Principles

Operation	Mechanical	Thermal
Control	Lubrication	Insulating

3. Components

Cylinder	Crosshead	Governor
Piston	Boiler	Controls
Valve	Rod	Vane
Flywheel	Condenser	

4. Fuels

Coal	Oil	Atomic

5. Engineering standards

Efficiency	Clearances	Power
Materials	Torque	Ratings

6. Applications

Industrial	Stationary	Recreation

C. Electric Motors, Generators

1. Types

D.C.	Repulsion	Two-phase
A.C.	Synchronous	Three-phase
Induction	Single-phase	

2. Principles

Operating	Mechanical	Controls

3. Components

Armature	Brushes	Bearings
Slator	Slip rings	Frame
Commutator	Controls	Leads

4. Engineering standards

Efficiency	Materials	Torque
Insulation	Circuits	Power

5. Applications

Transportation	Construction	Domestic
Industrial	Stationary	Recreational
Agricultural		

II. Power Transmission

A. Electrical

Generation	Conduction	Transforming

B. Mechanical

Belt	Gear	Pressure
Chain	Screw	Fluid
Crank	Shaft	Sound wave

C. Hydraulic

Pumps	Fluid	Motors

D. Pneumatic

Vacuum pump	Compressor	System

III. Basic Materials

Ceramic	Plastics	Textiles
Metal	Rubber	

IV. Basic Occupation and Occupational Fields

A. Management

Administration	Finance	Records
Supervision	Legal	Sales
Personnel	Purchasing	Plant engr.

B. Technical, Scientific

Researchers	Mathematician	Tradesmen
Chemists	Engineers	Services
Physicists	Mechanics	

C. Production

Molders	Blacksmiths	Technicians
Machinists	Welders	Electricians
Assemblers	Inspectors	Patternmakers

D. Design, Development

Researchers	Inventors	Designers

V. Representative Functional Components

Research	Physics	Mechanisms
Invention	Models	Controls
Design	Materials	Construction
Development	Processes	Manufacture
Engineering	Principles	Services
Experiment	Standards	Operation
Testing	Systems	Management
Chemistry	Circuits	Utilization
Safety		

THE TRANSPORTATION INDUSTRIES

Transportation development in the United States is an integral part of all industrial development. It has become as essential in the American way of living as has communications. Both are considered as basic socializing agencies. The increasing specialization in economic activity which has accompanied industrialization has made people individually and socially interdependent for nearly all of the material needs in living. Without equivalent developments in transportation, this interdependency would not be possible. Transportation takes raw materials to the factory and delivers products to every community in the country. It moves materials through the processing in the factory. People depend on the automobile to the extent of over 600 billion passenger miles annually, and the common carriers provide some 150 billion. For this study the transportation industries include both the manufacture of the equipment and the operation of the transportation systems.

Airways, Spaceways

I. Aircraft Types

Airplane	Glider	Rocket
Helicopter	Blimp	Space ship

II. Powerplants

  A. Types

Reciprocating	Turbo-prop	Jet
Turbine	Rocket	

  B. Components

Ignition systems	Electrical	Cooling
Fuels and systems	Hydraulic	Mechanical

III. Aircraft Structures

  A. Materials

Metals	Plastics	Ceramics
Textiles	Rubber	Wood

  B. Fastening

Welding	Bolting	Sewing
Bonding	Riveting	

  C. Components

Fuselage	Stabilizer	Landing gear
Wing	Rudder	Instruments
Accommodations	Controls	Communications

IV. Aircraft Transport Operations

  A. Instruments

Engine	Flight	Communications

  B. Navigation

Dead reckoning	Charts	Radio
Maps	Celestial	Radar

C. Meteorology

Weather	Instruments	Reports

D. Services

Maintenance	Cleaning	Repair
Inspection	Lubrication	Rebuilding

E. Operation Levels

Private	Commercial	Military

F. Legislation

Local	Military	Testing
State	Licensing	Safety
C.A.A.	Regulation	

V. Basic Occupations and Occupational Fields

A. Management

Administration	Finance	Records
Supervision	Legal	Sales
Personnel	Purchasing	Plant eng.

B. Technical, Scientific

Research	Mathematics	Mechanics
Chemistry	Aerodynamics	Navigation
Physics	Electronics	Servicemen

C. Production

Lofting	Assembly	Test
Manufacture	Inspection	

D. Operations

Pilots	Traffic	Licensing
Crews	Passenger	Communications
Services	Freight	Military

E. Design, Development

Research	Materials	Testing
Experiment	Structures	Processes
Engineering	Standards	Safety

VI. Representative Functional Components

Research	Models	Manufacture
Invention	Lofting	Operation
Design	Materials	Services
Experiment	Structures	Controls
Engineering	Processes	Communications
Testing	Standards	Powerplants
Development	Fastening	Military
Regulation	Safety	Management
Legislation	Human factors	Evaluation
Integration		Utilization

Highway Vehicles

I. Types of Vehicles

Automobile	Truck	Miscellaneous

II. Basic Materials

Ceramics	Metals	Rubber
Leather	Plastics	Textiles

III. Vehicular Components

A. Internal Combustion Engines

Gasoline	Turbine	Diesel

B. Electric Power

Motors	Current	Controls
Drives		

C. Fuel Systems

Carburetion	Injection	Supercharging

D. Ignition Systems

Battery	Distributor	Spark plugs
Magneto	Coil	Wiring

E. Electrical Systems

Battery	Generator	Lighting

F. Lubrication Systems

Engines	Drives	Chassis

G. Cooling Systems

Liquid	Air	

H. Starting Systems

Electric	Gasoline	Auxiliary

I. Hydraulic Systems

Brakes	Steering	Lifts

J. Drives

Transmission	Transfer case	Differential
Torque convert.	Clutch	2-wheel
Overdrive	Drive shaft	4-wheel

K. Body, Chassis

Frame	Suspension	Steering
Unitized	Shock absorber	Body

L. Brakes

Mechanical	Electric	Pneumatic
Hydraulic		

M. Tires

Types	Sizes	Grades

IV. Basic Occupations and Occupational Fields

A. Management

Administration	Finance	Records
Supervision	Legal	Sales
Personnel	Purchasing	Plant engr.

B. Technical, Scientific

Research	Mathematics	Operators
Chemists	Engineering	Craftsmen
Physics	Mechanics	Services

C. Production

Operator	Inspector	Finisher
Assembler	Tester	Technician

D. Design, Development

Engineer	Modeler	Industrial design.
Inventor	Artist	

E. Transportation Systems, Bus and Truck

| Terminals | Scheduling | Services |
| Routes | Dispatching | Operation |

F. Allied Fields

Petroleum	Parts mfg.	Agencies
production	Tire mfg.	Salvage
Service station		

V. Representative Functional Components

Research	Operation	Systems
Invention	Selection	Mechanics
Design	Purchase	Service
Experiment	Regulations	Safety
Engineering	Powerplants	Management
Testing	Chassis	Materials
Models	Mechanisms	Processes
Manufacture	Circuits	Legislation
Distribution	Safety	Utilization

Highways

I. Basic Components

| Roads | Bridges | Grade separations |
| Streets | Turnpikes | Parking |

II. Engineering Elements

Surveys	Costs	Materials
Soil tests	Contracts	Processes
Estimates	Standards	Supervision
Planning	Safety	

III. Construction Elements

A. Materials

| Rock | Brick | Timber |
| Concrete | Bituminous | Steel |

B. Processes

Cutting	Rolling	Forms
Filling	Pouring	Coffer dams
Grading	Finishing	Piling
Tamping	Oiling	Ballast

C. Equipment

Earthmovers	Shovels	Tampers
Dozers	Draglines	Mixers
Clams	Back hoes	Finishers
Oilers	Rollers	Markers

IV. Services

Repairs	Preserving	De-icing
Painting	Weed control	Snow removal

V. Traffic Controls, Regulations

Local	Controls systems	Standards
State	Signs	Penalties
National	Enforcement	Safety

VI. Basic Occupations and Occupational Fields

A. Management

Administration	Finance	Records
Supervision	Legal	Sales
Personnel	Purchasing	Services

B. Technical, Scientific

Research	Engineering	Maintenance
Chemistry	Hydraulics	Repair
Mathematics	Communications	

C. Production

Surveys	Oiling	Rolling
Grading	Topping	Forms
Laying	Finishing	Structures

D. Design, Development

Community planning	National planning	Engineering
Regional planning	Traffic patterns	

VII. Representative Functional Components

Research	Presentations	Construction
Invention	Materials	Structures
Design	Processes	Regulation
Development	Equipment	Safety
Engineering	Principles	Legislation
Experiment	Services	Management
Surveys	Standards	Maintenance
Models	Evaluation	Utilization

Railways

I. Types

Common carriers	Street	Industrial

II. Car Types

Passenger	Mail	Freight

III. Track

Standard	Road bed	Bridges
Narrow	Yards	Tunnels
Monorail	Spurs	

IV. Powerplants

A. Types

Steam	Electric	Gasoline
Diesel	Turbine	Experimental

B. Locomotives
   Freight   Industrial   Yard
   Passenger

V. Railway Operations

A. Trains
   Agent   Controls   Crews
   Dispatcher

B. Terminals
   Yards   Elevators   Freight houses
   Stations   Docks

C. Services
   Section crews   Car barns   Bridge and bldg.
   Round houses   Signal   Engineering

VI. Basic Occupations and Occupational Fields

A. Management
   Administration   Finance   Records
   Supervision   Legal   Sales
   Personnel   Purchasing   Plant engr.

B. Technical, Scientific
   Research   Mechanics   Technicians
   Engineering   Tradesmen   Servicemen
   Electronics   Operators   Traffic

C. Production
   Manufacture   Inspection   Tradesmen
   Assembly

D. Design, Development
   Engineering   Invention   Industrial design

E. Operations (See V.)

VII. Representative Functional Components

Research	Standards	Structures
Invention	Materials	Construction
Design	Processes	Services
Engineering	Products	Management
Experiment	Manufacture	Power plants
Models	Utilization	Safety
Development	Operation	Legislation
Controls	Regulation	Evaluation
	Safety	

Waterways

I. Carriers

Liners	Tankers	Yachts
Freighters	Ferries	Boats
Barges	Merchantmen	Naval types

II. Powerplants

A. Types

Steam	Gasoline	Outboard
Diesel	Electric	Inboard

B. Propulsion

Screw	Paddle wheel	Sail

III. Ship, Boat Building

Design	Marine engr.	Materials
Experiment	Lofting	Processes
Model	Standards	Finishes
Test	Structures	Manufacture

IV. Shipping Operation

Scheduling	Piloting	Sailing
Loading	Communications	Services
Unloading	Docking	Terminals

V. Basic Occupations and Occupational Fields

A. Management

Administration	Finance	Records
Supervision	Legal	Sales
Personnel	Purchasing	Plant engr.

B. Technical, Scientific

Research	Communications	Services
Engineering	Operators	Technicians
Marine archit.	Tradesmen	

C. Shipbuilding

Operators	Inspectors	Craftsmen
Assemblers		

VI. Representative Functional Components

Research	Standards	Regulation
Invention	Materials	Powerplants
Design	Processes	Services
Development	Manufacture	Shipping
Experiment	Models	Communications
Engineering	Inspection	Management
Architecture	Operation	Utilization
Testing	Products	Equipment
Controls	Legislation	Safety

Conveyors

I. Basic Types

Assembly line	Elevator	Belt
Escalator	Pipe line	Link

II. Drives

Electric	Automatic controls	Instruments
Hydraulic		

III. Applications

Loading	Parts processing	In-plant

Unloading	Bulk carriers	Commercial
Transporting	Lifting	Transcontinental
Parts transfer	Lowering	

IV. Basic Occupations and Occupational Fields

A. Management

Administration	Finance	Records
Supervision	Legal	Sales
Personnel	Purchasing	Plant engr.

B. Technical, Scientific

Research	Engineering	Operators
Metallurgy	Electronics	Technicians
Mathematics	Mechanics	Hydraulics

C. Production

| Manufacture | Assembly | Inspection |

D. Design, Development

| Research | Materials | Principles |
| Design | Engineering | Components |

E. Services

| Installation | Operation | Repair |
| Maintenance | | |

V. Representative Functional Components

Research	Manufacture	Operation
Invention	Processes	Controls
Design	Construction	Automation
Engineering	Structures	Materials
Development	Principles	Services
Models	Installation	Management
Applications	Legislation	Safety
Presentations	Standards	Evaluation
		Utilization

THE ELECTRONIC INDUSTRIES

The first electronic product manufactured for mass consumption was the radio receiver, the development of which was dependent on the vacuum tube. With further research and experiment the transmitting characteristics were applied to other uses; the most significant one for industry is probably that of electronic controls in automatic production. The importance of electronics for all of industry is implicit in the fact that more money is being spent annually for research in this group of industries than in any other included in this study. According to present thinking, the more automatic that machines become, the more electronic they will be.

I. Fields for Applications

    A. Industrial

Computers	Transfer	Measurement
Controls	Correction	Regulation

    B. Communications

Radio	Telephone	Telegraph
Radar	Recording	Television

    C. Therapeutics

Electrotherapy	Electroencephalograph
Neurocalograph	Ultrasonic wave
Electrocardiogram	Pacemaker

    D. Research

Radiotelescope	Betatron	Electron microscope

    E. Accounting

Calculating	Statistics	Sorting
Records	Computations	

    F. Transportation

Meteorology	Communications	Controls

    G. Household

Air conditioning	Lighting	Controls
Communications	Cooking	Musical

H. Personal

| Hearing aids | Communication | Psychogal-vanometer |

II. Basic Materials

| Metals | Plastics | Textiles |
| Ceramics | Paper | Woods |

III. Representative Products

Receivers	Telephones	Intercom
Transmitters	Amplifiers	Detectors
Hearing aids	Computers	Oscilloscopes
Public address systems	Phonographs	Cameras
Generators	Telegraph	Conductors
Instruments	Television	Components

IV. Basic Technical Components

Electricity	Measurement	Generators
Magnetism	Circuits	Motors
Electron theory	Condensers	Transmitters
Current	Inductance	Rectifiers
Cells	Transformers	Converters
Conductors	Relays	Tubes, transistors

V. Basic Occupations and Occupational Fields

A. Management

Administration	Finance	Records
Supervision	Legal	Sales
Personnel	Purchasing	Plant engr.

B. Technical, Scientific

| Physics | Metallurgy | Technicians |
| Mathematics | Engineering | Craftsmen |

C. Production

| Manufacture | Inspection | Installation |
| Assembly | Test | |

D. Operation

Field	Industrial	Governmental
Studio	Military	Private

E. Design, Development

Research	Engineering	Industrial Design
Invention		

VI. Representative Functional Components

Research	Integration	Standards
Invention	Principles	Manufacture
Experiment	Theories	Installation
Design	Circuits	Operation
Development	Systems	Services
Engineering	Materials	Management
Physics	Processes	Legislation
Mechanics	Components	Safety
Safety	Controls	Utilization

INDUSTRIAL RESEARCH:
THE INDUSTRY OF DISCOVERY

Research and development produce new materials and new processes which affect new products and new services, which bring new industries, which in turn bring new occupations, and then more products. Altogether this involves cycles of searching, discovering, developing, producing, and perfecting, which bring about the dynamics of an ever-changing technology. Much research is carried on today by private research corporations with their own facilities and staffs. Expenditures for basic research, where the purposes are purely for the discovery of new knowledge without regard to its immediate application in products, is a new venture for industry. Private industrial research firms spent about four billion dollars for research in 1953; in 1960 this had grown to approximately eight billion.

I. Basic Types of Research

A. Pure: exploration of the universe

B. Applied: Solutions to contemporary problems

II. Drives to Industrial Research

    A. The New:

Materials	Uses	Sources
Methods	Solutions	Products
Knowledges	Applications	Ideas

    B. The Better:

Materials	Products	Applications
Methods	Solutions	Sources

    C. The Greater:

Efficiency	Simplification	Safety
Economy	Comfort	Potential
Convenience	Production	Usefulness
Luxury	Sales	Durability
Operating ease	Aesthetics	Distribution

    D. Lessened:

Labor	Supervision	Weight
Maintenance	Repair	Size
Costs	Complexity	

III. Fields for Industrial Research

    A. Manufacturing

Materials	Products	Machines
Processes	Tools	Distribution

    B. Construction

Materials	Processes	Safety
Structures	Fasteners	

    C. Transportation

Materials	Controls	Operation
Media	Safety	Regulation

    D. Power

Materials	Principles	Systems
Mechanisms	Circuits	Application

E. Electronics

| Applications | Components | Computers |
| Circuits | Controllers | Automation |

F. Services

| Tools | Instruments | Diagnosis |

G. Management

| Human engr. | Labor saving | Health, safety |

IV. Basic Occupations and Occupational Fields

A. Management

Administration	Finance	Records
Supervision	Legal	Distribution
Personnel	Purchasing	Services

B. Technical, Scientific

Chemists	Craftsmen	Draftsmen
Physicists	Designers	Writers
Engineers		

V. Representative Functional Components

Library	Design	Products
Searching	Drawing	Operation
Inventing	Models	Testing
Discovery	Construction	Measuring
Experiment	Materials	Evaluating
Creating	Processes	Refining
Study		Limitations
Integration		Utilization

THE SERVICE INDUSTRIES

The services industries were established in response to the need for skilled technical servicing to keep the many and diverse products of industry in operation for the consumer, whether this be in the home, business, or industry itself. Dewhurst (39, p. 731) gave the following estimates on service workers (exclusive of domestic service) as one class of the experienced civilian labor force: in 1940,

7.6% of the force were service workers; in 1950 the percentage was 8.0; and in 1953, 8.4%. In 1953 there was approximately one service worker for two industrial production workers. Indications are that the percentage of service workers will increase; at present, approximately seven million are so employed.

I. Basic Categories as Functional Components

    A. Maintaining

Refueling	Sharpening	Cleaning
Lubricating	Turning	Balancing

    B. Repairing

Breaks	Leaks	Adjustment
Wear	Shorts	

    C. Rebuilding

Renewing	Refinishing	Testing
Replacing	Inspecting	

    D. Installing

Assembly	Venting	Securing
Plumbing	Wiring	

    E. Refinishing

Removal	Resurfacing	Repainting

II. Service Areas

    A. Industrial

        1. Power

Generation	Transmission	Distribution

        2. Transportation

Powerplants	Railway	Waterway
Vehicles	Airway	Conveyors

        3. Communications

Industrial	Commercial	Personal

4. Construction

Equipment	Refrigeration	Communications
Housing	Furnishings	Structures
Air condition.	Floors	Painting
Plumbing	Roofing	Glass
Electrical	Lighting	Conveyors

5. Production machines

Machine tools	Controls	Systems

B. Commercial

Construction	Equipment	Product

C. Domestic

Housing	Appliances	Recreation

D. Miscellaneous

Musical instr.	Medical care	Military
School		

III. Basic Occupations and Occupational Fields

A. Management

Administration	Finance	Sales
Supervision	Legal	Records
Personnel	Purchase	Equipment

B. Technical, Scientific (See II. for Service Areas as Occupational Fields)

Engineers	Machinists	Electronics
Technicians	Electricians	Refrigeration
Installers	Finishers	Appliances
Mechanics	Welders	Communications

IV. Representative Functional Components

Research	Diagnosis	Products
Invention	Repair	Tools
Circuits	Rebuilding	Test equipment
Systems	Refinishing	Instruction

Mechanisms	Materials	Safety
Testing	Processes	Utilization
Standards		

INDUSTRIAL MANAGEMENT

An industry is considered to have two basic divisions: the productive and the nonproductive. The former is that part which earns the profits, and in a manufacturing industry, for example, it includes the departments actually making the product. The nonproductive part of the industry includes all of those departments which are needed to make production possible, but which are supported by the productive division. Management in industry is involved in both the productive and the nonproductive ends.

The technical aspects of industry have been developed through research, invention, and experiment, as have those of management. Here research has produced simplified systems of organization, production control, records, training, and such. The drive to increased efficiency employs methods analysis for simplification of work and for increasing production. It also results in an increasing use of mechanization and is leading to automation. Industrial psychology, psychology applied to industry, is a relatively new force in management. It is effective in the solutions to problems involving the human side of industry and is a tool of management. Human engineering is now a new body of subject matter for study in the management of industry.

I. Management as Organizational Method

  A. Primary Functions
    1. Establishment of objectives
    2. Establishment of lines of authority
    3. Assignment of responsibilities
    4. Recognition of human element

  B. Primary Organization Structure
    1. Development of operational systems
    2. Establishment of records systems
    3. Establishment of operating rules, regulations

    4. Exercise of leadership

  C. Types of Organization
    1. Line, scalar: direct flow of authority from supervisor to sub-supervisor, to worker
    2. Line and staff: the staff organization assisting the line organization
    3. Functional: several supervisors involved in the decisions
    4. Committee: final authority or limited authority; advisory or educational

II. Elements of Management as Functional Components

  A. Administration

Stockholders	Legislation	Statistics
Finance	Accounting	Credit

  B. Supervision

President	General mgr.	Foreman
Vice presidents	Superintendents	Leaders

  C. Personnel Relations

Employment	Safety	Insurance
Promotion	Health	Recreation
Discharge	Training	Food services

  D. Distribution

Sales	Advertising	Customer relations
Promotion	Packaging	Publicity

  E. Research

Experiment	Development	Processes
Application	Materials	Testing

  F. Product Development

Engineering	Aesthetics	Testing
Design	Evaluation	Drafting

  G. Production Planning

Planning	Material control	Routing
Purchasing	Scheduling	

H. Production

Parts mfg.	Sub-assembly	Final assembly
Finishing	Inspection	Testing

I. Plant Engineering

Standards	Tool design	Tool storage
Methods	Tool mfg.	Maintenance

J. Plant Services

Stores	Salvage	Shipping
Stock	Traffic	Transportation

K. The Society of Industry

Structure	Goals	Solutions
Levels	Problems	Influence

From Industries Analyses to Subject Matter

The preceding grouping and classification of industry included the basic categories of manufacturing, construction, power, transportation, electronics, management, research, and services. When analyzed, subject-matter content for industrial arts is revealed. These analyses now serve as guides for curriculum construction, from which courses of study for any level may be prepared. Such an approach to curriculum is not unknown to industrial arts. In fact, it has proved very workable. But any one of the individual outlines is not sufficiently complete as to require no further development for use in curriculum building. Each outline is to serve as a guide not only to the study of the respective industry but to a more complete development of the contained body of content. Any structure employed in such analyses must be sufficiently basic as to be representative, and it must be representative over a reasonable period of time. Consequently, in the selection of the divisions and subdivisions lies the key to usefulness. The structures employed herein seem to meet the requirements of representativity and durability fairly well. They have been used by the author for more than two decades. We hope that they will be good for another.

The functional components stand as individual bodies of knowledge, concepts, principles, or practices which may be studied. This idea will be developed later in the continuing search for subject matter.

TO DISCUSS, TO DEBATE, TO DECIDE

1. How can research be considered an industry?
2. What agency of the Federal government provides statistical information on industries?
3. Why must today's petroleum refineries be automated?
4. The foods industries have not usually been included for study in industrial arts. Can they be justifiably included?
5. The rubber and chemicals industries are not usually a part of industrial arts. What laboratory facilities would be essential to their study?
6. Does weaving give adequate representation to the textile industry?
7. What other basic areas of the woods industries, in addition to furniture, can be studied?
8. What relationship exists between the industries analyses and the functional components?
9. How could a teacher make use of one of the industries analyses in the laboratory?
10. What criteria should be used in adapting an industries analysis for study in the elementary school?

(Above) An early screw factory. Workmen here are cutting screws by hand as was the method before Henry Maudslay invented his screw-cutting lathe in 1800. With this it was possible to make an infinite number of identical screws and to cut screws of different pitches from one master lead screw through the use of change gears. (Courtesy: The DoAll Company.)

(Below) One of the world's largest crankshafts meets one of the smallest. The large crankshaft, weighing more than thirty tons, is being turned on a 120-inch lathe. It is to be used on an 1,800-ton pipe extrusion press. 120,000 pounds of counterweights were used to balance the forging during its 45-day turning operation. The small crankshaft is for a model airplane engine. It weighs .44 ounces. No task is too large nor too small for today's industry. (Courtesy: United States Steel Corporation.)

Industrial Arts:
A Reconsideration
of Its Functions

. . . technical education . . . is creative experience while you think, experience which realises your thought, experience which teaches you to coordinate act and thought, experience leading you to associate thought with foresight and foresight with achievement. Technical education gives theory and a shrewd insight as to where theory fails.

—Alfred North Whitehead, *The Aims of Education.* (New York: The Macmillan Company, 1929.)

Goals, objectives, and purposes for industrial arts have been studied and proclaimed for half a century. Those expressed in the earlier concepts have remained essentially unchanged through the years. This suggests that they were so fundamental, definitive, and inclusive as to have withstood the test of time. Whether or not they were, they are still with us. Emphasis and the methods of implementation alone change. Following the *Ohio Prospectus* in 1934 *(73)*, many state standards for industrial arts were revised with the new terminology and emphasis. Gordon Wilber's use in 1954 of desirable behavior changes *(94)* represents a philosophical reconsideration of objectives, which is in keeping with the current concern that education effects behavior changes in the individual. But Hostetler's study (82, pp. 11-22) as it identifies many of the accepted objectives, may suggest that such miscellany in purposes can only multiply confusion about objectives. (See p. 231)

A set of objectives for education in general is of little assistance for industrial arts, mathematics, or any of the other subject fields. Such programs must obviously make contributions to the whole of the educative purpose, but in so doing they must, first of all, have unique contributions by which they can stand on their own. By standing on its own objectives, each program can define its functions and identify its contributions. One of the purposes in a rethinking of industrial arts is to discover means for strengthening the structure so that it can stand firmly by itself. Another is to find ways of restructuring it so that it can either stand more firmly or take a new stance. Any fundamental consideration of objectives for American industrial arts is fundamental only as it is based on a rather clear understanding of the kind of person needed for a refining, strengthening, and advancing of the American way of life. Industrial arts objectives must contribute to his understanding of the culture in which he is growing, developing, and serving. They must enable him to gain a rather clear inventory of his own capacities as a human and charge him with a faith in human potential so that he can find increasing meaning for his own living as he interacts with his environment.

Industrial arts rightfully will aim at understanding the influences of technology on culture and will assist the individual in finding and developing his own capacities for improving this culture. Industrial arts will provide for the interaction of the individual with his technological environment in such manner as to draw him out to his fullest. He can best understand the technology as he becomes a party to it. In so doing, he comes to understand himself and his culture and thus finds meaning and purpose for his very being. But the "new" industrial arts has a concern even beyond this. This industrial arts will have as its all-encompassing goal the *advancing of technology* through the advancing of the human, who in turn advances through his understanding of technology. Each student is to be charged with that responsibility.

The following list of outcomes is rather typical of such statements as have appeared in industrial arts literature for several decades. Each item requires a score when used for evaluation purposes.

1. Proficiency in the use and care of hand tools.
2. Proficiency in the operation and care of machines.
3. Knowledge and skill in the wise use of industrial products.
4. Knowledge and understanding of the properties and uses of important raw materials.
5. Information concerning industrial occupations.
6. Ability to make practical applications of industrial arts skills at home.
7. The use of industrial arts in the leisure time activities of pupils.
8. The development of desirable attitudes toward work.
9. The development of appreciations of good workmanship.

Such statements emphasize some few unique contributions of industrial arts but they largely originate in, and are directed to, a concept which assigns highest value to technical competence and skill. We can legitimately ask whether such statements show concern for the development of the total of industrial arts and of the total of the student. The values represented are limited enough to suggest the answer. Such statements imply an inanimacy about industrial arts, so much so that neither the teacher nor his pupils can get very excited about it. This may account for the industrial arts graduate of the university or college who sees his job as "teaching shopwork" and his only challenge as introducing a better project now and then. Such a challenge, has not enough stimulation, invigoration, or inspiration to last the young teacher for his lifetime. It is no wonder, then, that his enthusiasm soon cools to boredom. He gets to believing that his greatest contribution to his profession is to complain. Nobody understands what industrial arts is. Nobody seems to consider it educationally respectable, not even the parents and especially not the administration. His shop has become the dumping ground for ill-mannered and incapable pupils. He takes the defensive against the school system and sees himself as standing alone for a program which he assumed was essential. Because this man is common, industrial arts over the country assumes the defensive, the position it has held since the middle fifties.

Such statements of purposes do not lead to understanding the technology and the role of the human in it. They lead nowhere except to the end of a dead-end street. We need statements of objectives that lead us along broad avenues of human experience to a full view of the technology, that man-made phenomenon to set all men free.

INDUSTRIAL ARTS FOR THE WHOLE CHILD

Industrial arts as one subject-matter program in the school makes its own unique contributions to the whole of education. But a feeling of doubt seems always to accompany a study of typical statements of objectives—doubt that these statements really identify the good that industrial arts can do. When all subject-matter programs in the school have their own unique contributions, supposedly all of them added together result in producing the kind of persons America needs, so far as schooling can.

This principle, which holds that education must be concerned with the whole child, has attracted a rather extensive following among educators. It rests on the assumption that one can analyze the individual so that his needs can be classified in terms of mathematics, history, industrial arts, and such. And when all facets of the school experience are added, they theoretically amount to a concern for the whole child just as enough apples added together make a bushel. For the child, however, this may not be true. And one reason may be that we really do not know the whole child well enough that we can tell when all of the necessary parts of his education are present.

If we propose that each subject-matter program be concerned with and directed to the whole child, this immediately requires an intensive search for meaning within that subject matter. It necessitates an understanding of what a whole person is and then an understanding of the full meaning of the subject matter. When these are achieved, mathematics for example, becomes tremendously more significant not only for the mathematician himself but for the student who may never be a mathematician. This student may gain greater growth and development toward the level of living of which humans are capable if he understands the meaning and purpose of mathematics and thus achieves a degree of liberation, at least from the common blind biases that mathematics exists for the sake of mathematics and mathematicians.

We propose here that industrial arts be concerned with the whole child if it finds justification for its existence. If it is to achieve full educative stature and respectability, even among its own disciples, however, it must be based on concern for the entire human. In no way does this imply that industrial arts can and should assume the full task of the entire educating of the child. It rather advises that in-dustrial arts can never become really important, really necessary, unless the teacher sees it as functioning fully for the whole child. The child who comes to the laboratory is always the whole child. Statements of objectives and purposes must then include concern for the child as well as for the technology. The student in industrial arts should understand its objectives so that he can grow with them. If he does not have them as his guide, he will devise his own, and they may not be in harmony with those of the teacher.

FUNCTIONS FOR THE NEW INDUSTRIAL ARTS. The term function is used here in preference to that of objective or purpose. It includes objec-tives and purposes and at the same time suggests a program of action. It encompasses values, directions, measures for evaluation, and impli-cations for means to the accomplishment of the mission.

The functions proposed for the industrial arts envisioned in this study are the *technical*, the *occupational*, the *consumer*, the *recrea-tional*, the *cultural*, and the *social*. They bear resemblance to the statement of functions in the *Ohio High School Standards* (59, pp. 10-12), to the purposes of industrial arts as expressed in the *Ohio Prospectus*—(73, pp. 93-94), and even to the outcomes of industrial arts as seen by Bonser and Mossman (20 pp. 14-16). The first five derive directly from the technological culture. The last, social, con-cerns the individual as the social creature who not only creates the technology but also must learn to live with it in the field of work as well as in leisure.

In the section following these functions are analyzed in outline form. The analyses serve at least five purposes. In the first place, they will enlighten the person who has wondered what industrial arts really is. Secondly, the analyses serve to identify the nature of industrial arts more completely, thus facilitating the definition of its scope and the setting of the limits to its province. They show us that there is much more good in industrial arts than may have been sus-pected. Thirdly, they may serve as guides in the selection of subject matter. Fourth, they serve as a basis upon which to evaluate industrial arts, and fifth, they may serve as sources of specific goals and ob-jectives. Altogether they support a reconsideration of the functions of industrial arts.

THE TECHNICAL FUNCTION:
THE SCIENCE OF THE INDUSTRIAL ARTS

Throughout the evolution of industrial arts, as described in Chapter I, the objective of technical skill has been most influential in determining the nature of the curriculum. Likewise, it has been most effective in shaping the physical shop or laboratory in which the curriculum is carried on. The industrial arts teacher is critically judged by his own professional fellows for his own technical competences rather than by his skill in teaching children. Industrial arts students often measure their own growth and development through industrial arts by their increasing technical competences rather than by their achievements as expressed in the other functions. The industrial arts program in undergraduate teacher education is likely directed most strongly to the accomplishment of the technical function. This attention to the technical does not necessarily mean that this function is the most important of the six although a great many industrial arts teachers would place it thus. It undoubtedly receives the most attention. But this could also be because it is the most readily accomplished and its achievements the most easily measured.

The technical function is well expressed by Wilber, in *Industrial Arts in General Education*, in his list of "Important Objectives of Industrial Arts":

1. To explore industry and American industrial civilization in terms of its organization, raw materials, processes, and operations, products, and occupations.
2. To develop a certain amount of skill in a number of basic industrial processes (94, pp. 42-43).

The American Vocational Association's *A Guide to Improving Instruction in Industrial Arts* includes "Shop Skills and Knowledge" among a list of nine objectives for industrial arts. Analysis of this objective is made in terms of "Student Behavior Changes Which Characterize the Objective":

1. He will be familiar with the common hand tools and be able to perform the common operations associated with them up to a standard compatible with his maturity level.
2. He will be familiar with the common industrial machines.
3. He will be able to use the common machines safely and effectively.

4. He will be able to perform the operations involved in doing simple jobs or in making simple projects.
5. He will be able to solve the problems that are involved in common types of construction and repair.
6. He will realize his limitations in handling and using common tools and machines (8, p. 28).

With the preceding as background, the following analysis of the technical function is made. It represents an interpretation of the technical mission of industrial arts. As such, it is an attempt to reflect the concept and spirit of industrial arts as herein conceived.

The Technical Function for the New Industrial Arts

Industrial arts seeks to acquaint the student with the technical principles and practices employed by industry as it provides materials, products, and services. It develops technical competences with materials, tools, machines, and products. In so doing, industrial arts involves the student during his search for better ideas and better ways in projects that require creating, problem-solving, designing, constructing, and developing. From this the student is expected not only to gain understandings and appreciations of contemporary technology, but to contribute to an advancing of that technology.

I. *Technical Elements* (Knowledges, Skills, Understandings, Appreciations)

A. How industry discovers, mines, refines, manufactures, classifies, distributes materials.

B. How industry employs technical processes and scientific principles to convert materials into products.

C. How industry designs, produces, uses, services machines and equipment.

D. How industry provides housing for industry, business, government, schools, homes.

E. How industry provides transportation of materials, products, animals, and people.

F. How industry produces, transmits, and utilizes power.

G. How industry provides, operates, and services communications media and systems.

H. How industry employs research in the development of materials, processes, products, and industries.
I. How industry employs organization, management, personnel, records, controls in the production of goods and services.
J. How industrial products are used, operated, maintained, and serviced in industry, government, business, home, school.
K. How the student can convert materials into products and projects by means of representative processes with machines and tools.
L. How the student can employ materials, processes, and products in the development of ideas and in the solutions to problems.

II. *Industrial Components*

A. Basic Materials

Types	Qualities	Manufacture
Kinds	Standards	Test
Sources	Processes	Use

B. Basic Processes

Hand	Chemical	Electrical
Mechanical	Thermal	Natural

C. Basic Products

Invention	Distribution	Use
Design	Structures	Test
Manufacture	Construction	Services

D. Basic Services

Power	Communication	Security
Transportation	Recreation	Household

E. Basic Industries

Manufacturing	Transportation	Research
Construction	Electronics	Services
Power		

III. *Representative Functional Components*

A. Industrial Design

Engineering	Styling	Models
Psychology	Redesign	Evaluation

B. Planning

| Estimating | Problem-solving | Drawing |
| Analyzing | Scheduling | Evaluating |

C. Inventing

| Imagining | Discovering | Experimenting |
| Creating | Legislating | Developing |

D. Presentations of Ideas

| Drawings | Models | Cut-aways |
| Photographs | Mock-ups | Charts |

E. Materials

Types	Sources	Manufacture
Kinds	Qualities	Test
Standards	Processes	Uses

F. Standards

| Interchangeability | Measures | Limits |
| Modular units | Symbols | Tolerance |

G. Processes

| Hand | Chemical | Electrical |
| Mechanical | Thermal | Nuclear |

H. Structures

| Joints | Fastening | Strengths |
| Frames | Unitized | Loads |

I. Construction

| Fitting | Assembly | Testing |
| Fastening | Inspection | Modification |

J. Mechanisms

| Generation | Motion | Machines |
| Transmission | Controls | Mechanics |

K. Circuits

| Regulating | Amplifying | Visual |
| On-off | Audio | Power |

L. Formulas

| Mathematical | Recipes | Mechanical |
| Chemical | Electrical | Empirical |

M. Manufacturing

| Materials | Assembly | Testing |
| Parts | Finishing | Shipping |

N. Inspection

| Standards | Testing | Procedures |

O. Systems

| Hydraulic | Thermal | Pneumatic |
| Electronic | Cooling | Automated |

P. Operation

| Control | Regulation | Capacity |
| Safety | Limitations | Utilization |

Q. Service

| Maintaining | Adjusting | Cleaning |
| Repairing | Lubricating | Rebuilding |

R. Products

| Selection | Testing | Manufacture |
| Use | Appraisal | Distribution |

THE OCCUPATIONAL FUNCTION: VOCATIONAL ORIENTATION

The inclusion of an occupational function may provoke a controversy within the industrial arts profession. Neither Woodward's manual training, Bennett's manual arts, nor Bonser's industrial arts included such a function. The *Ohio Prospectus* does refer to a vocational purpose:

> INDUSTRIAL ARTS is one of *Practical Arts*, a form of general or non-vocational education, which provides learners with experiences, understandings, and appreciations of materials, tools, processes, products and of the vocational conditions and requirements incident generally to the manufacturing and mechanical industries (73, p. 93).

Industrial arts is commonly seen as nonvocational in the sense of training for a particular job. However, the provision above for ". . . experiences, understandings, and appreciations of . . . the vocational conditions and requirements incident generally to the manufacturing and mechanical industries," suggests that industrial arts has a responsibility of a vocational nature. It has become increasingly important through the years that industrial arts provide the student with these experiences, understandings, and appreciations. Two reasons seem especially logical. One is that a study of American industry without concern for its occupations would be little more than a technical study. The second is that as industry becomes increasingly large, automatic, and complex, a young man or woman has increasing difficulty seeing himself as a part of it or making occupational choices. Then, too, with industrial arts centered on technology, a study of how man earns a living here is fundamental to a full comprehension of technology.

The occupational emphasis in industrial arts will vary with the level of the program. In the elementary school industrial occupations are studied to reveal how people earn livings. In the secondary school study and activity are occupationally oriented and directed to the search and discovery of talents. Trial occupational experiences are integrated with study and work. The student logically expects to find salability for his industrial arts competences since all of industrial production and services lead to the same. This economic by-product adds a degree of stature to the student's experience in industrial arts. The following analysis of the occupational function identifies the nature of an educational service which industrial arts should logically provide.

The Occupational Function in the New Industrial Arts

Industrial arts provides an orientation to the ways in which people earn their livelihoods in occupations within the technology. It acquaints the student with the nature, qualifications, purposes, and values in such occupations and helps him to see possible opportunities for himself therein. Industrial arts offers opportunity for the student to get exploratory, try-out experiences in basic industrial occupations.

I. Nature of the Occupational Considerations

   A. Jobs that Industries Provide

   B. How People Earn Their Livings in Industries

C. Changing Nature of the Job
D. Changing Concept of Work
E. Requirements for a Successful Work Experience
F. Opportunities for Private Business
G. Educational Requirements and Opportunities

II. Representative Occupational Information

A. Orientation

| Opportunities | Qualifications | Status |
| Requirements | | |

B. Guidance

| Testing | Counselling | Follow-up |
| Inventory | | |

C. Exploration

| Reading | Field trips | Interviews |
| Films | | |

D. Selection

| Criteria | Health | Evaluation |
| Techniques | Safety | |

E. Try-out

| Industrial arts | Co-op programs | Part-time work |
| Salable skills | | |

F. Entrance

| Applications | Employment | Credentials |
| Interviews | Evaluation | |

G. Rewards

| Salaries | Incentives | Security |
| Satisfactions | | |

H. Promotion

| Training | Experience | Responsibility |

III. Representative Functional Components

A. Competences

| Knowledges | Interests | Skills |
| Appreciations | | |

B. Attitudes

Work	Co-workers	Government
Supervision	Success	Values

C. Knowledge of Self

Interests	Abilities	Potential
Aptitudes	Try-out	Weaknesses

D. Occupational Information

Opportunities	Selection	Reward
Qualifications	Entrance	Evaluation

To the above categories of curricular components should be added the items in II.

THE CONSUMER FUNCTION: AN ENLIGHTENED UTILIZATION

The consumer function defines the contribution of industrial arts to an enlightened utilization of the products and services provided by industry. It is directed largely to the individual as the consumer of these products and services. Industry itself is the great consumer in the American economy, but study of this is included in the studies of industries themselves. The function seems to have first appeared in the literature of the profession at about the time when the manual training and manual arts concepts were being superseded by that of industrial arts. This appearance was a logical consequence of the realization that one finds no statement or inference concerning a consumer function in Richard's proposed change in terminology (see Chapter I). Probably Bonser and Mossman first sensed the logic of such an objective in an educational program derived from a study of industries. They expressed a concern for consumer education in industrial arts in their statement on "Outcomes of the study of Industrial Arts":

> . . . One who has properly studied the industries should: . . . be able to buy and use industrial products of good quality in material and construction and well adapted to their purposes, at costs that are reasonable; to care for what is secured so that it will remain serviceable in its fullest possible measure; to repair or supervise repairing, when it can be done to advantage; and intelligently to substitute inexpensive for expensive products when this is needed. This is the economic outcome (20, pp. 14-15).

The *Ohio Prospectus* (73, p. 94) in its definition of industrial arts gives as one purpose: ". . . ability to choose and use the industrial products wisely . . ." In the chapter on "Objectives and their Meanings" the *Prospectus* includes consumer knowledge and Appreciation:

> Five principal meanings are also identified as belonging to this objective. These include: *selecting, testing, operating, maintaining,* and *judging.* The objective applies from the time one even considers a product of industry until it is fully consumed. Considerable significance is seen for the development of this objective in Industrial Arts classes because of its widespread application to the many products of industry and to the increasing emphasis now being placed on intelligent consumption.
>
> Woods, metals, appliances, plans, foods, tools, machines, garments, one's home, communication, transportation—all are things which one consumes and are therefore significant phases of content material, or subject matter, which will contribute to the achievement of the consumer knowledges and appreciations purpose (73, p. 54).

The outline analysis immediately following indicates the content of the consumer function. This function has become of increasingly vital concern in a daily living where a simple economic tenet holds that spending what one earns is as important as the earning itself. As products used in day-to-day living are changed and improved, they frequently become more technically complex, even in operation. Appliances for the home are good examples. Unless the consumer is able to keep reasonably current with such developments, and thus is able to choose and use the products more wisely, he becomes dependent on others for help and then substitutes hope for wisdom.

The Consumer Function in the New Industrial Arts

Industrial arts seeks to enlighten the student in his role as a consumer of industry's materials, products, and services. The consumer is here involved in selecting, purchasing, using, and evaluating. Wise consumption requires understandings of materials, processes, structures, design, and aesthetics to arrive at intelligent decisions involving function, durability, quality, economy. The goal is consumer competency.

I. Nature: Selection, Use, and Care of the Products of Industry

   A. The Economic Aspect: Spending wisely what one earns is as important as earning.

   B. The Personal Aspect: Individual needs, interests as measures of wise selection.

   C. The Social Aspect: Needs and benefits to the group as measures of wise selection.

   D. The Technical Aspect: Qualitive standards as relative to function, structure, materials, design. Operation, care and maintenance as elements of utilization.

   E. The Appraisal Aspect: Assessment of economic, personal, social, and technical values.

II. Representative Functional Components

   A. Function

    How well does it accomplish its function?
    How easily, simply does it operate?
    Is it easily serviceable and maintained?
    Is there a good choice of mechanisms, circuits, formulas?
    Is there a good relationship of size and weight to function?

   B. Structure

    Is it structurally sound, sensible?
    Is the new idea in structure better than the old?
    Is construction appropriate to function and materials?
    Is replacement of parts a desirable feature?
    Does it express an imaginative solution to a problem?

   C. Durability

    Will it function as long as desired?
    Is it too durable?
    What compromises have been made for the sake of durability?
    Is the selection of materials and structures appropriate to durability?
    Does the manufacturer stand behind it?

   D. Materials

    Are appropriate materials used?
    Could less expensive materials suffice?

Are the materials repairable?
Is excessive care in use required?

E. Economic
   Is it a bargain if you do not need it immediately?
   Which is wiser, repair or replacement?
   Is depreciation a factor?
   Is the most expensive one the best?
   How do maintenance costs compare with those of a similar product?

F. Aesthetic
   Does its beauty originate within itself?
   Is its beauty refreshing, imaginative?
   Will it promote harmony within its environment?
   Is its beauty enduring, or faddish?
   Does it reflect on the good taste of its owner?

G. Cultural
   Does it reflect the best out of the past, or is it just old?
   Does it effectively represent the contemporary spirit?
   What contributions does it make to the material culture?
   Does it reflect fine craftsmanship, superior ingenuity?
   What great names are associated with such products?

H. Safety
   Is the product adequately protected electrically, chemically, mechanically?
   Is the operator adequately protected from shock, burns, fumes, and the like?
   Is it structurally safe?
   Are its materials appropriate to safety?
   Will it be a hazard to others?

I. Personal
   Does it lend real pride to possession?
   Does its possession reflect favorably on the owner?
   Does it really enhance finer living?
   Does it make one's work easier?
   Does it increase the owner's respect for the work of his fellow man, and appreciation of the Greater Wisdom?

J. Social
  What effects will its purchase and possession have on others?
  Is selection made as a concession to conformity?
  Are social standards affected by its possession?
  What legislative elements are involved?
  What does it contribute to an improved standard of living?

K. Use
  Are the controls simple, effective, easily accessible?
  Is special care required?
  Is special instruction, skill required?
  Is it "fool-proof"?
  Does ability to use it contribute to the growth and achievement of the operator?

L. Appraisal
  Is the owner happy with it?
  Has it met with social approval?
  Does it function as intended?
  Has it made the desired contribution to a finer living?
  How can it be improved?

THE RECREATION FUNCTION: RE-CREATION IN DISCRETIONARY TIME

The "worthy use of leisure time" was one of the original Seven Cardinal Principles of education. It was probably John Dewey, however, who stimulated professional educational thinking on the subject when in 1916 he explained his concept of Work and Play in the curriculum, in his *Democracy and Education*. He pointed out:

> . . . Education has no more serious responsibility than making adequate provision for enjoyment of recreative leisure; not only for the sake of immediate health, but still more if possible for the sake of its lasting effect upon habits of mind. . . (37, p. 241).

Until the depression years of the thirties, recreation as worthy use of leisure time was given little public attention except through parks and playgrounds. However, with the arrival of a forced leisure for which Americans were unprepared, both economically and culturally, national attention was quickly focused on the problem of what to do for adults and out-of-school youth who had more spare time than they could put to good use. The Federal Government during this period attempted to restore the economic and social equilibrium of the nation with emergency programs of work, training, and recreation. During these times, also, industrial arts announced the inclusion of recreation among its functions. The two major professional announcements of the period included the recreational function in their statements of position. The first of these, the *Ohio Prospectus*, in a section on unemployment and leisure, pointed out the following:

> Much of the wholesome recreation of people is associated with material things. . . .
> . . . The American people have never been led to experience the deep satisfactions and lasting pleasures to be derived in avocational interests possible of development in the arts. It is natural for people to want to make things. The rapid spread of home workshops and increasing sale of small power machines during the depression testify to the growing popularity of homecrafts, avocational interests, or hobbies (73, pp. 35-36).

In its definition of industrial arts the *Prospectus* concluded with this statement:

> The subject of industrial arts, while encompassing all age and school levels, is justified in secondary-school areas for such purposes as . . . the development of avocational and vocational interests . . . (73, p. 93).

The second publication, *Industrial Arts, Its Interpretation in American Schools*, included recreation among the industrial arts which apply to all levels of public education from the elementary grades through college. Among its several references to the subject is the following: ". . . Through such a program the pupil . . . increases in ability . . . to use effectively his recreational time . . ." (81, p. 1).

In the years since the *Interpretation* the recreation function has become increasingly important for industrial arts. The length of the workweek in industry has decreased with new technological developments to today's approximately thirty-eight hour workweek, and it is expected to decrease even further for the same reason within the next few decades.

The National Industrial Conference Board (29) made a survey on Leisure Time and Leisure Spending in the United States, 1939 versus 1955, which is suggestive of the importance attached to leisure by the American public. Even though the figures will not match those for today, the indicated trends can be projected to the present with reasonable accuracy. The Board found that in 1939 approximately five billion dollars was spent on leisure while, by contrast, in 1955 approximately twenty-one billion was spent. The survey also disclosed that leisure time has increased measurably during the period. In 1939 only 37 per cent of the hourly industrial employees had a five-day week, while in 1954 93 per cent had a five-day week. In 1939 only 46 per cent had paid vacations; in 1956, the figure was 96 per cent. In 1939 14 per cent had paid holidays, and in 1956 the figure was 96 per cent. Apparently a strong relationship exists between these data: the more leisure time, the greater the spending for recreation. This deduction is hardly startling, but the trend toward an increasing leisure for the industrial employee is as obvious as the increasing willingness to spend to enjoy it. This raises the possibility for the industrial arts educator of educating the American to spend both his leisure and his money more wisely. The analysis to follow describes the nature of the recreation function for industrial arts.

The Recreation Function in the New Industrial Arts

Industrial arts provides opportunity for development of wholesome discretionary time, re-creative interests deriving from creative and constructive experience with materials, tools, and machines. The student is encouraged to explore, to experiment, and to develop ideas which are essentially expressive of himself. The recreation function complements the technical and the occupational functions. The latter originate in the concern for the work side of living; the recreation function is industrial arts' concern for the intelligent use of discretionary time.

I. The Recreation Elements

  A. Recreation as Liberation

    1. Freedom from conformity
    2. Freedom from boredom
    3. Freedom for the pursuit of interests
    4. Freedom for self-discovery
    5. Freedom for individualism

B. Recreation as Human Growth and Development
   1. Growth in abilities, skills
   2. Growth in appreciations, understandings
   3. Growth in wisdom, knowledge
   4. Growth in satisfaction, achievements

C. Recreation as Rehabilitation
   1. Restoration of the physical
   2. Regeneration of the emotional, spiritual
   3. Retraining for skills
   4. Therapy as treatment
   5. Development of a "new" self

II. Applications of Recreation Through Industrial Arts

   A. Crafts
      1. Creating with materials and processes
      2. Constructing with hand, tool, machine
      3. Collecting

   B. Therapeutics
      1. Therapy
      2. Rehabilitation
      3. Retraining

   C. Economics
      1. Do-it-yourself savings
      2. Design, construction, repair, maintenance, refinishing
      3. Commercialization

   D. Community Service for Industrial Arts
      1. School recreation programs
      2. Community agency recreation programs
      3. Private agency recreation programs
      4. Recreational leadership training programs

III. Representative Functional Components

   A. Materials and Self-expression

Prospecting	Conservation	Qualities
Manufacturing	Design	Construction
Reclamation	Development	Evaluation

B. Processes and Self-expression

Tools	Mastery	Construction
Machine tools	Invention	Utilization
Machines	Refinement	Evaluation

C. Products and Self-expression

Operation	Maintenance	Service
Collection	Study	Utilization

THE CULTURAL FUNCTION:
UNDERSTANDING THE MATERIAL CULTURE

The cultural function for industrial arts has as its major concern the development of understandings and appreciations of the American culture as it is and has been influenced by man's mastery of materials. The cultural function is also industrial arts' contribution to the fundamental purpose of all education as a social institution: the understanding of the culture of which the student is a part. Considered thus, the cultural function is accomplished by the study of the *material* culture, which includes essentially the sum total of man's ways for using materials.

Precedent for the inclusion of the cultural function in the mission of industrial arts seems to have begun with Bonser. Bonser, writing with Mossman, proposed to make industrial arts educative as well as constructive; and they envisioned as a third outcome for "one who has properly studied the industries" the following:

> Love that which is beautiful, and be able to select and use products which are beautiful in themselves, which are well adapted to the particular purpose for which they are chosen, and which fit harmoniously the surroundings in which they are placed. This is the art of aesthetic outcome (20, p. 15).

Although Woodward was concerned with other than an aesthetic purpose in his manual training, Bennett made a strong plea for it in his manual arts. The final chapter of Bennett's *Art Training for Life and for Industry* (14, pp. 49-61) even proposes a national school of industrial arts to preserve and perpetuate the manual arts and crafts as an important part of American culture.

The *Prospectus* devotes a chapter to "Contributions of the Material Heritage" in which a case is made for an enrichment of the industrial arts experience through study of the *material heritage*:

The student who has learned to know styles in furniture, architecture, rugs, silverware, china, and other objects of common use is prepared to surround himself with those things which an integrated taste tells him can supply lifetime satisfaction. One who knows the various forces—racial, individual, symbolic, material, national, etc.—which have entered into the making of the common articles of every day use is stimulated constantly to fuller enjoyment of those things and is keenly interested in the source and direction of those forces. Through recognizing the significance of the material heritage, the school establishes a closer relationship between its program and the enduring contributions of the time (73, p. 42).

The objective under consideration in the *Prospectus* is called the "aesthetic and cultural." This is consistent with the common connotation of culture as refinement in taste. However, the opening statement below for the study describing the cultural function for the new industrial arts gives it greater dimension than that of refinement. This cultural function also appears to be a resultant of several of the other functions since appreciations and understandings derive from interests, knowledges, and experiences. The following analysis is offered.

The Cultural Function
for the New Industrial Arts

Industrial arts acquaints one with the culture of which he is a part. He gains appreciation of the great materials achievements of the past and of the men and women who made them. He acquires standards of quality by which to understand and enjoy the finer material things in living. He gains understanding of the technology in its role as a great civilizer. He comes to sense the spirit of the technology which has moved his country to its high standard of living and to realize technology's role in keeping America great. In effect the student becomes culturally competent in a technological society.

I. Cultural Elements

    A. Record of the Origins and Development of American Industry

    B. Record of Major Achievements with Materials: natural, synthetic, alloys, transmutations

    C. Record of Technological Inventions and Discoveries

D. Evolution of Processes and Processing with Materials

E. Record of Technological Development in Other Countries

F. Record of Great Men and Women in the Technology: industrialists, engineers, scientists, inventors, designers, craftsmen

G. Standards for Appreciation of the Products of the Arts and · Crafts

H. Standards for Appreciation of the Products of Industry

I. Standards for Appreciation of Craftsmanship

J. Realization of the Impact of Technology on the American Way of Living

II. Representative Functional Components

A. Materials and the Material Culture

Nature vs. synthetic	Scientific achievements and
Identification	goals
Uses of materials	Quality standards
	Materials sources

B. Processes and the Material Culture

Basic types of processes	Controls in processing
Evolution of processes	Automatic processing
Standard processes	Hand vs. machine processing

C. Products and the Material Culture

Product development	Quality standards
Product identification	Engineering standards
Design standards	Standard parts

D. Tools and the Material Culture

Tools and civilization	Standards in tools
Evolution of tools	Quality in tools
Man, the tool-user	Design in tools

E. Machines and the Material Culture

Evolution of machines	Machines, man, and automation
Man vs. machine	
Materials and machines	Design in machines
	Machine tools

F. Aesthetics and the Material Culture

Primitive products	Aesthetic standards
Cultural styles	International influences
Classic achievements	Contemporary tastes

G. Man and the Material Culture

Materials in the civilizing process	Materials and security
	Materials and opportunity
Materials expression as native	Materials of the future
Humanism vs. materialism	

THE SOCIAL FUNCTION:
MAN, THE MASTER OF THE MACHINE

The preceeding functions of industrial arts proposed for this study emphasize student growth and development through technical competencies, consumer education, occupational intelligence, personal recreation, and cultural appreciations. All of these tend to be largely personal and individual in direction with respect to the student. The social function is included to give added meaning and value to these other functions because it concentrates on the development of competences which are characteristically personal-social. In the process it gives meaning to the American way of technological living and helps the student find himself in this technological environment.

The *Prospectus* used the term "personal-social" to identify this function of industrial arts, but the emphasis there was largely on the "personal":

> PERSONAL-SOCIAL TRAITS. Pupils in an Industrial Arts laboratory learn to work together both as leaders and followers. What and how they produce is reflected in the smooth operation of their particular organization.
> Social intelligence is becoming more and more important for individual success in all walks of life. Secondary-school graduates too often become misfits and failures because they have not learned how to work with people. It is not necessary to stifle individuality, but rather essential to offer opportunities to teach teamwork and responsibility.
> . . . The operation of a *pupil-personnel organization* permits the development of desirable personal-social traits in individual pupils . . . (73, p. 56).

The Ohio Standards (59, p. 199) emphasized the social side of the objective, but consumer, cultural, and economic implications were also evident.

Boyd H. Bode, in *Industrial Arts and the American Tradition* for the literature of Epsilon Pi Tau, the international honor society for industrial arts and industrial-vocational education, added a spiritual dimension to the social values of industrial arts. He stated the following:

> It is presumably agreed that industrial arts must provide something more than a set of skills plus such items of information as are necessary to make these skills effective. What is the "something more"? It is obviously social, in the first instance. It calls for a form of social organization which will provide opportunity for continuous growth in the practice of industrial arts, as over against a type of organization which would make robots of our young people. Such opportunity for growth is what is meant by the reference to the spiritual potentialities which reside in the practical activities of everyday life. In order to keep open the door to such opportunity, it is necessary to have a social organization which can make readjustments as they may be required; which is to say that industrial arts is committed to a democratic philosophy of social organization (*18*, p. 7).

Bode's "spiritual potentialities," which so far as this writer is able to deduce from a study of the brochure, have little relationship to the moral and ethical human living. Bode seems rather to be attempting to elevate and to dignify industrial arts by suggesting that a potential for human growth exists in the practical activities of life, including industry. This potential which he terms spiritual includes the intellectual and the creative and enables one to find meaning in these practical activities. Whether he intended a moral connotation or not, the thought is a provoking one; it sets one to conjuring up visions and values in industrial arts which can make it truly liberal in the cultural sense. Do you believe that there are moral and ethical values in industrial arts?

The following analysis interprets the social function for industrial arts used in this study.

The Social Function
for the New Industrial Arts

Industrial arts develops the traits that are necessary for successful social relations. Industrial arts provides opportunity for the student to develop his own native, individual potential for problem-solving, reasoning, creating, and constructing in an environment of materials, tools, machines, and energies. In so doing, the student comes to know himself, to discover and extend his interests, to find purpose for his own existence, and, thus, to be better equipped to deal harmoniously with others. Likewise industrial arts helps him to arrive at social understandings, appreciations, and concerns and to develop social abilities, all of which contribute to his social competence in adapting to a technological culture.

I. The Social Elements

   A. Personality Development
      1. Personality inventory
      2. Self-study and appraisal
      3. Discovery of aptitudes
      4. Development of abilities
      5. Self-expression
      6. Expansion of interests
      7. Creative imagining

   B. Social Competence
      1. Social adjustment, adaptation
      2. Ability in the democratic process
      3. Citizenship
      4. Social freedoms, responsibilities
      5. Moral, spiritual values
      6. Leadership, followers

   C. Society and the Individual
      1. The individual in a technological society
      2. The individual in industry
      3. Technology and the standard of living
      4. Legislative aspects of the technology
      5. Social progress and economic development
      6. Industry and the democratic process

II. Representative Functional Components

   A. Personality Inventory
      Strengths   Weaknesses   Potential

B. Personal Attitudes

Work	Morals	Service
Responsibility	Initiative	Growth
Leadership	Achievement	Learning

C. Development of Talents

Discovery	Application	Guidance
Identification	Mission	Evaluation

D. Leadership

Qualities	Significance	Followership
Types	Goals	Evaluation

E. Group Dynamics

Nature	Goals	Creativity
Values	Techniques	Conformity

F. Personnel Management

Organization	Responsibilities	Values
Authority	Incentives	Problems

G. The Society of Industry

Structure	Legislative control	Management
The individual	Labor	Problems

Some Reflections. The six functions accepted here for the new industrial arts are essentially six areas of mission, values, objectives, outcomes, guides to development, and criteria for evaluation. Although the analyses appear to be most encompassing, we must remember that industrial arts does not take care of the full needs of the student even in the areas of the technical, the occupational, the consumer, the recreational, the cultural, and the social functions. Industrial arts serves the individual only within the framework of the technology. Total education is concerned with many more facets of the culture than the technological.

All six of the functions are assumed applicable at any grade level and in any part of the complete program of industrial arts. But all are not equally so for all students. Nor should we expect that all are fully operable at any one time or for any period of time for each student. They have too much breadth, too much depth, and too great a potential of application. We do not energize and activate these functions by merely opening the door to the laboratory or by turning a switch. They are guides to program development and operation, to facilities planning, to curriculum selection and implementation, and to discovering and developing human potential within the context of the technology. We are concerned with the maximum development of each student through industrial arts; but because of individual differences in background and capacity, the functions become uniquely applicable for the individual. Although so concerned, we are not intent on shaping the individual to a predetermined pattern. The new industrial arts must make maximum provision for individualization of experience. The research and development emphasis throughout the new program makes a point of this, and it is premised on the hypothesis that learning is itself an individual process.

Within each statement of function lie numerous specific objectives and values which can be singled out for attention. They are so numerous, however, as to suggest the virtue in brevity. Should we need a compacted statement of objectives for industrial arts, we may use the following:

1. Technical competence
2. Occupational orientation
3. Consumer competence
4. Recreational liberation
5. Cultural appreciations
6. Social competence

Objectives are commonly as general as these. But if there is virtue in brevity, there is also danger that meaning will be concealed. One major problem facing industrial arts today is the diversity of opinion on its mission. This is evident among us in the profession as well as among school administrators, parents, and even the students. For example, look at Ivan Hostetler's chapter "What Objectives Should be Emphasized in Industrial Arts?" in the U.S. Office of Education Conference Report titled *Improving Industrial Arts Teaching* (82 pp. 11-22). With twenty-five objectives collected, the question of emphasis is indeed pertinent. Hostetler proposes four major objectives as unique to industrial arts but points out that other specific objectives supplement these. His major objectives are:

1. To develop in each student an insight and understanding of industry and its place in our culture.
2. To discover and develop talents of students in the technical fields and applied sciences.
3. To develop technical problem-solving skills related to materials and processes.
4. To develop in each student a measure of skill in the use of common tools and machines.

Again in the interest of specificity and singleness of direction, we may assume that the new industrial arts has as its overall objective the advancing of the human and his technology. Teaching knowledge, understanding, appreciations, and skills are not enough. These must lead to something. In this case they must lead to a realization of human potential within the framework of the technology, which in turn results in an advancing of the very technology with which our subject-matter treats.

TO DISCUSS, TO DEBATE, TO DECIDE

1. Are the terms aims, objectives, goals, outcomes, functions really synonomous? What are the differences, if any?
2. What are the differences in connotation between the terms "shop" and "laboratory"? What differences would one expect to find in the respective classrooms?
3. Orientation is sometimes given as a function of industrial arts. Is it an end or is it a means for industrial arts?
4. Industrial arts is not a vocational subject in the sense of trade training. How can its occupational function be justified?
5. Is any one of the functions especially unique to industrial arts? Why?
6. Does industrial arts need the six functions? Cannot one or more be eliminated so as to narrow its mission and give a greater chance for success?
7. Do all of the functions require equal emphasis by the teacher?
8. In a program of industrial arts recreation, would the recreational function alone be involved?
9. What possible relationships exist between the technical and social functions?
10. What evidence can there be for the accomplishment of any one function?

(Above) A machine shop typical of the 1900 era. Overhead line shafts transmitted the power of a central steam engine, and later, an electric motor. Countershafts provided different speeds for individual machines. Precision was dependent on the accuracy of the machine tool and the skill of the machinist. (Courtesy: The Bettmann Archive Inc.)

(Below) Today's machining can be controlled by magnetic tape. Here, an automatic milling machine for aircraft spars takes its orders from instructions recorded on the tape shown in the control cabinet. Precision of a mathematical quality is built into both machine and its control. (Courtesy: Minnesota Mining and Manufacturing Company.)

Subject Matter
for the New
Industrial Arts

*If there is any one factor most responsible for the phenomenal
economic progress of the United States in the twentieth century, it is the enthusiasm with which we as a people have
tried to create better ways and conditions of working and
living . . .*
— Thomas J. Watson, Jr., *Goals for Americans,
The Report of the President's Commission on
National Goals.* © 1960, by The American
Assembly. Prentice-Hall, Inc., publisher.

To this point, in the search for subject matter
reflective of technology the following has been done:

1. Industrial technology has been identified and described.
2. A system for the classification of American industries was set up.
3. Analyses were made of the industries in the classification.
4. The functions of industrial arts were reconsidered.

The next step, which is to follow, is an examination of the analyses
of the industries and of the functions of industrial arts for subject
matter, with recommendation for their utilization. Three major

sources of subject matter serve for the development of the curriculum for industrial arts: the industries analyses, the functional components derived from the industrial analyses, and the functional components drawn from the functions of industrial arts.

The Industries Analyses as Subject Matter. The outline analyses of the industries in Chapter IV identify the general nature and extent of basic American industries. For purposes herein these analyses become *outlines of subject matter for the study of specific industries or groups of industries.* Before course guides or courses of study are prepared from these outlines, they may require more detailed analysis. The basic structure used for the manfacturing industries —materials, processes, products, and occupations—seems proper for use in the respective courses of study. These were also used in the other industries outline when and as it seemed best. The problem in developing such structures for the study of the industries is to find a pattern which is sufficiently fundamental that it can remain rather constant over a period of years and at the same time to permit the curriculum builder to reflect the significant industrial changes which continue to appear. The author hopes that the structures used herein meet this requirement, but it should be remembered that other patterns may be fully as fundamental and authoritative. In the use of the industries analyses for subject matter, we assume that the content is basic, fundamental, and minimal rather than maximal. It is still to be amplified and enriched with experiment and test in actual laboratory practice.

The industries analyses may be used directly as course outlines by the teacher. He may draw on these as guides in the development of course outlines for particular levels or for units of study of any length. He may use them as guides to the development of courses of study. He may use them as guides for student study and research. To illustrate the latter, a single item may be selected from any of the analyses; for example, the item Structures in the outline of The Construction Industries. A student may make a study of wood structures, showing details of joinery and the relationships of parts as currently used in housing construction. A similar study may reveal changing structural practices in the evolution of wooden housing. From such research the student could design a piece of furniture or a cottage employing modifications of historical structural techniques.

These applications suggest that the outlines themselves are rich sources of subject matter, full of ideas for student study, research, and projects. It would be virtually impossible to identify all of the curricular potential in any one of them. The imaginative teacher will find much more than he can use, even in a lifetime of teaching.

When the magnitude of the subject matter involved in each of the industries analyses appears to be overwhelming, as it often does, the logical reaction is to call on some method of selectivity to choose the most important elements. Before this is done, let us pause to reflect a bit. Is it not good that we in industrial arts experience the sensation of being overwhelmed by the magnitude and importance of our field? For too long we have practiced clipping the wings of industrial arts to keep it from soaring to heights of service. Until we do get excited about its educative potential, we cannot expect the layman to show much enthusiasm for it. Everything in the industries analyses is important; every industry is essential. The selective process will obviously be used when adapting the outlines for a particular group or grade level. But the danger lies in the measures used for the selection. Traditional conditioning causes us to look for familiar elements and to delete those which are not understood. However, the redirecting and enriching of the traditional program depends upon elements presently unfamiliar. The new professional spirit that must accompany the new industrial arts suggests that we look at the entire pattern of subject matter revealed in the industries analyses as our province, and if we do not know all about this new province, we should begin to study.

THE FUNCTIONAL COMPONENTS
AS SUBJECT MATTER

The functional components in each of the industries analyses appear as basic elements of the industries. Each becomes a block of subject matter in itself with applications to be found in each of the industries. In this role we refer to them from this point on as *curricular components*. A single component is a result of a searching for subject matter, a searching for a common denominator which can be considered basic, fundamental subject matter. We assume, then, that a subject-matter program for each of the industries can be derived from an analysis of the respective functional (curricular) components. Since these components are representative of industries in general, and since they then become fundamental, anyone of them can become a block of subject matter for study. Its applications will be found in all of industry.

The detailed study of the functions of industrial arts also revealed components of subject matter which were labeled functional. They are reflective of both the industrial and the professional or philosophical influences on industrial arts and resulted when the functions themselves were probed rather deeply for meaning. Like the components drawn from the industries analyses, these are elements of subject matter and we shall include them as curricular components.

THE MASTER LIST OF CURRICULAR COMPONENTS. The total of the curricular components drawn from the industries analyses and those from the functions of industrial arts becomes a master list of basic blocks of subject matter. Simple addition here will reveal more than five hundred. Many of these appear to be duplicates but, owing to differences within the many industries for which a component appears, this may not be altogether true. Take molds, for example. There are many types of molds as well as different principles of operation which appear in an industry-wide study of molds and molding. Consequently, there may be less duplication from one particular industry to another than appears on the surface. For compilation into a master list of components, however, it seems best to minimize the repetition of terms. In the preparation of the list from the many items, a process of condensation rather than elimination was involved. The one hundred categories of subject matter remaining (see Fig. 6-1) should constitute fundamental subject matter to be drawn from a study of industry for industrial arts; they are so seen here.

UTILIZATION OF THE CURRICULAR COMPONENTS. Utilization of the curricular components may proceed from two basic directions. The first requires a selection of the components appropriate for the grade level or the maturation level of the student. The second assumes that all of the components are applicable on any grade level but in varying degrees of concentration. Each approach is functional and readily justifiable. In both cases detailed content studies are necessary before the components can be used. We cannot feasibly include here such

**MASTER LIST OF CURRICULAR COMPONENTS
AS CATEGORIES OF FUNDAMENTALS IN SUBJECT MATTER**

Advertising	Hobbies	Preserving
Analysis	Human engineering	Principles
Assembly	Inspection	Processes
Automation	Installation	Problems
Chemistry	Instruments	Production
Circuits	Integration	Products
Communications	Interpretation	Quality
Components	Invention	Records
Computers	Investigation	Recreation
Concepts	Jigs	Refinement
Conservation	Labor	Regulation
Construction	Legislation	Reproduction
Consumer	Lubrication	Representations
Controls	Machines	Research
Creativity	Maintenance	Safety
Decoration	Management	Salvage
Design	Manufacturing	Selectivity
Development	Materials	Services
Diagnosis	Mathematics	Solutions
Dies	Measurement	Specifications
Discovering	Mechanics	Standards
Distribution	Mechanisms	Structures
Drawing	Mechanization	Supervision
Editing	Mining	Supplies
Engineering	Molds	Surveys
Eqiupment	Models	Synthetics
Exhibits	Occupations	Systems
Experiment	Operation	Techniques
Evaluation	Organization	Testing
Fastening	Physics	Theories
Finishes	Planning	Tools
Fixtures	Power	Transportation
Government	Presentations	Utilization
Graphics		

Fig. 6-1.

analyses for the entire master list. Several typical outline analyses follow.

The Materials Component: How industry discovers, produces, refines, reclaims, replenishes materials.

1. Types of materials

Natural	Metallic	Liquid
Synthetic	Organic	Gaseous
Mineral	Solid	

2. Sources of materials

Local	Transportation	Tariffs
National	Restrictions	Research
International	Legislation	Chemistry

3. Supply of materials

Limits	Natural	Replenishment
Availability	Synthetic	Conservation
Reclamation	Regulation	Demand

4. Qualities

Grades	Limitations	Standards
Specifications	Control	Measurement
Characteristics	Prices	Scales

5. Manufacture of materials

Processing	Testing	Research
Refining	Packing	Chemistry
Inspecting	Preserving	Limitations

The Processes Component: How industry employs technical and scientific principles, machines, and men for converting materials into products.

1. Types of processes

a. Hand

| Types | Advantages | Skills |
| Techniques | Limitations | Safety |

b. Mechanical

Types	Controls	Limitations
Principles	Automation	Safety

c. Chemical

Nature	Controls	Limitations
Principles	Automation	Safety

d. Thermal

Types	Controls	Limitations
Uses	Principles	Safety

e. Electrical

Nature	Controls	Limitations
Applications	Principles	Safety

f. Natural

Weathering	Seasoning	Gravitation

2. Tools

a. Types

Processing	Assembly	Measurement

b. Applications

Techniques	Developments	Care, safety

c. Design

Problem analysis	Drawing	Pilot models

d. Manufacture

Casting	Heat treat	Sharpening
Forging	Fabrication	Test

The Products Component: How industry produces products and services.

1. Types of product, services

Industrial	Construction	Consumer
Commerce	Security	Institutional

2. Research and development

Product	Facilities	Objectives
Sales	Methods	Inventions

3. Product design

Objectives	Techniques	Controls
Criteria	Aesthetics	Changes

4. Manufacture

Process	Planning	Test
Assembly	Inspection	Controls

5. Distribution

Local	International	Transportation
National	Systems	Advertising

6. Services

Types	Techniques	Facilities
Systems	Standards	Legislation
Controls	Regulation	Safety

The Machines Component: How industry produces the means to produce.

1. Types

Production	Unit	Portable
Experimental	Combination	Stationary

2. Applications

Manufacturing	Transportation	Electronics
Power	Construction	Communications

3. Principles

Mechanical	Hydraulic	Thermal
Electrical	Pneumatic	Chemical

4. Operation

Control	Limitations	Qualifications
Set-up	Test	Safety

5. Production devices

Molds	Jigs	Forms
Dies	Fixtures	Guides

6. Design

Problem analysis	Standards	Drawing
Research	Systems	Development
Mechanisms	Circuits	Pilot models

7. Manufacture

Casting	Heat treat	Testing
Forging	Assembly	Evaluation
Fabrication	Adjustment	Modification

The Services Component: How industry keeps operative the products which it provides.

1. Power

Motors	Turbines	Controls
Engines	Distribution	Transmission

2. Transportation

Airway	Seaway	Space
Highway	Railway	Conveyor

3. Manufacturing

Materials	Machines	Tools

4. Communications

Graphic arts	Electronic	Electrical

5. Housing

Building	Refrigeration	Ventilation
Plumbing	Electrical	Preservation

6. Domestic

Appliances	Furnishings	Apparel

7. Recreational

Vehicles	Hobby equipment	Do-it-yourself equipment
Sports equipment	Musical equipment	Home workshop

8. Miscellaneous

Military	Medical	Government

THE FUNCTIONS OF INDUSTRIAL ARTS AS SOURCES OF SUBJECT MATTER

The functions of industrial arts are a third source of subject matter. The use of the functions of the new industrial arts (technical, occupational, consumer, recreational, cultural, social) for the development of a subject-matter program is not common, yet it is fully legitimate. In fact, this is an excellent means for putting the functions to functional tests, to show how really functional they are. The preceding reconsideration of the functions in Chapter V is proposed here as a source of subject matter. The outline analyses of each of the six functions of industrial arts may be used in different ways for curriculum development. They may serve wholly or in parts as guides for the selection of units of study, as in the technical function. They may serve as guides to the development of complete programs, as with the recreation function.

To illustrate further how these functions may be used in curriculum development, the following pattern for deriving subject matter is suggested. This becomes a framework for a structure of subject matter drawn from technology. Then typical applications of this pattern are given for all of the industries categories. Study of these typical applications should suggest many more.

A PATTERN FOR DERIVING SUBJECT MATTER FROM THE FUNCTIONS

Technical
Materials, processes, tools, machines
Theories, principles, applications
Construction, operation, utilization
Mechanisms, circuits, systems
Maintenance, repair, service

Consumer

Selection, including comparative quality, standards, function, and the
    like
Purchase, including comparative costs, trade-in, guarantee
Use, including operation, safety, care, maintenance
Evaluation, including the functional, economical, social

Occupational

Opportunities for men and women
Requirements, qualifications, education, experience
Rewards, incentives, status, hazards, values

Selection: interests, aptitudes, permanence, security
Occupational retraining

Cultural

History and development
Great people and great achievements
Contemporary status, influences of the technology
Trends, future developments
Meaning in the technology

Recreational

Hobby possibilities and the home workshop
Club activities and organizations
Supplies and facilities
Materials, tools, machines, and hobbies
Great hobbyists and their hobbies

Social

Relationships of the technology to the standard of living
Legislative aspects of the technology
Significance of industrial society to the individual
World impact of American technology
The individual in a technological society

THE CERAMICS INDUSTRIES

Technical

Ceramic materials: types, nature, uses, limitations
Ceramic processes, principles, techniques
Kiln operation, firing, furnace, lehr operation
Ceramic glaze formulation, applied chemistry
Mold principles, and construction

Consumer

Ceramic materials versus other materials in products
Standards of quality and aesthetics in ceramic products
American versus foreign ceramic products

Clay products versus glass products
Ceramic products and a finer living

Occupational

Job opportunities in the ceramic industries
College preparation, apprenticeship, vocational training
The role of research and engineering in ceramics
Opportunities for women
Rewards, hazards, health, safety

Cultural

The history of American pottery
The story of porcelain
The story of glass and glassware
Famous potters and pots
Contributions of ceramics to architecture

Recreational

Hand-made pottery as a home hobby
Enameling on metals
Plaster casting
Glass blowing
Design, construction of potters wheel, kiln, and the like

Social

Ceramic products and the rising standard of living
Restoration of mined land
International economic aspects of ceramic production
Clay working as self-expression, self-realization
The changing nature of the job in the ceramic industries

THE CHEMICALS INDUSTRIES

Technical

Principles and practices of battery charging
Principles and practices of electroplating
Molecular formulas and glaze compounding

Principles and practices of alloying
Principles and practices in photographic film manufacture

Consumer

Paint formulas and paint quality
Selection of adhesives
Effects of solvents in paints
Obtaining maximum strength in concrete
Uses and limitations of various kinds of plastics

Occupational

Job opportunities in the chemicals industries
Opportunities for women
Requirements, qualifications
Nature and extent of college preparation
Rewards, hazards, health, safety

Cultural

Paints and finishes throughout history
Identification of ceramic glazes
Outstanding chemical achievements and chemists
Science and chemistry of the future
Remaking nature through chemistry

Recreational

Making ceramic glazes
Preparing paints, finishes
Electroplating at home
Photo developing at home
Chemical coloring of metals

Social

Impact of chemistry on living
Legislative controls and chemicals
Automation and the chemical industries
Applied chemistry and self-expression, self-realization
Natural materials as sources of chemicals

THE FOODS INDUSTRIES

Technical

Farm machinery, mechanisms, operation
Principles, practices in refrigeration
Principles, practices in electronic cooking
Appliance maintenance and repair
Principles, practices in atomic food preservation

Consumer

Appliance selection by mechanisms, circuits, principles
Safety and home appliances
Maintenance requirements of appliances: finishes, controls,
  mechanisms
Styling standards

Occupational

Job opportunities in industrial food production
Job opportunities in farm machinery production
Job opportunities in kitchen appliance manufacture, service
Opportunities for women
Incentives, rewards, health, safety

Cultural

History and development of farm machinery
Inventions, inventors in food production industry
Industrial food production today
Styles, designs in tableware, dinnerware
History of utensils

Recreational

Farm tool and equipment design, invention
Farm workshop planning, equipping, using
Design, make ceramic dinnerware
Design, make dinnerware
Design, make tableware of wood, plastics, paper, and the like

Social

Industrial food production and the standard of living
Home kitchen appliances and the standard of living
Legislative aspects of industrial food products
Food production research and development, and health standards
Trends in kinds, forms, preservation of consumer foods

THE GRAPHIC ARTS INDUSTRIES—DRAWING

Technical

Engineering elements, principles, theories
Projections, pictorial representations
Standard practices
Drawing materials, tools, machines
Interpretation of drawings

Consumer

The role of the drawing in production
Reading drawings, charts, graphs
Making functional sketches, drawings
Appreciations, understandings of architectural services
Relationships of drawing and planning

Occupational

Job opportunities in industrial drawing
Relationships of drawing to engineering
Opportunities for training, advancement
Opportunities for women
Apprenticeship requirements in the printing industries

Cultural

The history of graphic representation
The development of the alphabet
Styles of letters and lettering
Facility with drawing as a language
Appreciations of intellectual aspects of drawings

Recreational

Sketching for fun
Drawing as a means to designing
Collecting: examples of letter styles for hand lettering
Planning the home workshop
Home planning by means of drawing

Social

Drawing as the universal language
Drawing as a means to problem-solving
Drawing as a means to self-expression, self-realization
The importance of drawing in industry
Development of drawing as communication among peoples

GRAPHIC ARTS—PHOTOGRAPHY

Technical

Photographic principles, processes, techniques
Engineering, scientific application
Scientific principles and practices
Use of photographic equipment
Photographic lighting

Consumer

Types and uses of cameras
Types and uses of photographic supplies
Criteria of good photography
Legislation affecting photography
How to make photographs

Occupational

Job opportunities in the industry, business
Opportunities for training, experience
Technical qualifications for various jobs
Opportunities for women
Occupational rewards, hazards, incentives

Cultural

History and development of photography
Famous photographers, inventors
Appreciations of photography
Scientific developments of the future
Competitions, salons, shows

Recreational

How to take and make good pictures
Equipping, planning the home darkroom
Participating in photo competition
Photography club membership
Collecting outstanding photos

Social

Photography as common communication
Photography as self-expression
Photography and the law
Photography and its role in education
Photography as a tool for modern industry

GRAPHIC ARTS—PRINTING

Technical

Comparison of basic printing processes and principles
Color process printing
Platemaking processes
How books are published
Type face identification

Consumer

Measures of quality in printing
Economics of book collecting
Aesthetic considerations in printed materials
Measures of quality, standards in paper
Comparative costs of printing

Occupational

Opportunities in the printing industries
College preparation, apprenticeship, vocational training
Printing as a small business
Opportunities for women
Rewards, hazards, incentives

Cultural

History and development of printing
History of book, magazine, newspaper publishing
Great names in printing through the years
Great achievements in printing
Identification of type faces

Recreational

Printing as a home hobby
Book plate collecting
Block printing
Silk screen printing
Book collecting

Social

Printed communications and the standard of living
Printed communications and the standard of education
Printed communications and national, personal freedom
Printed communications and the development of industry
Printing as a means of self-expression, achievement

THE LEATHER INDUSTRIES

Technical

The manufacture of leather from skin, tanning chemistry
The manufacture of shoes
Leather decorating processes
Physical, chemical qualities of leather
Leather cutting die design

Consumer

Care of leather goods
Leather versus imitations, synthetics

Qualities of good design in leather products
Comparative qualities of different kinds of leathers
Identification of leathers

Occupational

Job opportunities in the leather and leather products industries
College preparation, apprenticeship, vocational training
Opportunities for the small business
Opportunities for women
Rewards, hazards, incentives

Cultural

The history of shoes
Primitive uses for leather
Famous achievements in leather
Significant inventions, discoveries
Leather products and good dress

Recreational

Hand leather working as a hobby
Leather decoration
Pattern making for leather projects
Braiding, knotting, lacing
Shoe, glove, purse design and construction

Social

Leather products and the standards of living
Foreign competition in leather manufacture
Leather working as a means to self-expression, achievement
Economic competition with synthetics
Production of skins as industries

THE METALS INDUSTRIES

Technical

How metals are mined
How metals are refined
Theory and practice in alloying
Basic processes for shaping metals
Nature, qualities of different metals

Consumer

Advantages, disadvantages, of metal products
Welding versus casting versus pressing in quality products
Preserving, protecting metals from corrosion, weather, and the like
Quality standard in fine metals
Identification of common metals in products

Occupational

Job opportunities in the metals industries
College preparation, apprenticeship, vocational training
Occupational outlook in the metals industries
Opportunities for women
Occupational rewards, hazards, incentives

Cultural

Prehistoric metal working
Influences of metal technology on the standard of living
A history of gold mining in the United States
The role of metals in atomic energy
The story of medieval armor

Recreational

Establishing the home workshop foundry
Equipping a home machine shop
Jewelrymaking at home
Coil collecting
Design, construction of home workshop equipment

Social

Metals and international relations
Legislative controls of metals
Metals and the national security
Geographical sources of strategic metals
Metal working as self-expression, achievement

THE PAPER INDUSTRIES

Technical

Types of pulp materials
Chemical treatment of pulp

The Fourdrinier process
Types, uses of paper
Paper integration with plastics

Consumer

Kinds, grades of papers
Identification of papers by quality
Paper sizes, weights, finishes
Economical purchase of paper
Types, uses of plastic impregnated papers

Occupational

Job opportunities in the paper industry
Job qualifications, requirements, education, training
Geographic distribution of paper industries
Occupational rewards, hazards, incentives
Opportunities for women

Cultural

The history of hand-made paper
The development of the paper industry
Fine papers and good taste
Great names and achievements in paper
Historic papers, documents

Recreational

Making hand-made paper
Useful articles from discarded papers, cartons, and the like
Collecting samples of foreign papers
Paper, cardboard construction, sculpture
Making model buildings, cities, and the like of cardboard

Social

Paper and its influence on civilization
Paper and printing as socializing agencies
Paper consumption and the nation's wood supply
World sources of pulp materials
Hand-made papers as marks of individuality

THE PLASTICS INDUSTRIES

Technical

Types, characteristics of plastics
Basic manufacturing processes
Applied chemistry
Mold and die design principles, practices
The future of plastics

Consumer

Qualities, uses of plastics materials
Synthetics versus natural materials
Types, uses of adhesives for home and school
Qualities of good design in plastics
Plastics finishes for wood, metal, and the like

Occupational

Job opportunities in the plastics industries
Qualifications for technical positions, education, training
The need for research personnel
Occupational rewards, hazards, incentives
The future of the industry

Cultural

The story of the discovery of plastics
The history of the plastics industry
Great men and achievements in plastics
Plastics materials before the synthetics
Aesthetic principles and plastics

Recreational

Plastics as a home workshop material
Jig, fixture design for forming plastics at home
Making plastics at home
Repairing plastics products
Casting liquid plastics

Social

The impact of the synthetics on the technology
Plastics products and the standards of living
The scientific revolution in industry
Plastics as stimulus to creativity, invention
Economic aspects of natural versus synthetics competition

THE RUBBER INDUSTRIES

Technical

Applications of chemistry and engineering
Comparison of types of rubber
Making synthetic rubber
Making tires and rubber toys
Bonding rubber to metal

Consumer

Rubber types and their uses
Rubber versus plastics in products
Preserving rubber products
Proper usage of rubber products
Repairing of rubber products

Occupational

Job opportunities in management
Technical-scientific jobs in the industry
The nature of production jobs in the industry
Maintenance jobs in the industry
Education, apprenticeship, training

Cultural

The history of rubber
The discovery of vulcanization
The invention of the tire and its development
New uses for rubber
The role of rubber in the development of our country

Recreational

Rubber toymaking
Rubber forming, molding, dipping in the home workshop
Design and construction of rubber sports equipment
Rubber moldmaking from plaster castings
Development of projects from discarded rubber products

Social

The rubber industry and the government
International aspects of the rubber industry
Contributions of rubber to the standard of living
Impact of synthetic rubber on natural rubber consumption
Contributions of American rubber companies to the development of
Southeast Asian and African countries

THE TEXTILES INDUSTRIES

Technical

Pattern design for textile weaving
Manufacture of synthetic thread
Printing processes for cloth
Types of looms, operating principles
Manufacture of metallic thread

Consumer

Types of weaving patterns in textile materials
Identification of quality in fabrics
Comparative advantages of natural and synthetic textiles
Personal selection of clothing
Marks of good decorative design on fabrics

Occupational

Job opportunities in the textiles industries
The geography of textiles manufacturing
Opportunities for women
Technical qualifications, requirements, education, training
Occupational rewards, hazards, incentives

Cultural

Weaving and textiles among the ancients
The story of the development of the factory
How rugs are woven
Great achievements, inventions among textiles
The romance of dyes and dyeing

Recreational

Construction of hand looms
Construction of rope, cord machines
Textiles decorating, printing
Fabrication of neckties, aprons, shop coats, and the like
Knitting, braiding, knotting

Social

The sweatshop and textile production
Textiles imports, exports, nature, extent, effects
Textiles around the world
Impact of synthetics on cotton, silk, wool production
Textiles industries statistical status

TOOLS AND MACHINES INDUSTRIES

Technical

Metals machining processes
Kinds, properties, uses of metals
Basic mechanisms
Electrical control circuits
Principles, practices in hydraulic, pneumatic systems

Consumer

Identification of good tools
Essential features of good machine tools for school and home
Properties of materials and quality of tools, machines
Single-purpose versus multi-purpose machine tools
Maintaining school and home workshop machines

Occupational

Job opportunities in the tool and machine industries
College, apprenticeship, vocational training
Personal qualifications for success
Social-economic status of industrial positions
Occupational rewards, hazards, incentives

Cultural

The story of the wheel
The evolution of the factory
The nature and possibilities of automation
The story of interchangeable parts
Great inventions and inventors

Recreational

Design, construction of tools and machines for the home shop
Design and construction of jigs, fixtures
Development of experimental machines
Design of new, improved tools

Social

Application of power units to machines
Contributions of the machine to the standard of living
The role of leisure in a technological society
Automation: a new look at machines
Automation: key to the future
Creative imagination versus machine intelligence

THE WOODS INDUSTRIES

Technical

Wood materials: types, nature, uses, limitations
Processes in lumber manufacture
Operation of woodworking tools, machines
Engineering and design principles applied to wood
Structures in woods, strengths, limitations

Consumer

Identification of kinds of woods
Advantages and disadvantages of wood in products
Types, varieties of products made from wood
Knowledge of finishes used on woods
Identification of good design in wood products

Occupational

Job opportunities in forestry, tree farming
Job opportunities in wood products manufacture
Job opportunities in the field of woods chemistry
College preparation, apprenticeship, vocational training
Rewards, incentives, hazards

Cultural

Famous trees in history
Early furniture designers and their contributions
Identification of period styles in furniture
Famous wood buildings in history
Study of early American wood products for antique collectors

Recreational

Woodworking as a home hobby
Tree planting, care, identification
Collecting native and foreign wood samples
Do-it-yourself activities at home
Restoration of wood antiques

Social

Contributions of wood to the standard of living
Government programs of reforestation, parks, and the like
Forest conservation as national, state, local problems
Woodworking as self-expression, self-realization
The new woods industries and scientific development

THE CONSTRUCTION INDUSTRIES

Technical

Practices in framed structures
Theories, principles of modern heating systems
House painting and repainting principles, practices
Lighting principles and practices
Reading architectural plans

Consumer

Grades, sizes, standards of building materials
Types of construction, advantages, costs
Economies in heating plant operation
Functional, aesthetic considerations in decorating
Marks of quality in houses

Occupational

Occupational opportunities in construction industries
Opportunities in architectural design, engineering
Qualifications for technical, trade, engineering jobs
Nature and extent of apprenticeship, training, college
Occupational rewards, hazards, incentives

Cultural

Identification of architectural styles
Contributions of the great architects
Historic architecture around the world
Contemporary versus period styles
History of American architecture

Recreational

Do-it-yourself in home maintenance
Design, construction of model homes, buildings, cities
Furniture refinishing
Hand weaving upholstery fabrics

Social

Housing developments and the standard of living

Legislative aspects in building construction
Slum clearance through community, government programs
Housing styles and geography
Relationships of construction and city planning

THE POWER INDUSTRIES

Technical

Theory, principles of internal combustion engine
Theory, operation of carburetion systems
Theory, principles of electric motors
Theories, applications of hydraulics
Adjustment, tune-up practices

Consumer

Selections of engines, motors for home, farm, recreation
Computation of operating costs
Qualities of lubricants, fuels
Comparison of features of automobile engines
Materials used in engines, motors

Occupational

Occupational opportunities in power products manufacturing
Opportunities in research, engineering
Occupations in services, installation, maintenance
Nature, extent of training, education, apprenticeship
Occupational rewards, hazards, incentives

Cultural

The standard of living in the days of muscle power
The development of hydro-electric powerplants
Great inventions, inventors in the field of power
Power and interplanetary travel
Stationary powerplants of the future

Recreational

Design, construct engines for model boats, airplanes, and the like
Outboard motor operation, maintenance

Bicycle motor service, repair
Rebuilding engines
Experimental jet, rocket engines

Social

Mechanical power and the standard of living
Legislative, governmental aspects of power
The individual and man's quest for power
Mechanical power and the elimination of work
Social control of mechanical power

THE TRANSPORTATION INDUSTRIES—AIRWAYS

Technical

Engineering, aerodynamic theories, principles
Aircraft nomenclature
Aircraft operation
Aircraft engines manufacture
Aircraft and engines servicing

Consumer

Private flying
Governmental regulations for safety
Types, features of private aircraft
Qualifications, licensing of service personnel
Commercial air travel, potential, costs, and the like

Occupational

Job opportunities in commercial aviation
Job opportunities in aircraft manufacturing
Job opportunities in military aviation
Job opportunities in meteorology, electronics, and the like
Rewards, incentives, hazards, education, training

Cultural

History of man's attempt at flight
The story of the Wright brothers' flight
Great achievements, flights, people

From pony express to air mail
The development of aircraft powerplants

Recreational

Learning to fly
Design, building flying model airplanes
Collecting, building scale models of world aircraft
Glider design, construction, flight
Developing experimental models

Social

Aviation and the world's standard of living
Aviation and international relations
Aviation and international security
Aviation and competition in transportation
Implications of interplanetary travel

TRANSPORTATION—CONVEYORS

Technical

Engineering principles and practices in conveyors
Industrial installations, applications, operation
Pipe line construction and operation
Pipe, tube manufacture: steel, aluminum, glass, and the like
Automatic controls systems on conveyors

Consumer

Economics in pipe line transportation
Materials, services made available by pipe lines
Legislative aspects of transcontinental conveyors
Right-of-way, lease, purchase, and the like
Safety in the use of elevators and escalators

Occupational

Automation and employment opportunities
Opportunities in construction, operation of pipe lines
Opportunities in plumbing, pipefitting
Opportunities in electronic controls
Opportunities in conveyors services

Cultural

Early Roman water systems
Early American city water systems
History, development of transcontinental pipe lines
Great achievements in conveyors development
Future possibilities of conveyors systems

Recreational

Design, construct model elevators, escalators, and the like
Do-it-yourself plumbing, pipefitting
Adapt winches, hydraulic lifts to farm equipment
Develop models of factories of the future
Install a water system for a summer cabin

Social

Automation and the standard of living
Economic competition in transportation
Pipe line systems and the national health
Government regulations, controls
Bulk commodity transportation of the future

TRANSPORTATION—HIGHWAY VEHICLES

Technical

Operating principles of the internal combustion engine
Principles of transmission, ignition system, and the like
Automobile driving instruction
Nomenclature of the automobile
Engineering aspects of automobile safety

Consumer

Considerations in the selection of an auto, bicycle, and the like
Economics of automobile operation
Safe operation of the automobile
Legislative aspects of highway transportation
Practical automobile servicing at home

Occupational

Job opportunities in automobile manufacturing industries
Opportunities in vehicle servicing
College preparation, vocational training
Opportunities for women
Rewards, incentives, hazards

Cultural

History and development of the automobile
Great inventions, inventors
Principles of good design applied to the automobile
Kinds, characteristics of materials in the automobile
Interior furnishings and good taste in the automobile

Recreational

Design, construct models of automobiles
Restoring antique automobiles, engines
Collecting photos, insignias of automobiles
Design, construct soap box racers
Design, construct powered miniature automobiles

Social

Effects of the automobile on the standard of living
Needed safety, regulatory legislation
The automobile and social status
The vehicle industry and its contribution to employment
Vehicular transportation and city planning

TRANSPORTATION—HIGHWAYS

Technical

Concrete design, characteristics, applications
Principles, techniques in surveying
Development, drawing of surveys
Elements of traffic engineering
Fundamentals of city planning

Consumer

Knowledge, understanding of traffic regulations
Acquaintance with correct highway legislation
Development of skills in safe driving
Methods of financing road, street construction
Awareness of community traffic safety problems

Occupational

Job opportunities in highway engineering
Civil service opportunities, education, training
Opportunities in traffic control
Opportunities in heavy equipment operation
Rewards, incentives, hazards

Cultural

Famous early roads and the settlement of the West
Outstanding achievements in bridges
History of traffic legislation
Contemporary leaders in city planning
Highways of the future

Recreational

Development of model bridges, road systems, and the like
Design, construction of molds, forms for concrete construction
Highway travel by automobile
Voluntary safety patrol service
Design, drawing of animated road maps

Social

Highway development and the national standard of living
Highway development and the national security
Relationships of local, state, national highway planning
Legal aspects in highway construction
Standardization of traffic controls, regulations

TRANSPORTATION—RAILWAYS

Technical

Railway powerplants, principles, operation
Railway nomenclature

Railway automatic controls, signals
Manufacturing of railway equipment
Maintenance, services of railway equipment

Consumer

Governmental regulation, rates, service
Extent of railway service in the United States
Railways as competitive transportation
Traveling by rail: nature, accommodations, and the like
Railroad transportation and safety

Occupational

Job opportunities in railroading
College preparation, apprenticeship, vocational training
The occupational future in railroading
Rewards, incentives, hazards

Cultural

Opportunities in railway equipment manufacture
The story of early railroads in the United States
History-making trains, locomotives
Railroads and the settlement of the West
European contributions to railroads
Great achievements, inventors, pioneers

Recreational

The development of a model railroad
Construction of model trains
Design, construction of model railroad equipment
Development of railroad-type playground equipment
Collecting pictures of famous trains, locomotives

Social

Railroads and the national standard of living
Railroads and industrial development
Legislation and government regulation of railroads
The significance of railroads in the national economy
Future status of railroad development

THE ELECTRONICS INDUSTRIES

Technical

The electron theory
Basic electronic circuits
Functions of electronic components
Applications of electronics in automation
Applications of electronics in the home of the future

Consumer

Electronic versus mechanical controls
Criteria of quality in the selection of electronic appliances
Safety instructions for television operation
Repair versus replacement
Economics in the operation of electronic equipment

Occupational

Opportunities in the electronic industries
Personal, technical qualifications, education, training
The occupational future in electronics
Opportunities for women
Occupational rewards, incentives, hazards

Cultural

The history of electrical discoveries
Great inventors, inventions
Biography of Edison
The development of commercial television
Contemporary developments in electronics for a finer living

Recreational

Ham radio operation
Electronic gadgetry
Home electronics workshop development
Radio control for model boats, airplanes
Short-wave radio listening and foreign language study

Social

Electronics development and the standard of living
Legislative, governmental regulation
Electronic communications as socializing agency
Electronics as an aid to human growth and development
Electronics takes over human thinking

INDUSTRIAL RESEARCH

Technical

The tools of research
The scientific method
Research as an industry
Relationships of research and development
Research and the new materials

Consumer

Economic values of research
Research to outmode current products
Research and health, safety, longevity
Research and aesthetic qualities, standards
Research and the supply of consumer products

Occupational

The work of the chemist in research
The work of the physicist in research
The role of mathematics in scientific research
College preparation, nature and extent
Rewards, incentives, hazards

Cultural

Role of the creative intellect in human experience
Famous scientific achievements, scientists
Relationships of research and invention
Relationships of industrial research and social progress
Nature, extent of the fields of industrial research

Recreational

Inventing
Constructing experimental models
Developing machine-tool competencies for experimental work
Exploring among materials and processes
Experimental industrial chemistry

Social

Contributions of research to a finer living
Substitutes for research and their effects
Governmental versus private research
Exploration of the universe and the Master Plan
Freedom to question, to search, as essentials to human growth and
    development

THE SERVICES

Technical

Operating principles of refrigeration systems
Heating systems, types, operation, adjustment
Electronic instruments: radio, television, and the like
Internal combustion engines

Consumer

Understanding of machine operating principles
Recognition of need for service
Identification of type of service needed
Product selection and probable service
Knowledge of personal service limitations

Occupational

Opportunities in services in industry
Qualifications for service positions, education, training
Opportunities for private enterprise in services
Opportunities in services for business
Rewards, incentives, hazards

Cultural

Understanding of circuits, systems, mechanisms in functional
    relationships

The appreciation of the unique problems of the engineer and of the
stylist in effecting functional design
Awareness of the role of the consumer in the success or failure of
products

Recreational

Equipping the home workshop for servicing
Repairing appliances
Adapting old parts, machines to new ones
Rebuilding gasoline engines
Collecting a technical library

Social

Product service and the standard of living
Product service, a new American necessity
Product models, a key to production
Role of the consumer in automated industrial development
Foreign products and service

INDUSTRIAL MANAGEMENT

The pattern being used for derivation of subject matter by function does not fit the area of industrial management. Instead, the following analysis is proposed to structure student-teacher relationships and to reflect industrial management. It also serves as an outline of management as subject matter.

I. Organizational Plans
   A. Line: the teacher is the authority
   B. Line and Staff
      1. The teacher is the authority, with several students as staff assistants
      2. A student is the authority, with several students as advisers and with the teacher as consultant
   C. Functional: several student departmental supervisors collaborate as the authority
   D. Committee
      1. Executive committee of students with teacher as adviser
      2. Student adviser committees
      3. Student educational committees for discussions, group projects, and the like

    E. Informal
      1. Student-teacher direct relationship
      2. Students assume functional responsibilities; the teacher only teaches
  II. Organizational Charts
    A. Structural Relationships
    B. Lines of Authority Defined
    C. Fix Responsibility
    D. Standard-practice Instruction

REPRESENTATIVE STUDENT EXPERIENCE UNITS

The student experience units which follow are representative of the types of industrial arts programs we envision. They are considered typical of subject matter and projects, but they are by no means complete and fixed as listed. However, with further development they could become a virtual catalog of learning situations.

Class units, including visitations, discussions, and projects, emphasize learning situations involving the entire class. A maximum of student participation in organization and management is desirable. In class projects a basic requisite for success is complete division of responsibility so that each student makes essential contributions.

Group units involve small numbers of students, perhaps two to five, with one student acting as team leader. The project undertaken requires careful preplanning with periodic review by the teacher. Each member is assigned an essential responsibility, and from this point he assumes the obligation of detailed planning and completion of his assignment. Effectiveness of any class or group undertaking can be increased when the students understand the qualifications and duties involved in leadership and in followership. These exist as elements of subject matter within the social function and can be taught.

The *individual units* suggest involvements for single students without concern for the group or the class, except as they set high or low standards for student achievements. The most successful individual project not only results in a maximum of student growth and development but stands as a measure of overall excellence for others to attain or to surpass.

Production projects may involve groups or entire classes for their development. Principles and techniques of effective organization and management are applicable. When a class engages in a production project, as in the production laboratory (see Chapter IX), the chart, Fig. 9-10, p. 320, shows a general plan of organization. This may be expanded or condensed depending on the class size. Such a project may begin with meetings of the directors, which include the entire class. Proposals for production items may originate with the class or in projects created by students in the research and development program. The proposals are presented and evaluated, problems of production are identified, and project finance is studied. A vote determines acceptance or rejection of the project. When a project is accepted, a general manager is elected, and he in counsel with the teacher appoints the key personnel of the managerial staff. At this time the resource persons to be drawn from local industry are proposed and invited. Typical duties of the managerial staff and their offices are suggested on the chart. When the production is completed, the directors in a final meeting evaluate the undertaking, make recommendations, and dissolve the organization.

THE CERAMICS INDUSTRIES

Class Units

Visitations

Dinnerware manufacturing
Art pottery manufacturing
Glass products manufacturing
Enameled metal production
Portland cement plant

Discussions

Ceramic products in the home
New scientific developments in ceramics
The grinding of optical, camera lenses
The chemistry of glazes
Geographical, geological aspects of ceramic materials

Class projects

Sponsor community ceramics hobby club
Sponsor science-ceramics seminars
Sponsor industrial ceramics products show
Sponsor school assembly programs; glass blowing, throwing
Construct concrete walks, benches, and the like for school
    grounds

Group Units

    Design, construct concrete recreational equipment for community
        park or school grounds
    Design, construct flower planters for classrooms
    Concrete construction work at homes of needy persons
    Arrange ceramic exhibits for school
    Conduct ceramic demonstrations for elementary classes

Individual Units

    Design, develop pottery, dinnerware, insulators, resistors
    Glass blowing, forming, experimental bodies
    Enameling on metal: research, experiment on common metals
    Plaster mold design and construction
    Concrete fish pools, garden furniture

Production Projects

    Clay, wall, hearth, table tile
    Pottery favors for teachers, school visitors
    Enameled metal fishing lures
    Saleable souvenirs for community celebrations
    Flower planters, vases for hospitals

THE FOODS INDUSTRIES

Class Units

    Visitations

        Modern dairy farm
        Modern automatic dairy
        Appliance manufacturing plants
        Candy manufacturing plants
        Cereal manufacturing plants

    Discussions

        Principles, operation of food preservation systems
        How the home refrigerator works
        How electricity produces heat for cooking
        How a vacuum bottle keeps food hot or cold
        Practices in table settings
        Design, decoration for dinnerware, silver

    Projects

        Sponsor industry-agriculture fairs

Servicing farm machines and tools for needy families
Construction of farm buildings or equipment for sale
Design, construct scale models of farms of the future
Cooperative interchange with home economics

Group Units

Design, construct a garden tractor and implements
Design, construct feeders, brooders for 4-H members
Convert auto or truck into a utility tractor
Design, construct utility trailers
Design, construct portable air compressor

Individual Units

Design, construct garden tractor, attachments
Design, construct utility trailer, feeders, and the like
Rebuilding, repainting farm machines
Design, construct forms for concrete construction
Plan the electric power system for a farm

Production Projects

Garden vegetable identification markers
Storage crates for a fruit grower
Bird houses, feeders for county-wide distribution
4-H club insignia
Ceramic dinnerware, wood tableware

THE CHEMICALS INDUSTRIES

Class Units

Visitations

Paints, finishes manufacturing plant
Commercial photo processing plant
Glass products plant
Steel smelting plant
Electroplating plant

Discussions

Why plaster of Paris returns to gypsum rock
Why rubber stretches
Why adhesives hold materials together
The effect of exposure to light on photo film
Why ceramic products are permanent

Class projects
  Invite a chemist to speak and demonstrate before the class
  Arrange a clinic on paints for do-it-yourself fans
  Arrange a clinic on color photography processing
  Arrange exhibits showing the manufacture of adhesives, paints,
    and the like

Group Units
  Collaborate in the development of ceramic glazes
  Compound photographic solutions from formulas
  Conduct tests on adhesive strengths
  Develop synthetic jewels
  Measure moisture content of lumber

Individual Units
  Bath-mix and make glazes
  Experiment and report on the bonding of plastics
  Experiment and demonstrate bonding of woods to metals
  Explain and demonstrate the deflocculation of clay
  Explain and demonstrate the sensitizing of paper, metal, and the
    like

Production Products
  Grind, calcine metals for ceramic colors
  Electroplate projects made in industrial arts
  Etch designs in glass, metal projects
  Process a quantity of roll film
  Heat treat tools made in industrial arts

THE GRAPHIC ARTS INDUSTRIES—DRAWING

Class Units
  Visitations
    Industrial drafting rooms
    Engineering design division of industry
    Aircraft and boat lofts
    Architects' studios
    Industrial design studios
  Discussions
    Role of drawing in industrial arts
    Role of drawing in industry

How to read technical drawings
Nature and values of standard drafting practices
Supplementary information included on a drawing
Class projects
Make a survey and map of the community, park, and the like
Make a landscape plan for a new school, playground
Collect and exhibit types of industrial drawings
Make drawings of a proposed industrial arts laboratory
Compile an encyclopedia of drawings

Group Units
Make a set of working drawings of a boat
Design and make the drawings for a midget auto
Restyle an automobile by means of drawings
Design the record charts for a production project
Compile a file of project ideas for industrial arts

Individual Units
Make a set of drawings for a "dream" car, boat, airplane
Make a drawing of a proposed home workshop
Make drawings for furniture for one's own room
Make an organizational chart for a local industry
Make a progress chart for a fund raising campaign

Production Units
Set up design and drawing competitions for sports cars, yachts,
airplanes, motor scooters, home workshops, industrial arts laboratories, and the like
Produce quantities of prints from drawings

GRAPHIC ARTS—PHOTOGRAPHY

Class Units
Visitations
Camera and supplies manufacturing
Lens grinding plant
Movie studio
Commercial photo studio
Photographic salons
Discussions
Characteristics of films and papers

Principles and practices in camera operation
Qualities of good photographs
Chemical-physical nature of the development process
Photography and science
Class projects
Organize a camera club in school or neighborhood
Sponsor photographic competitions
Photographic yearbook for industrial arts
Photograph school classes
Provide school photographic service
Group Units
Sponsor school photography club
Arrange for photographic exhibits in school
Design and construct photographic equipment
Keep photo record of industrial arts projects, activities
Utilize experimental photography
Individual Units
Learning to take photographs
Darkroom techniques
Design, construct equipment: printer, enlarger, and the like
Photo exhibiting in competition
Experimental photography
Production Projects
Take photos of industrial arts students
Manufacture equipment, accessories
Produce an industrial arts yearbook
Produce souvenir school albums
Photograph school functions

GRAPHIC ARTS—PRINTING

Class Units
Visitations
Newspaper plant
Book, magazine publishing plant
Commercial printing plant
Commercial engraving plant
Silk screen printing plant

Discussions
  The role of the printed word in American living
  Comparison of the basic printing processes
  How paper money is printed
  How a photograph is reproduced in printing
  The story of a book
Class projects
  Exhibits showing printing processes, bookmaking, and the like
  Conference on new developments in printing with experts
  Advertising printing for school carnival, open house
  Book repairing for the school library
  Magazine binding for teachers, library, and the like
Individual Units
  Learning to set type
  Platemaking, cutmaking
  Printing distinctive personal stationery
  Constructing a silk screen outfit
  Planning a home printing shop
Group Units
  Publishing a neighborhood newspaper
  Publishing an industrial arts class newspaper
  Design, construct equipment for home print shop
  Collecting old books, magazines for an exhibit
  Compiling an encyclopedia of printing ideas
Production Projects
  Publishing an industrial arts departmental newspaper
  Producing school activity posters
  Printing souvenirs for industrial arts, school, and the like
  Manufacturing paper
  Designing and printing book jackets for textbooks

THE LEATHER INDUSTRIES

Class Units
  Visitations
    Leather tannery
    Leather products manufacturing
    Leather supply warehouse

Shop of a professional leather craftsman
Museum exhibits of ancient leather products
Discussions
The manufacturing of leathers
Leather and leather products of the ancients
The chemistry of tanning
Selection of leather goods
Equipping of a home workshop for leather work
Class projects
Sponsor shoe grooming campaign in school
Sponsor neighborhood leather-craft clubs
Training program in leather craft for recreation leaders
Sponsor exhibit of antique leather products
Assist elementary teachers with leather-craft instruction
Group Units
Tanning small skins
Leather products manufacture for sale
Design, make school jackets, belts, and the like
Conduct leather-craft instruction for community groups
Sponsor leather-craft hobby show
Individual Units
Design and make projects of leather
Tan a small animal skin
Develop patterns of lacing, braiding
Make dies for cutting identical leather parts
Dye leather
Production Projects
Industrial arts department souvenirs for visitors
Bookmarks for all students in school
Leather gloves for the class
Die design and construction
Machines for making leashes, lanyards, and the like

THE METALS INDUSTRIES

Class Units
Visitations
Steel mills
Mining operations
Metals research laboratories

Metals products manufacturing
Foundries

Discussions

How stainless steel is made
Methods for welding metals
Precious metals refining, grading
Grades, sizes, shapes of steel
Principles and practices in metal plating

Class Projects

Construct model steel mill, rolling mill
Conference with a metallurgist
Design, construct playground equipment
Christmas toy rebuilding project
Compile an encyclopedia of metals products

Group Units

Design, construct home workshop machines
Sponsor metal-craft hobby clubs
Design, construct a camping trailer
Design, construct school bicycle racks
Demonstrate metal forming processes to elementary classes

Individual Units

Camping and home workshop equipment
Research and experiment with powdered metals
Identification tests for various metals
Research and experiment in making alloys
Comparative tests for forgings and castings

Production Projects

Metal toys for Christmas distributions
Metal favors for P.T.A.
Bicycle accessories
House numbers
Picnic grills, coolers, and the like

THE PAPER INDUSTRIES

Class Units

Visitations

Pulpwood lumbering
Papermaking plant

Paper supply company
Paper carton manufacturing
Boxboard, wallboard manufacturing
Discussions
How paper is made from pulp
The operation of the Fourdrinier machine
The chemistry of papermaking
Paper selection for industrial arts printing
Types, grades of papers
Class projects
Demonstrate papermaking in elementary classes
Arrange an exhibit showing industrial papermaking
Conduct a salvage paper drive to finance a production project
Make and decorate wastepaper receptacles for school use
Demonstrate papier-maché work to elementary classes
Group Units
Set up a papermaking unit and produce paper
Collect, identify samples of paper from manufacturers and jobbers
Develop paper crafts
Demonstrate paper crafts to elementary teachers and pupils
Make decorations and decorate the laboratory for a party
Individual Units
Construct papermaking equipment for home and school use
Construct cardboard models of buildings, cities, and the like
Experiment, test with plastic-paper laminates
Design decorative cardboard boxes, containers for production
projects
Make Christmas decorations
Production Projects
Paper stock for greeting cards, for photography
Make decorations for school carnivals, dances, and the like
Make costumes, masks for parties, dances, and the like
Make papier-maché toys for Christmas distribution
Make industrial arts department souvenirs

THE PLASTICS INDUSTRIES

Class Units
Visitations
Chemical-plastics manufacturing
Plastics products manufacturing

Mold and die manufacturing
Industrial plastics research
Department store to find and classify plastics products
Discussions
    Plastics as substitute materials
    Industrial integration of plastics with other materials
    Predicting the future of synthetics
    Advantages of plastics
    Identification of plastics types
Class projects
    Exhibit of plastics products of good design
    Demonstrations with plastics for elementary classes
    Student demonstrations for the P.T.A. and other groups
    Conference with plastics chemist
    Salvage, repair plastic toys for needy children

Group Units
    Design, construct plastics forming jigs
    Design, construct instruction aids
    Design, construct presses for molding plastics
    Design, construct plastics heating equipment
    Design, construct metal dies for casting, molding

Individual Units
    Experiment, test plastic adhesives
    Design, develop plastic fishing lures
    Design, construct forming jigs
    Experiment, test with plastic paints
    Design, develop a plastic product

Production Units
    Plastics souvenirs for industrial arts open house
    Plastics dishes, spoons for industrial arts party
    Plaster molds for casting liquid plastics
    Decorative tiles of polyester resins
    Plastic laminates

THE RUBBER INDUSTRIES

Class Units
    Visitations
        Rubber manufacturing plant
        Tire manufacturing plant
        Rubber toy factory

Foam rubber manufacturing plant
Museum exhibits on rubber
Discussions
The story of rubber, to synthetization
The importance of rubber as a material
How synthetic rubber is made
How tires are made
The future of rubber
Projects
Student bicycle and auto tire inspection program
Rubber toy repairing, redecorating
Rubber molds for plastics or plaster casting
Rubber stamp design
Upholstering with foam rubber
Group Units
Exhibits depicting the story of rubber, tires, and the like
Design, construction of rubber processing equipment for home
workshop
Research project on automobile accidents caused by faulty tires
Individual Units
Rubber stampmaking
Rubber cuts, platemaking
Repair of rubber products
Foam rubber·upholstery
Waterproofing fabric
Production Projects
Rubber molds
Rubber toys
Toy balloons
Vibration dampers
Novelties, souvenirs

THE TEXTILES INDUSTRIES

Class Units
Visitations
Cotton plantation
Cotton gin
Textiles manufacturing plants
Clothing manufacturing plants
Rubber tire manufacturing plant

Discussions

The role of textiles in the standard of living
Relation of the textiles and plastics industries
Identification of common textile weaves
Textile products in the home
Automation in the textiles industries

Class projects

Sponsor dress-up days at school
Arrange exhibits illustrating the story of textiles
Arange exhibit showing the manufacture of nylon
Arrange exhibits of fabrics, weaves, fibers
Sponsor textiles crafts hobby clubs

Group Units

Construct a variety of types of hand looms
Weave material for and make scarfs, ties, purses, and the like
Demonstrate textile decorating: stencil, block, and the like
Fabricate camping equipment: sleeping bags and the like
Plan exchange project with home economics group

Individual Units

Construct camp equipment: knapsacks, cases, and the like
Weave a necktie
Braid cord, rope for leashes, halters, and the like
Make a shop apron, shop coat
Decorate luncheon sets, head scarfs, and the like

Production Projects

Industrial arts shop aprons
School banners, pennants
Decorated neckties, head scarfs as school souvenirs
Make hand looms for elementary classes
Die cut felt favors for sale at school carnival

TOOLS AND MACHINES INDUSTRIES

Class Units

Visitations

Tool and die division of the large industry
Automated industries: powerplant, refinery, dairy, and the like
Job-type machine shop
Tool manufacturing industry
State employment office

Discussions
  How dies are made
  How jigs are used in auto and aircraft production
  Effects of automation on the job
  Equipping the home workshop
  Different methods for cutting metals by machines
Class projects
  Sponsor community, neighborhood do-it-yourself show
  Sponsor community, home workshop equipment show
  Sponsor invention competition for students
  Promote antique tool exhibit
  Promote neighborhood workshop centers
Group Units
  Design, construct machine tools for the home workshop
  Design, construct jigs for production in plastics, metals
  Design, make embossing stamps for leatherworking
  Make sets of clay modeling tools
  Service, overhaul home workshop machines
Individual Units
  Construct a home workshop machine
  Recondition hand tools
  Develop experimental mechanisms
  Make a set of tools
  Make a useful application of a hydraulic system
Production Projects
  Produce home workshop equipment: jig saws, wood lathes, wheels,
    photoprinters, and the like
  Produce small steam, gasoline engines, and the like
  Make dies and produce plastic souvenirs
  Make bending jigs for forming metal bookracks, jewelry
  Design and produce hand tools, stamps, and the like

THE WOODS INDUSTRIES

Class Units
  Visitations
    State and national forests or tree farms
    Lumber manufacturing mill
    Furniture factory
    Boat manufacturing plant
    Museum exhibits of woods, woods industries

Discussions
  The future of the woods industries
  The sharpening principles for wood tools
  Identification of products made from the tree
  Kinds of lumber and lumber products for house construction
  Means, devices for fastening woods
Class Projects
  Annual tree planting on school grounds
  Sponsor a school whittling competition
  Tree care program for school grounds
  Construct a garage, shed, chicken house, and the like for sale
  Sponsor wood hobby crafts clubs
Group Units
  Make house repairs for a needy family
  Construct a boat, swimming raft, and the like
  Build a pre-fabricated cabin, clubhouse
  Design and construct dog houses, hutches, feeders, and the like
  Refinish woodworking benches for school shop
Individual Units
  Design and construct a piece of furniture
  Design and make a model of a home workshop
  Learn to sharpen each common type of wood tool
  Rebuild, refinish a piece of furniture
  Build a boat of marine plywood
Production Projects
  Produce an item of furniture for each class member
  Produce a small item for each classroom: planter, shelf, and the
    like
  Produce model airplane, boat, automobile kits
  Manufacture wood toys for an orphanage, children's home
  Manufacture wood accessories for the Red Cross

THE CONSTRUCTION INDUSTRIES

Class Units
  Visitations
    Community housing project under construction
    Construction of a large school or industrial building
    Home furnishing department of a large department store
    Unique contemporary buildings by renowned architects
    House pre-fabricating plant

Discussions
  Functional, aesthetic considerations in house planning
  Functional, aesthetic considerations in city planning
  How great architects work
  Comparisons of construction materials
  The house, building of the future
Class projects
  Sponsor clean-up, paint-up campaigns in school, community
  Arrange exhibits showing evolution of house designs
  Sponsor model house design competition
  Sponsor industrial arts laboratory planning competition
  Sponsor furniture project design competition
Group Units
  Design and construct cabins for a recreation camp
  Repair broken sidewalks on school grounds
  Design, construct industrial arts display cabinet
  Design, construct a model of a community improvement project
  Design, make model of a crafts center for a summer camp
Individual Units
  Design and draw plans for a summer cabin
  Plan and redecorate one's room at home
  Plan and remodel a basement for a recreation center
  Refinish, repair furniture
  Design, construct furnishings for a recreation room
Production Projects
  Community street markers
  Bird feeders, pet cages for elementary classrooms
  Dog houses, bird cages to be sold
  Build a garage, cabin, outdoor fireplace for a client
  Paint a house for a needy family

THE POWER INDUSTRIES

Class Units
  Visitations
    Hydro-electric power station
    Steam-electric power station
    Automobile engine manufacturing plant
    Model-airplane engine factory
    Aircraft engines maintenance center

Discussions
  How power is produced by heat
  How an electric motor is driven
  How power measurements and ratings are made
  The operating principles of the reaction engine
  Theories of simple machines: lever, pulley, plane, and the like
Class projects
  Safety campaigns in handling automobile horsepower
  Auto, motor scooter, motorbike inspection campaign
  Model-airplane, boat, auto competition
  Electrical safety campaign in home, farm, school
  Exhibits on the evolution of mechanical power
Group Units
  Design, construct miniature gasoline, steam engines
  Model of electric power station and transmission system
  Overhaul and service lawn mower engines
  Restore an old automobile engine
  Construct an instructional mock-up of a rocket engine
Individual Units
  Design, construct miniature engines
  Design, construct miniature powered cranes, bulldozers, and the
    like
  Operate engine tune-up instruments
  Adapt electric motor or gasoline engine to a machine
  Design, build powered auto scooter, motorcycle, and the like
Production Projects
  Manufacture model steam, gasoline engines
  Manufacture garden tractors
  Manufacture small automobiles for street use
  Manufacture adaption kits for engine to bicycle
  Manufacture parts for converting engines for inboard boats

THE TRANSPORTATION INDUSTRIES—AIRWAYS, SPACEWAYS

Class Units
  Visitations
    Aircraft terminal, control tower
    Government weather station
    Aircraft museum

Aircraft manufacturing plant
Model-airplane meets, shows
Discussions
  Theory of flight
  Theory of flight propulsion
  Recent developments in aircraft science
  Present status of expert thinking on space travel
  Air travel in 2,000 A.D.
Class projects
  Sponsor school model-airplane club
  Sponsor community model-airplane meets, shows
  Sponsor flight experience for students, flying club
  Develop a model-airplane flying field
  Meetings with aeronautics experts

Group Units
  Develop experimental flying models
  Develop jigs for shaping, assembling parts
  Instruct groups in model-airplane flying, construction
  Demonstrate indoor flying for elementary students
  Enter local, state, national competition

Individual Units
  Develop original designs in models
  Construct radio control for powered flight
  Cooperative work experience at an airport
  Construct models of historic aircraft
  Construct model-airplane service kit

Production Projects
  Develop and produce model kits for class competition
  Develop and produce model-airplane service kits
  Design and produce insignia for model-airplane club
  Design and produce plastic canopies
  Make molds and cast ships for model space station

TRANSPORTATION—RAILWAYS

Class Units
  Visitations
    Modern railroad terminal
    Railroad locomotive repair shops
    Dispatching office of a large railroad

Trip in and through a modern train
Engineering offices of railroad
Discussions
Locomotive design, operation
Foreign developments in trains
How railroad traffic is regulated, controlled
The workings of a railroad block system
How rails are made
Class projects
Make an excursion by train
Build a model railroad for use in elementary grades
Set up a model railroad for use in industrial arts
Sponsor a community model railroad club
Show films on railroads for all school students
Group Units
Organize a school, neighborhood model-railroad club
Design, construct a model railroad for industrial arts use
Develop, construct a controls system for a model railroad
Learn trainman's signals
Make a traveling exhibit on the development of railroads
Individual Units
Construct a miniature working steam engine
Develop experimental trains for a model railroad
Repair, service electric model locomotives
Develop mechanical equipment for a model railroad
Demonstrate principles of steam Diesel engines
Production Projects
Manufacture toy trains
Manufacture parts, accessories for a model railroad
Produce railroad club insignia
Publish a story of railroads with photos of models
Make souvenir ceramic oilers, locomotive penny banks, and the
like

TRANSPORTATION—VEHICLES

Class Units
Visitations
Automobile engine factory, assembly plant
Automobile body stamping plant

Bicycle, transportation toy factory
Highway patrol station to observe auto inspection, driver examination
City bus terminal and repair shops
Discussions
How power is produced in an engine
Principles of automatic transmissions
Driving safety for young drivers
Bus, truck systems operation
Economic significance of the automobile in the United States
Class projects
Conduct auto, bicycle safety inspections for students
Promote community auto, pedestrian safety campaign
Conduct all-school power model-auto speed contests
Rebuild an antique automobile
Construct devices for automobile driver tests
Group Units
Conduct model sports car design competition
Rebuild an automobile to sell
Overhaul an engine
Restyle an automobile body
Build mock-ups of transmission, ignition system, and the like
Individual Units
Engine adjustment, tune-up
Comparative study of auto engine specifications
Car top carrier
Install turn signals
Engine trouble-shooting experience
Production Projects
Traffic control signs for school grounds
Windshield ice scrapers
Mono-wheel trainers for automobile
Tow cables from surplus parts
Emergency trouble lights

TRANSPORTATION—WATERWAYS

Class Units
Visitations
Shipbuilding, boat manufacturing plants
United States naval base

Excursion by boat
Ship terminals, docks
Canals, locks, river, waterways developments
Discussion
    Applications of physical laws to boats
    How ocean-going ships are controlled
    Procedures in boat building
    Operations of canal, river locks
    National and international laws affecting shipping
Class projects
    Sponsor boating, sailing club
    Sponsor model-boat competition
    Sponsor demonstrations on boating safety
    Arrange for a class meeting with an expert on navigation
    Construct models of famous ships for instructional use

Group Units
    Model-boat design and construction
    Diving gear design and construction
    Fishing tackle design and construction
    Ice boat construction
    Motorboat, canoe construction

Individual Units
    Build a full-size boat
    Design and build powered model boats
    Convert an air cooled engine to inboard use
    Construct surf board, water skis
    Design and construct camping equipment for boats

Production Projects
    Full size boats, canoes, ice boats
    Water sports equipment
    Produce plans and kits for a model boat competition
    Toy boats
    Diving apparatus

TRANSPORTATION—CONVEYORS

Class Units
    Visitations
        Pipe line installations
        An automatic manufacturing plant
        Factory employing assembly lines

Modern dairy
Glass tube manufacturing plant
Discussions
Advantages of pipe line transportation
Kinds of materials used in pipe, tube systems
Automation as automatic control or as parts transfer
The story of the "Big Inch"
Overland conveyor systems, a new form of transportation
Class projects
Arrange with experts a public program on automation
Make scale models of machines to equip a typical factory: pottery, paper mill, and the like
Compile an encyclopedia of applications of conveyors
Arrange exhibits showing conveyor systems of the future

Group Units
Develop a working model of an automatic machine
Design, construct a conveyor system for industrial arts use in a production project
Design, construct a miniature working model of a conveyor for use with a model railroad
Individual Units
Weld glass tubing
Develop an experimental model of automatic processing
Weld steel pipe, tubing
Make joints in copper tubing systems
Design, construct coal elevator for model railroad
Production Projects
Manufacture conveyor loaders for model railroad systems
Produce parts for an assembly line for industrial arts
Set up a conveyor system for glazing pottery
Set up a conveyor system for painting projects
Set up a conveyor system for drying printing ink

TRANSPORTATION—HIGHWAYS

Class Units
Visitations
State highway engineering offices
Highway, bridge construction project

Heavy road machinery factory
Municipal traffic court
State highway patrol headquarters
Discussions
The current automobile accident record, causes
The problem of the teen-age driver
Unsafe driving practices observed in the community
Designing for safer highways, streets
Needed traffic legislation, community, state, national
Class projects
Establish, conduct school safety patrol
Conduct school safe driving campaign
Establish, conduct school traffic court
Survey community for more effective traffic control
Design, construct scale models of community developments

Group Units
Develop instructional aids for driver training
Repair concrete walks on the school grounds
Design, construct model bridges, grade separations
Design, construct model of the city of the future
Develop a parking plan for the school grounds
Individual Units
Pass a safe driving examination
Draw a map of the community showing traffic regulations
Make forms for and lay a concrete walk, steps, and the like
Blacktop the home driveway
Design, construct highways, bridges for model trains
Production Projects
Design, manufacture street markers for new community streets
Design, make school safety patrol insignia
Design, make welcome signs for entrances to city
Design, construct bridges, highways, towns
Design, construct model electric traffic controls

THE ELECTRONICS INDUSTRIES

Class Units
Visitations
Television-radio broadcasts

Electronics equipment manufacturing
Electric powerplants
Movie technical laboratories
Automatic factory
Discussions
Inside a vacuum tube
Applications of the electric eye
Applications of electronic computers
How sound is produced electronically
Electronics and national defense
Class projects
Displays on the development of radio, television, and the like
Collect old radios, television sets to salvage parts
Write, film a movie on industrial arts activities
Prepare a radio program on industrial arts
Sponsor radio-controlled model-airplane flights
Group Units
Construct oscillators and learn code
Install private telephones in shop, home
Establish an amateur radio station
Organize a school electronics club
Arrange electronic demonstrations for elementary pupils
Individual Units
Construct transistor pocket radio
Construct electronic garage door control
Construct hi-fi record player and cabinet
Construct radio control for a model airplane
Construct a code practice set
Production Projects
Assemble portable transistor radios
Assemble kits of electronic test devices
Design and construct hi-fi cabinets
Fabricate radio chassis
Construct television antennae

INDUSTRIAL RESEARCH

Class Units
Visitations
Governmental aircraft research stations
Museums of science and industry

A five-and-ten cent store to search for unique ideas in products
An industrial research laboratory
A Frank Lloyd Wright building
Discussions
Where do ideas come from?
The design process
How patents, copyrights are obtained
The need for research in the American way
How to work and think scientifically
Class projects
Encourage development of unique, imaginative solutions to problems by placing premiums on them, *i.e.*, competitions, awards, scholarships, recognition. Set up school awards for outstanding creative achievement.

Group Units
Collaborate on development of experimental machines, designs, model aircraft, autos, boats, ceramic glazes, electronic controls, electrical applications, musical instruments, and the like

Individual Units
Individual research, experiment, development among materials and processes in search of new applications, new design ideas, improved and refined applications, inventions, and the like
Materials analysis and testing
Design and testing of structures in wood, metal, plastics, and the like

INDUSTRIAL MANAGEMENT

Class Units
Visitations
Design division of a large industry
Production planning division of a large industry
Industrial relations divisions of a large industry
Materials handling and control operations
Safety department operations
Discussions
Elements of human engineering
Labor-management relations
Unionism and the standard of living
Qualities of leadership
Training for leadership

Class projects
>Design, equip, operate a materials control system
>Design and operate an effective tool control system
>Design and operate a student organizational system
>Design and operate a safety control plan
>Evaluation and revision of the above systems after trial

Group Units
>Operate an industrial health and safety program in industrial arts
>Operate a materials salvage project
>Plan a program for the discussion of problems in industrial management, using resource persons
>Propose a floor plan arrangement for carrying out a production project

Individual Units
>Design and construct a management chart for the laboratory
>Audit the material control records for the laboratory
>Draw up a requisition for needed supplies
>Inventory materials and supplies

RESEARCH

Class Units
>Visitations
>>Research centers in manufacturing industries
>>University science laboratories
>>Private testing laboratories
>>State highway engineering laboratories
>>Federal engineering and testing laboratories
>Discussions
>>The role of research in today's industry
>>The nature of research in yesterday's industry
>>How to get ideas
>>The nature of the human imagination
>>The creative process with materials, tools, machines
>Class projects
>>Brainstorming problems
>>Developing measures for identifying creativity in materials
>>Evolving an idea through design and development
>>Judging a common product
>>Conducting an opinion poll on the design of a student project

Group Units

Refine the design of a project

Develop a solution to a technical problem

Develop a mock-up to demonstrate the functioning of a system, circuit, and the like

Try for a better idea in the processing of a material

Individual Units

Propose a solution to a technical problem in research style

Design a unique project and identify its strengths and weaknesses

Evaluate a design or solution proposed by another student

Propose an application for a mechanism, circuit, system, and the like

Develop a mock-up of a mechanism, circuit, system, and the like

Production Units

Ideas developed in the industrial arts research laboratory are not put into production there. They are readied for production. Manufacture takes place in the production laboratory (see Chapter IX)

THE SERVICES

Class Units

Visitations

Modern auto, bus, truck service facilities

Locomotive roundhouse

Aircraft rebuilding shops

Radio-television repair shops

Industrial maintenance shops

Discussions

How a watch keeps time

Functions of components in a radio

Auto ignition tune-up

Control systems in automatic washers

When should an amateur not tinker?

Class projects

Servicing industrial arts equipment

Servicing appliances for needy families

Bicycle safety service campaign

Sharpening project for kitchen cutlery

Toy repairing for distribution to needy children

Group Units

    Trouble shoot a "rough" automobile engine
    Construct jigs for, and sharpen ice skates
    Overhaul lawn mower, garden tractor engines
    Test and charge storage batteries
    Operate a vacuum tube tester

Individual Units

    Repair electric appliances
    Construct test equipment for appliance service
    Draw the electrical circuit for a toy train
    Trouble shoot a model-airplane engine
    Disassemble, clean, lubricate, assemble a bicycle brake

Production Projects

    Assemble electrical test equipment
    Assemble portable transistor radios
    Spray paint the toys repaired in the class project
    Sharpen neighborhood knives, scissors
    Collect, replace faulty cords in lamps, irons, and the like

Some Reflections on Subject Matter

The first source of subject matter, the industries analyses, revealed a potential of industrial arts subject matter which can be used as is in the laboratory. However, further derivation may be desirable when fitting the content to particular grade levels or courses. A curriculum so structured is perhaps the most logical and the easiest to develop.

Because industries of all kinds have common elements, common denominators as it were, these, too, may be used as a second source in curriculum construction. They were analyzed and identified as curricular components in a master list (see Figure 6-1). The use of such components as units or blocks of content is particularly suitable in studies intended to search out concepts, principles, theories, and practices which characterize industry broadly and generally.

The analyses of the six functions of industrial arts serve as the *third* major source of subject matter. The representative subject matter derived from the functions suggests their adaptability to curriculum building. Although the content included is as broad as industrial arts itself, certain of these analyses may be used as resources for such study units or courses as occupations in industry, consumer economics, and cultural studies. The content for the recreational function may serve as a guide to the development of industrial arts recreation programs. The substance in the occupations function may be that for the curricular component, occupations.

Possible combinations of subject matter drawn from the three sources are probably unlimited. We recommend that experimental curricula be set up on all levels and that a nationwide search be begun to find the most effective curricula. At this writing several such searches are known to be under way, and in each case the parties involved are enthusiastic about the potential as well as about the results which have begun to appear.

The typical experience units carry the subject matter discussed here into the laboratory. They are intended as ideas and suggestions to prompt better ideas and suggestions. Many more possibilities may be drawn.

TO DISCUSS, TO DEBATE, TO DECIDE

1. How can the industries analyses actually be used in developing a course guide or course of study?
2. Which would be preferable to use in building a curriculum, the industries analyses or the curricular components?
3. How could the six functions serve for the construction of a curriculum? Does this out-of-the-ordinary approach have any advantages?
4. Make an exhaustive study of one of the industries for subject matter by function. Start with any one given and carry it beyond the suggestions already given.
5. What are the reasons for emphasizing principles in industrial arts subject matter?
6. Where can we get the factual information necessary to implement the occupation function in any particular industry?
7. Do possibilities exist for correlated studies between industrial arts and other courses?
8. Can you conceive of a more efficient transportation system for moving people into and out of cities than is now in use?
9. What are the values for the individual student in a group unit or in a production project?
10. How many items can you add to a list of representative student experience units?

(Above) The portable power-plant of the early 1900's was the steam tractor. Introduced for farm use, these bulky tractors weighed approximately twenty tons and yet delivered only about twenty draw-bar horsepower. This one is pulling a six-bottom plow. (Courtesy: International Harvester Company.)

(Right) The business end of today's mighty farm tractor. Weighing almost fifteen tons, with four-wheel drive and 180 draw-bar horsepower, it is designed to serve farms with acreages of 1000 and up. In America, such farms now number approximately 130,000. (Courtesy: International Harvester Company.)

VII

The New
Industrial Arts:
The Project

The "civilized man" may be defined as someone who is at home in his own time and place; it is my belief that to be a civilized American today one must be aware of the mainspring of contemporary America—its technology—as Americans of a hundred years ago were aware of the soil.
—Mitchell Wilson, *American Science and Invention.*
(Copyright 1954. By permission of Simon and Schuster, Inc.)

The project has been an integral and a conspicuous part of industrial arts throughout its existence. Even though frequently questioned, its educative role and worth remain rather constant. The time-worn issue of project, a means or an end, remains unsettled even though many a teacher or graduate student has startled himself with his discovery that the project as a means to an end opens doors to higher values than he had before seen for industrial arts. The teacher who tells the parent that he is more interested in her child than in the child's project never fails to receive a parental blessing.

When the project is relegated to the role of means, it becomes insignificant in itself, and because it then becomes largely busy work, it is increasingly easy to doubt its value. But if the project is removed because of its weakness, industrial arts becomes academic. Then the ghosts of John Dewey swing into action, and the battle cry of learning-by-doing once again prompts a shift in the place of the project. In spite of the changing notions about the role of the project, one practice remains: the industrial arts teacher, the administrator, the parent, and the pupil himself invariably assess the value of the course according to the projects they see. The industrial arts teacher-educator and the state supervisor always look for the projects when they visit schools. The obvious: it is not industrial arts without the project.

In the new industrial arts, the project is neither means nor ends alone; it is both. It functions as one of the means for achieving the values of industrial arts, and thereby becomes a goal in itself. What the pupil does to the block of wood or chunk of clay is important because it is a strong measure of what that wood or the clay is doing to him. If we doubt the significance of the project for industrial arts, we are wiser to rethink this conclusion rather than to condemn the project. Perhaps we have never gotten the full worth from the project as an educative experience because of the many limitations placed upon it. How, for example, can a project truly liberate the pupil when it has been conceived, designed, simplified, systematized, and standardized by the teacher before he dares assign it to the child? The one who gets the most good out of this project and this processing is the teacher, not the pupil. So it is, with the spirit of inquiry prevailing, that industrial arts may properly rethink the project.

THE ORIGIN OF THE PROJECT IN WORK. The origin of the project in industrial arts can be traced to the time when work was first seen as an educative medium. When advocates of the concept of work as education, Pestalozzi and Froebel for instance, demonstrated their beliefs through experimental programs, they found that pupils needed something on which to work if they were to learn. First projects were often in gardening, animal husbandry, building construction, cooking, sewing, and such activities as were essential to the economic support of the experiment since the pupils were commonly poor and homeless children from the cities whose entire well-being was the responsibility of the school. Scandinavian sloyd as a formal course of instruction grew out of the concept of work as education, which in turn originated in rural homes where the family had to make the tools, utensils, clothing, and equipment needed for its own living. In these rural homes the father and mother instructed their children in the necessary arts and technics as a part of their growth and development.

THE PROJECT AS AN EXERCISE IN FUNDAMENTALS. With time Scandinavian educators began to see educative values in work projects and instruction and introduced them into the formal schooling for elementary pupils. In this new role the instruction and projects had to be organized into series of graded exercises to suit the maturity of the pupils. Thus, well-standardized projects in the form of graded exercises became the pattern for instruction in shopwork. In the early stages emphasis was placed on fundamental tool operation, and the exercises developed were largely disciplinary and without utility. By the time that Swedish sloyd was introduced to the United States, it had evolved into a system of graded instructional exercises centered in simple projects generally useful in the home. Emphasis was still on tool mastery, but because the project now had utility in itself, the leaders of the movement found the system easier to justify educatively. Woodward's early programs of manual training were based on formal exercises considered to be fundamental to an understanding of engineering and technology of the day. He made a strong plea on behalf of his manual training as general education.

THE PROJECT AS AN EXPRESSION OF THE AESTHETIC. Charles A. Bennett sought to enrich the educative experience in the manual training project by recommending a concern for its aesthetic treatment. He felt that the project as an experience would be complete, if in addition to its emphasis on tool mastery and utility, it incorporated principles of art and beauty. Bennett's recommendation was widely accepted and practiced, and it still influences the traditional industrial arts project so typical today. Whether Bennett's recommendation produced a completeness in the project has been debated for two generations. Critics have deplored the role artistry has played in industrial arts projects. Such criticism has often been well founded because the teacher so often thinks of beauty as an element to be added to the project rather than as an integral part of the whole.

THE PROJECT AS TRADE OPERATIONS. With national attention on trade training during the period of World War I, the project took on a different form in the hands of such leaders as Robert W. Selvidge. Then the project became an expression of the operations which tradesmen performed in their work, and it was arrived at through a process known as trade analysis. In its extreme form, the project became a formal exercise based on one or more of the tool operations which were practiced until a desired competence was achieved.

THE PROJECT AS TECHNICAL PROCESSES. The popularity of Bennett's manual arts soon liberalized the Selvidge concept and resulted in a utilitarian project which was an assemblage of technical processes, hand or machine. The measure of the project became the number of processes or operations involved in its construction. Function, aesthetics, and pupil interest were of secondary significance. This type of project is still dominant although attention to pupil interest, probably because of the acceptance of Dewey's doctrine of interest, has prompted a greater variety in the forms a project takes.

THE PROJECT AS A PROBLEM IN DESIGN. By 1950 the project appeared tired and worn from its many decades of manhandling. The need for rejuvenation coincided with the coming of age of the industrial designer. Industry's employment of the latter to create consumer product appeal suggested that the way to increase the appeal of industrial arts was likewise through design. Consequently, teachers' colleges here and there introduced courses in design or modernized existing ones, and the literature of the profession featured appeals for good design and short cuts and tricks for effecting it. Contests and exhibits of projects made provision for good design among their yardsticks. All of this attack on the project assumed that what was wrong could be cured by attention to design. Today industrial arts designers commonly consider that the project is complete when it exhibits conformity to accepted patterns of the so-called contemporary design.

THE PROJECT TODAY. The industrial arts project has gone through change in role and form but probably not through a complete development. The profession is still guessing at what the good project is because it is still guessing at the industrial arts curriculum. And it is still guessing at the curriculm because in reality the project has been the curriculum. The current general endorsement of design

quality as the measure of the project illustrates the tendency to sub-
scribe to proposals for the improvement of the project, with or without proof. The danger in such acceptance is in the possibility of
obscuring the real issue, and the real issue is the project.

THE NEW PROJECT IN THE NEW INDUSTRIAL ARTS

With technology serving as the basis of a new curriculum for industrial arts, the project becomes more significant. When accepted
for the new curriculum, the project will stand as a measure of
our understanding of technology and of the human. The problem is
to conceive of the project as truly reflective of the spirit of American
technology. In such a project the human and his creative and constructive powers will come into focus. The new project becomes
an expression of the involvement of the student and technology. By
definition, the project may be considered as an educational enterprise involving the solutions to numerous related problems and requiring the initiative of the student. The following outline analysis
pictures the new project in its three dimensions: the technological,
the human, and the professional, or industrial arts.

I. *The Project As Reflective of Technology*

   A. *The Materials*

      1. The project as an integration of materials
      2. The project as effective utilization of materials
      3. The project as a best choice of materials
      4. The project as proper materials in effective structural
         relationships
      5. The project as materials enhancement

   B. *The Processes*

      1. The project as an application of technical processes
      2. The project as an application of engineering practices and
         scientific principles
      3. The project as a resultant of the design process
      4. The project as the best choice of processes and structures
      5. The project as a product of machine processing

C. *The Quality Standards*
1. The project as an example of the pursuit of technical excellence
2. The project as technically respectable
3. The project as a demonstration of functional efficiency
4. The project as an example of material control
5. The project as employment of a measured durability, as permanence vs. obsolescence

D. *The Economics*
1. The project as an example of good judgment in economics
2. The project as value added to materials
3. The project as economical of time
4. The project as regard for the conservation of materials, natural resources
5. The project as an example of labor-saving

II. *The Project As Reflective of the Human*

A. *Human Resources*
1. The project as experience in creative imagining
2. The project as experience in problem-solving, reasoning
3. The project as a drawing out of talents
4. The project as an example of a better idea
5. The project as a demonstration of creative constructing

B. *Human Responsibility*
1. The project as acceptance of responsibility for effective planning
2. The project as requiring personal initiative, resourcefulness
3. The project as acceptance of responsibility for development of capacities
4. The project as a unique solution
5. The project as acceptance of responsibility in an environment of freedom

C. *Human Potential*
1. The project as a projection of personality
2. The project as a free expression of individuality
3. The project as an incentive to greater achievement

4. The project as re-creative experience
5. The project as means to human growth and development

III. *The Project As Reflective of Industrial Arts—The Professional*

Dimension

A. *The Technology*
   1. The project as essential to understanding technology
   2. The project as contributive to an advancing of technology
   3. The project as a materials expression of ideas
   4. The project as evidence of intelligence at work
   5. The project as suggestive of occupational opportunity

B. *The Student*
   1. The project as an achievement
   2. The project as real and meaningful experience
   3. The project as student-consuming, technically challenging
   4. The project as emphasis on individuality, reflection of self
   5. The project as a means to a greater idea

C. *The Profession*
   1. The project as educationally respectable
   2. The project as evidence of professional maturity
   3. The project as achievement of objectives
   4. The project as both means and end
   5. The project as culturally significant

A Rethinking of Project Design

Man is born with a potential for solving problems, for creating, for inventing. He has a brain with which to conceive and hands with which to implement. With these he is placed in a world of materials and energies. A reaction and an interaction occurs between man and material and energies. Man uses and strengthens his facilities in the utilization of the materials and the energies. This then is what the human postulate for the new industrial arts is. With this, industrial arts in its purest and simplest form is seen merely as the means to bringing the human with all of his talents into an environment of materials, tools, machines, products, and energies for purposes of interaction, leading to the fullest development of his capacities, and thus enabling him to find purpose in his own existence and direction for his efforts. The fullest development of the individual accompanies the fullest development of his expression with materials. This involves designing.

DESIGN: WHAT IS IT? The interpretation of technology accepted here (see Chapter II) is expressive of a philosophy of design. While this concept may be as broad and deep as technology, it is simple, logical, and pointed. Design is a process by which man finds and develops uses for materials; design is a process through which man makes materials serve man; design is a humanizing of materials. In this sense design is fundamental. It involves man with his natural talents for reasoning, problem-solving, creating, and constructing with materials. It permits him to express his native concerns for love, beauty, peace, goodness. It permits him to translate his purpose in living into materials. And hence as a designer, he becomes a philosopher. Further analysis of this concept reveals the multi-faceted role of design, but in total, design becomes the creator of technology because man is by nature a designer.

When design is considered as the creator of technology, the many facets of its role become apparent. Design is first of all *problem-solving*. When man as a creature is faced with a problem he has the facility for solving it. Animal tendency is to circumvent, to flee, or to fight.

Design then becomes *thinking* because thinking begins with a problem. Whether the problem is simple or complex, its solution logically begins with thinking. At this point design becomes imagining, ideating in the attempt to conceive of solutions. One idea suggests another in the process of ideation.

The search for a better way is now on, and design becomes that *search*. Perfection in the solution is relative to time, need, resources, and the designer. A design is perfect only for now; tomorrow it can be improved. Design to this point is leading somewhere. It points to discovery as the finding of a better way. But one discovery reveals another until the limits of time, intellect, and resources are reached.

In order, design then leads to *creating*, to originating in the search for a better way. It takes form in inventing and devising things as well as in methods of doing which have not existed before. This newness of solution is relative to the student and to the extent of his research. It may be conceived of as new only to the student. However, such confinement may result from a very limited searching for better ways.

Design now becomes *engineering*, the science of constructing. Here the idea, the solution, is translated into proposals of materials, structures, processes, and costs. This leads to the development of the solution where design takes on actual dimensions.

As this search for the better proceeds, design becomes a *refining* of the solution and an elimination of weakness. Now the designer can know that what he has achieved is good. He has found a better way.

DESIGN AND INDUSTRIAL ARTS. The concept of design developed above may be termed a *design approach to problem-solving*. Applied to industrial arts, this concept may serve as a design approach to industrial arts. Through the years when design has been applied to industrial arts, its emphasis has been largely on improving the aesthetic side of the project. Criticisms by people in the arts, to which industrial arts teachers have been particularly sensitive, were centered on a concern for beauty. Many design-conscious industrial arts teachers are directing their students to the so-called "contemporary" style, and seemingly they find some security there. But design education here is not the process of loading students on a bandwagon in a style parade.

If we accept the proposal of the design approach to industrial arts, the relationship of design and industrial arts is one of basics and fundamentals. It suggests a completeness, an integration, and an actual educative maturity for industrial arts. This design approach puts emphasis on the growth and development of the whole individual, and in the directions which that growth and development should rightly take. It requires the complete involvement of the individual as the means to his greatest growth and development.

The design approach to industrial arts puts faith in the intelligence and the natural aptitudes of the individual. It makes him responsible for finding a better way. Teacher-planned projects are not consistent with the design approach. These presume faith only in the intelligence of the teacher. This is in strong contrast to the spirit of the design approach.

The design approach to industrial arts puts emphasis on individual development through independent study in the search for unique solutions. This is consistent with the principle that people learn individually, not as groups.

The design approach to industrial arts makes the program one of *research and development*. In this atmosphere the student is concerned with the search for a better way. The teacher is involved in this as fully as the student, but for the purpose of promoting the maximum growth and development of the student.

The design approach to industrial arts assures industrial arts of a continuing timeliness, a continuing newness, a continuing growth and development. Standardization of pupil projects is not likely. Only the goals of this new industrial arts remain constant. The methods for reaching these goals change as the teacher himself continues to search for better ways of teaching.

The design approach to industrial arts assures it of an educative respectability and an intellectual distinction. Not only will such a program make good sense to the superior industrial arts teacher, but it will attract the attention of his academic colleagues as nothing else has done. His own status will be enhanced. His industrial arts will have a natural appeal for the superior student. Even the average and lesser student will achieve a level of growth and development far beyond that ordinarily assigned to him. Then, industrial arts can become essential to the all-round education of every American boy and girl.

DESIGN AND THE INDUSTRIAL ARTS TEACHER. We as industrial arts people are forever looking for short cuts. But there are no short cuts to good design any more than there are short cuts to the development of a philosophy of living. The design approach to industrial arts provides the teacher with a new and greater role. He is now the resource leader. The student uses him as consultant, advisor, and chief resource person. The very fundamentals of teaching industrial arts change as a methodology, dynamic as the new industrial arts itself, emerges. The teacher now finds himself surrounded by intelligence at work. His major responsibility is centered on inspiring his students to draw on intelligence to an even greater degree and stimulating them to seek even better ways. The design approach to industrial arts has the student thinking beyond the lesson and searching beyond the laboratory. The technical competence of the teacher is no longer the measure for the achievement of the student. The teacher, if his students are to continue to search for better ways, must continue to search for better ways in teaching in order to keep his students searching.

WHAT IS GOOD DESIGN IN INDUSTRIAL ARTS? To pull together the essence of the preceding discussion, let us say that good design has its basis in philosophy rather than in form, color, and texture. Design for industrial arts is a complex process involving, first of all, a concern for the growth and development of the student. This concern includes the student and what he does with materials—because what he does to them is a strong measure of what they do to him. Design for industrial arts, then, is more than an application of the processes of industrial design in the sense that in metals or woods or clay, for example, we draw on the basic processes of the respective industries.

Good design is good solutions to problems, which in industrial arts are both technical and human. Because these problems involve materials, processes, structures, mechanisms, circuits, systems, and such technical components, good design becomes good usage of the same. Thus, *effective function* becomes the first specific measure of good design because technology is built on that kind of excellence.

Because of the concern for the fullest development of the student and his natural capacity for thinking, imagining, creating, and constructing, a second measure of good design in industrial arts is that of *uniqueness of solution*. If the student has his own set of unique capacities, and we assume that he does, he is capable of uniqueness. His solutions, then, should reflect this essence of one-of-a-kind-ness. This requires freedom of expression along with the responsibility for expressing. Emphasis on uniqueness can make industrial arts itself unique as a course of instruction. This is a truly significant value which we would do well to develop and then to advertise. We have long talked of industrial arts as concerned with individualism through individual instruction. But this can produce sameness as well as uniqueness. At present, most of our courses seem geared to producing sameness.

Thirdly, good design is measured by *overall excellence*—the overall excellence already referred to. It demonstrates excellence in thinking, reasoning, imagining, creating, selecting, constructing. It represents the greatest excellence of which the student is capable at the time.

Fourth, good design reflects the *human personality.* This quality takes the project beyond function, beyond production and economics, and gives it that quality which shows that the designer cared enough to do his very best. The extra attention, the extra concern for details, the hope that someone else will love it too, all help to reflect the personality of the designer in the materials.

If, finally, we are searching for beauty in the new industrial arts project, we find it not in its conformity to rules, not in its reflection of the current trends in fashion, but because the beauty in the project is new, exciting, stimulating, and refreshing to us. It is beautiful because we can see in it a new, stronger, greater human. Beauty and goodness are one and the same to the philosopher and the poet. Can they not also be in materials?

THE PROSPECT FOR THE PROJECT. The thoughtful teacher will ask whether each project must meet all of the suggested qualifications. The three dimensions of the project identified, the technological, the human, and the professional (see p. 307) may never be achieved by any one student in any one semester. These dimensions describe the potential within the appropriate project. They are a challenge to both the teacher and student. Perhaps the student will not even gain the full value after a dozen years of industrial arts. Nevertheless, these dimensions will have guided him in the direction where the great values lie. They will have caused him to deliberate in the selection of the project. Copying from a magazine or a catalog will no longer satisfy him. Let us then, no matter on what level we teach, draw on these dimensions as measures for excellence and use them to assist us in elevating our concerns about the student and his project. All the dimensions in varying degree to be sure, can be found in the project which results in the greatest growth of the student. With them the project becomes much more than making something, and industrial arts itself becomes more than a course in making things.

Some Reflections. A new industrial arts will most likely require a new project. This project as described is considered to be of maximum dimension. The debate over the project as means or end goes on, and while it does, our concern here is to make something truly significant out of this unique feature of industrial arts. We may assume that there is much more value in the project than we usually get out of it. Great projects are bound to attract promising students to industrial arts as well as to keep its teachers growing. The good project provides as much learning for the teacher as for the student. The learnings may not necessarily be the same, however. Considerable emphasis is placed on the student-project relationship. The project has its greatest impact when it is conceived by the student, when it consumes him, and when it causes him to think on a grander scale. The new project is at the heart of the new industrial arts; no longer is the question one of project or related information, the nonfunctional dualism. The new project is a full package of human growth and development.

TO DISCUSS, TO DEBATE, TO DECIDE

1. Are children in the elementary school capable of research in industrial arts? How about those in the junior high school?
2. Analyze the issue of hand tools versus machines for industrial arts. Which instruction should come first?
3. Are hand-tool exercises justified?
4. Must formal instruction in drawing precede laboratory work?
5. Why have required projects been so commonly used in industrial arts?
6. Which is more pedagogically correct, the teacher-assigned project or the pupil-elected one?
7. When you are involved in an industrial arts project yourself, do you think of it as means or as end?
8. Is the junior high school student capable of designing his own projects? The elementary school child?
9. How can you account for the fact that over the country industrial arts projects are essentially alike, and that through the years they tend to remain essentially the same? Is this intentional standardization? Is this sameness a good idea?
10. What steps are involved in the development of a project?

(Above) A final assembly line in the production of Model T Ford cars during 1923. Henry Ford introduced the assembly line to American industry. It revolutionized assembly procedures by increasing production while simplifying labor. (Courtesy: Ford Motor Company.)

(Below) Final assembly in today's automobile plant is a continuous operation. The line keeps moving as the workers perform their highly specialized job skills. (Courtesy: Ford Motor Company.)

VIII

The New
Industrial Arts:
A Complete Program
to Reflect Technology

The greatest benefactor of the human race died more than half a million years ago. He was a hairy creature with a low brow and sunken eyes, a heavy jaw and strong tiger-like teeth. He would not have looked well in a gathering of modern scientists, but they would have honoured him as their master. For he had used a stone to break a nut and a stick to lift up a heavy boulder. He was the inventor of the hammer and the lever, our first tools, and he did more than any human being who came after him to give man his enormous advantage over the other animals with whom he shares this planet.

—Hendrik Willem van Loon, The Story of Mankind
(By Permission of Liveright, Publishers, N. Y.
Black & Gold Library.)

The new industrial arts is described here as a complete program. It is complete in that it provides for the maximum of service to a single individual and is capable of serving every one. Part I, Industrial Arts Education, includes the program for the

275

public school and the private school. Parts II, III, IV, V, VI, and VII occur beyond these schools on the collegiate level.

The subject matter earlier derived finds application throughout the entire program. No one level of the program can or should be concerned with the whole package of subject matter. No longer need the enterprising industrial arts teacher ask, "I now have thirteen areas in my shop, how many more do I need?"

I. Industrial Arts Education
  A. The elementary school: an introduction to the technology
    1. The primary grades: technology and the home
    2. The intermediate grades: technology and the community
    3. The upper grades: technology and the world
  B. The junior high school: the study of the manufacturing industries
    1. Grade 7: the graphic arts, paper, leather, textiles industries
    2. Grade 8: the ceramics, plastics, rubber, chemical, foods industries
    3. Grade 9: the metals, woods, tools, and machines industries
  C. The senior high school
    1. The power and transportation industries
    2. The electrical and electronic industries
    3. The construction industries
    4. Industrial production
    5. The services industries
    6. Industrial organization and management
    7. Research and development
  D. Industrial arts therapy
    1. Industrial arts as therapy
    2. Industrial arts as rehabilitation
    3. Industrial arts for the mentally handicapped
  E. Industrial arts recreation
    1. For the school
    2. For the community
    3. In the home

F. Industrial arts for the gifted
  1. Research and development program
  2. Industrial organization and administration

II. Industrial Arts Teacher Education

  A. For teaching in public, private schools
  B. For teaching in college, university, technical institute
  C. For administration, supervision
  D. For research, leadership, publication

III. The College Graduate Program

  A. Professional teaching, leadership
  B. Technical specialization, leadership
  C. Cultural-technological leadership
  D. Recreational leadership
  E. Research, development, publication

IV. Industrial Arts and the University

  A. Industrial arts as liberal arts
  B. Industrial arts recreation
  C. Industrial arts as vocational orientation

V. The Technical Institute and Community College Program

  A. Terminal technical programs
  B. Recreational leadership
  C. Cultural programs

VI. Industrial Arts Crafts—Technical Program

  A. For the professional craftsman
  B. For the industrial technician
  C. For the leisure-time craftsman

VII. Industrial Arts Professional Recreation

  A. For public, private schools
  B. For community programs
  C. For private agency programs

VIII. Industrial Arts Professional Therapy

    A. Industrial arts as therapy
    B. Industrial arts as rehabilitation
    C. Industrial arts for the mentally handicapped

INDUSTRIAL ARTS EDUCATION

The program in industrial arts education is proposed as complete in itself. Study of the proposal reveals that it is a structure with a definite base laid in the elementary school. To this is added the distinct schedule covering the junior high school, and on this is built the senior high school courses. A unique feature of this much of the program is that it involves particular, technological subject-matter content on each level. It is conceived of as developmental, continuous, directional. Each level makes its own content contribution to the growth and development of the student. Such unity of program should help to eliminate the rather common weakness of repetition. Presently the child on any level of industrial arts can expect to start at the bottom regardless of past instruction. In a secondary school woodworking course, for instance, a typical assumption is that what he had in the junior high school does not count. Should he take it in college, it is still assumed that he has not previously learned his ABC's of woodworking. So he starts once again at the bottom. This practice reflects badly on industrial arts as a whole. It suggests the lack of an overall program concept; instead two or three levels of courses exist, and each is independent of the others. Even the student cannot see evidence of his own growth. And the academician has proof for his contention that industrial arts is busy work; only the lazy and the inept are attracted to it.

The complete program herein proposed now gives industrial arts something to stand on and to stand for, something to build to, something to publicize and to sell. It is intended for all boys and girls, men and women regardless of educative potential.

THE ELEMENTARY SCHOOL PROGRAM

The child's introduction to technology begins at birth. From then on the person he becomes is influenced by the materials in his environment. The search for understanding of this environment begins in a formal way with his general schooling and his experiences in the new industrial arts. The level of arrangement of subject matter suggested here need not be considered fixed. The subjects of transportation and communication, for example, can be studied to advantage on any grade level. For purposes of correlation or integration with other school subjects, certain re-arrangements may be advantageous. However, the elementary program in total as recommended is basic to all of that to follow in the complete program. Its subject matter is relative to the child in a technological society. With a rather definite subject-matter content, the program requires competent instruction and appropriate facilities. The best teacher will be one with major preparation in industrial arts with emphasis on the elementary school, or one with major preparation for the elementary school with emphasis on industrial arts.

The following subject-matter outline should be considered as one of several possible structures suitable for the elementary school.

I. The Primary Grades: Technology and the Home

   A. Materials in the Home

      Identification: name, color, weight, texture
      Sources: local, national, foreign
      Characteristics: qualities, strengths, weaknesses
      Uses: furnishings, construction, toys, utensils, musical instruments

   B. Industrial Products in the Home

      Identification: name, function
      Sources: local, national, foreign manufacture
      Occupations: local, industrial, construction

   C. Tools and Machines in the Home

      Identification: name, use
      Sources: industries, cities, countries
      Operational principles: how they work
      Utilization: operation, care, safety
      Occupations: manufacturing, distribution, service

   D. The Use of Materials, Tools, Machines

      Project development: design, construction
      Materials selection: suitability, cost, sources

Functional considerations; purpose, durability, design
Simple structures: joints, fasteners, adhesives
Materials processing: use of tools and simple machines

II. The Intermediate Grades: Technology and the Community

A. Community Industries
Identification: size, location, importance, by-product
Location: local, distant, factors in
Products: types, manufacture of
Services: types, role of
Occupations: types, nature, importance

B. The Power Industry in the Community
Power and technology: muscles versus machines
Early sources of power: wind, water, steam
Electrical power: the power station, distribution
Electrical power in the home: utilization, safety
Portable power: engines, types, principles, uses

C. The Construction Industries
Influences of technology on construction in the community
Community planning: problems, development, model construction
Housing: architecture, types, construction
Legislation: zoning, codes, traffic regulation
Occupations: types, nature, importance

D. Uses of Materials, Tools, and Machines
Project development: design, development
Materials selection: suitability, cost, sources
Functional considerations: purpose, durability, design
Simple structures: joints, fasteners, adhesives
Materials processing: use of tools and machines

III. The Upper Elementary Grades: Technology and the World

A. Industries Around the World
Identification: by country, product, famous people

Location: geographic, economic, natural resources
Products: comparative study
Occupations: types, nature, comparison
World trade: role of technology

B. The Transportation Industries
Nature of transportation around the world
Roadway: auto, truck, highways
Railway: systems, operation, regulation
Seaway: ship, canal, terminal, systems
Airway: aircraft, systems, regulation
Occupations: types, nature, comparisons

C. The Communications Industries
Communications as a civilizing agency
Graphics: books, magazines, newspapers, drawings
Electronic: radio, television, radar
Photographic: processes, equipment, materials
Occupations: types, nature, comparisons

D. Industrial Arts Recreation
Technology and recreation: re-creation through materials
The home workshop: planning, developing
Hobbies: identification, possibilities
Family recreation through materials

E. Use of Materials, Tools, and Machines
Project development: design, construction
Materials selection: suitability, cost, sources
Functional considerations: purpose, durability
Simple structures: joints, fasteners, adhesives
Materials processing: use of tools and machines

The Junior High School Program

The complete program proposes that the study of the manufacturing industries be concentrated in grades 7, 8, and 9. The content of such courses can be derived from the industries analyses, supplemented with content from the analyses of the functions. Two basic plans for laboratory development are evident. In one, analogous industries are grouped for the grade levels. This has an advantage in that common elements, principles, techniques, and applications are readily discernible. This simplifies the preparation of instructional materials and economizes on laboratory equipment. The second plan employs single, comprehensive laboratories representing the entire grouping of the manufacturing industries. The large school would need several of these laboratories; the small school, perhaps only one.

The Senior High School Program

The seven areas for study in the senior high school program logically follow the study of the manufacturing industries in the junior high school. On the latter level the pupil gains a good acquaintance with the use of materials, tools, and machines, which is a preferred background for the types of study to follow. Two basic arrangements for the sequence of studies are apparent. In one, a single area may be studied per semester, with research and development made common to each. There is much in favor of such a plan especially when a rather complete, even though shallow, technical orientation of the student is of paramount importance.

The second sequence of studies permits the student to spend the entire school year in a single area. This makes good sense, too, especially when one realizes that even a single area is so broad and so deep that, at most, the student will not penetrate it completely. Thus, in the three years the student would concentrate in three areas. Added competences and meanings result from this concentration, but the problem of selection is not easy to solve. Some teachers may feel that the student is too immature and unsophisticated to choose wisely.

For the above-average student a year's concentration in research and development may truly open doors and windows for him. He has the time to develop intricate projects and to exhibit a growth and development not possible in a shorter course.

Before we accept one plan or the other, we must experiment. Without this we will have only reasoned recommendations to go on. No matter which plan, or combination of plans, is adopted, we should aim first at a full technological orientation of the student. This will provide the overall general education which we claim for industrial arts, and it will leave specialization to come later. The research and development program will not have much chance to demonstrate its qualities in less than a year of study for each student, however. The same can be said for the study of industrial organization and management.

Physics and mathematics are recommended as prerequisites to the courses in power and transportation and to electricity-electronics. Chemistry, physics, and mathematics should precede research and development. Sociology and economics should provide a functional basis for organization and management.

The production program provides for the study of the manufacturing industries through the use of production systems. From the research and development class come ideas ready for production. From the classes in organization and management come students seeking practical experience in managerial assignments. The student with less than normal gifts of intellect may also find opportunity for learning in this laboratory. He can gain real production experience as a machine operator, for example, or in some other work within his capacity. The production program requires diverse talents among its personnel just as in any one industry.

INDUSTRIAL ARTS THERAPY. Industrial arts therapy is intended to serve those for whom special treatment is recommended. The therapeutic effectiveness of work with materials for certain individuals is widely accepted. Appropriate experiences with materials, tools, and machines are prescribed as a means to individual rehabilitation. For the mentally handicapped, industrial arts is often the key to educative growth. Recognizing this, we should develop appropriate courses and programs under competent leadership and with adequately equipped facilities. This will preclude the use of industrial arts as a dumping grounds because the therapy program will assume full professional stature and because another program will be required for those who are normal or better.

INDUSTRIAL ARTS RECREATION. Industrial arts recreation in the school provides re-creation through materials, just as sports provide it through play. A special recreation laboratory is recommended. In this the student, the teacher, the community adult can find opportunity for self-expression without the pressures of grades, requirements, course of study, and such. Such a laboratory can then become a community center.

Industrial Arts for the Gifted. Industrial arts for the gifted as a facet of the complete program needs special attention. This is not because of the attention currently being given to this student, but rather because of the concern for technology and the individual within it. Advancement of the technology depends on superior human intellect. New materials, new processes, new products result from the exploitation of man's powers of reason, problem-solving, creativity, constructivity. The student identified as gifted here is not only the one we know who scores highly on today's intelligence tests, but also the one who has more than the normal amount of creativity, imagination, inventiveness, scientific curiosity, and other priceless attributes in the American way of life. Our first problem is to identify both types of these gifted individuals. The research and development program as specified in the secondary school schedule is intended for such students. The program of industrial organization and management is likewise intended for selected students who possess appropriate aptitudes and interests.

INDUSTRIAL ARTS ON THE COLLEGE LEVEL

Parts II through VIII of the complete program, in addition to being areas of service in the new industrial arts, are facets of the college-level program since they are directed to the preparation of college-trained personnel to carry on the programs.

The diagram, Fig. 8-1 of the New Industrial Arts on the College Level, shows the proposed relationship of the three levels of the program. The bachelor's level includes a broad base of liberal arts as general education. The block, fundamentals of technology, is laid on this base and provides the student with a general education centered in and influenced by technology. During this period he makes the decision on the area, or areas, of concentration which, while by necessity specialized, must also be broad.

The program on the master's level is supported by the strong undergraduate base and seeks to make the student a professional. This involves a re-defining of personal goals along professional lines, a realization and acceptance of professional responsibilities, and a dedication of purpose. Five areas for study and concentration are shown. Curricular provision must be made for the so-called professional courses applicable to teaching in the public school, the technical institute, and the community college, as well as for entry into university teaching. Provision for technical specialization assures additional technological content, essential to adequate teacher competence, confidence, understanding, and appreciation. Technical scholarship is encouraged to stimulate a desire for a continuing learning. Leadership potential must be assessed on this level, and provision for its development included. A formal research and development program here is integral and essential. Beginning at the undergraduate level and extending through the doctoral, such facility will attract research-minded students to the profession and eventually assure it of an extensive source of new information, on which the life of a profession depends.

The area on writing and publication reflects a need of the profession. Industrial arts at present suffers from the lack of an abundance of fresh literature drawn from technology and suitable to its purposes. Men with strong technical and professional backgrounds and a good command of communication can now be drawn into writing and publication.

The doctoral level begins on a base of professional specialization indicating the overall intent of the program. The student here is called on to pursue an area, or areas, for his concentration. These include, fields of higher education, scholarship, leadership, research, and publication, all of which are essential to the profession.

A Proposed Structure for a Program of Teacher Education for the New Industrial Arts

THE UNDERGRADUATE LEVEL. Teacher education occupies the key position in the orderly development of the new industrial arts. To arrange a program for implementing the concept herein presented

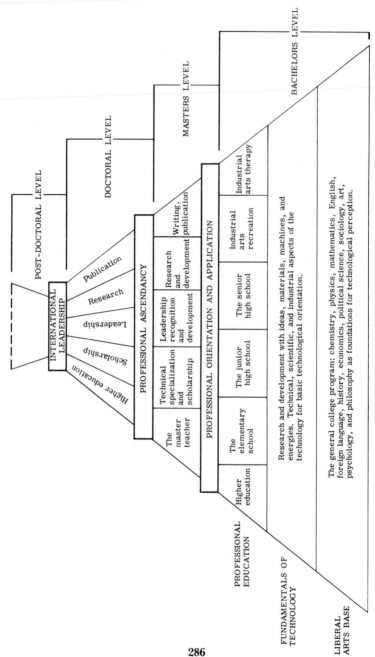

Fig. 8-1. A structure for industrial arts teacher education.

requires a willingness to lay aside patterns, precedents, and prejudices inherent in the old industrial arts. Any similarity between this proposed structure and the traditional is purely happenstance. When a curriculum is finally drawn from this structure, it will achieve its greatest strength when it builds on the new program in the secondary school.

I. The Liberal Arts Base

> The broad base on which the new industrial arts is built is a program of liberal arts studies: chemistry, physics, mathematics, history, psychology, sociology, economics, government, English, speech, foreign language, philosophy, and such. The sequence serves as general education for the student and as a foundation for an understanding of technology and its role in the civilizing process.

II. Fundamentals of Technology

> This block provides for knowledge, understanding, appreciation, and technical competences deriving from technology.

A. Technology and the Material Culture

> Orientation and exploration into the nature and influences of technology on contemporary culture.
> Technical, scientific, social, economic, political, and educational aspects of technology.

B. Technology and American Industry

> Origins, development, structure of American industry and its relation to technology.
> Derivation of subject matter

C. The Technology Laboratories

> These include a series of courses based on fundamentals in industrial materials and processes in manufacturing.

Woods Technology	Graphic Arts Technology
Metals Technology	Rubber Technology
Ceramics Technology	Chemical Technology
Plastics Technology	Foods Technology
Textiles Technology	Tools and Machines
Electrical-electronic	Technology
Technology	Paper Technology

D. Technical Research and Development

Technical research and development comprises a block of instruction in principles and techniques for the development of ideas in materials and processes.

1. Technical Graphics
   a. Graphic representation, as communications
   b. Graphic presentations or ideas
   c. Graphic solutions to problems
2. Technical Research
   a. Experiment, search, test, measurement
   b. Invention, discovery, application
   c. Reporting, evaluating, refining
3. Technical Design

   a. Engineering Design

Materials	Fasteners	Operation
Structures	Construction	Test

   b. Ideation: Creating with materials and processes

   c. Product Design and Development

Consumer research	Styling
Functional development	Evaluation

E. Advanced Technology

The laboratories included here identify areas for concentration of study.

1. The Production Laboratories
   Organization, finance, planning, scheduling, control, routing, manufacture, inspection of quantity production of products originating with research and development. The production laboratories give representation to the manufacturing industries: graphic arts, paper, leather, textiles, ceramics, plastics, rubber, chemical, foods, metals, woods, tools and machines. A separate laboratory may be set up for each manufacturing industry, or related industries may be combined into one laboratory with individual centers representative of those industries. In the smaller program, one production laboratory may be made flexible and adapted to serve the entire group of industries.

2. The Power and Transportation Laboratory
   The study of power, its development, transmission, and control as employed in technological cultures and as applied in transportation. The study of transportation media and systems as essential in industry and to American living.

3. The Construction Laboratory
   The study of the industry which provides housing for America, its materials, methods, problems, solutions, goals.

4. The Management Laboratory
   The study of principles and practices of industrial organization and management.

5. The Electrical-Electronic Laboratory
   The study and application of scientific principles in the field of electricity-electronics.

III. The Professional Education Block

The professional education block includes the levels of educational concentration available as major fields for teaching. The curriculum in basic education methodology is provided in the college of education. It involves fundamental principles and practices applicable to all levels, including higher education and recreation. The department of industrial arts builds on this base and gives special attention to industrial arts at the several levels. Student teaching experience may be gained in schools, in recreation programs, and in the college department of industrial arts for higher education.

A. Industrial Arts in Higher Education

   Industrial arts in higher education provides two distinct areas for concentration: teacher education, and industrial arts as liberal arts and recreation for college and university.

B. Industrial Arts for the Elementary School

   The curriculum is intended for teacher preparation in grades one through six, and includes special study on programs for the retarded and the gifted.

C. Industrial Arts for the Junior High School

   The junior high school level centers on the study of the manufacturing industries and includes the production laboratories as preparation. (See II, E, 1 above.)

D. Industrial Arts for the Senior High School

   This curriculum requires the selection of, preferably, two advanced technology laboratories for concentration.

E. Industrial Arts Recreation

   Industrial arts recreation is recommended as an area for major concentration leading to professional recreation leadership. The curriculum includes preparation for industrial arts recreation in school, college, community, and private agency programs.

F. Industrial Arts Therapy

   Industrial arts therapy as a field for concentration includes preparation for service in occupational therapy and rehabilitation as well as for work with the mentally retarded.

THE MASTER'S LEVEL

Five areas for concentration are proposed for the master's-level program in teacher education for the new industrial arts. From among these the sequences of courses can be planned to suit the needs and interests of the individual student. The master's program is directed to the preparation of master teachers for industrial arts and to the recognition and development of leadership potential.

I. The Master Teacher Sequence

This area will include courses in education and the liberal arts leading to a mastery of methodology and further understanding of the meaning of technology in American education and culture. Appropriate courses are provided in industrial arts educational methodology within the department of industrial arts. Content courses for technical concentration, including emphasis in research and development, will further strengthen the teacher.

II. The Technical Specialization Sequence

The technical specialization sequence provides for strengthening technical competences in the areas of concentration toward which the student has been building on the undergraduate level. The sequence will include provision for cooperative study in appropriate industries.

III. The Leadership Sequence

The leadership sequence is directed to the identification, development, and dedication of leadership talents. It includes courses embracing administration, public relations, program development and promotion, and experience in leadership assignments. The concern for professionalizing the student and for his personal refinement is widespread.

IV. The Research and Development Sequence

The research and development sequence provides for studies in depth in technical areas. Emphasis is on high quality research and development and on promoting the attitude of research already begun on the undergraduate level. This may be carried on at the university where facilities are adequate. Also recommended is that projects involve the use of industrial resources in personnel and facilities. High quality research on the graduate level will command the respect of industry and facilitate effective liaison.

V. The Writing and Publication Sequence

The writing and publication sequence is intended to encourage professional and technical writing and to provide instruction and experience leading to research reporting, thesis preparation, and writing for publication.

THE DOCTORAL LEVEL

The program for the doctoral level continues in the direction of concentration and leads to the ultimate objective of providing the high type of leadership and vision necessary to conceive and develop a new industrial arts. Superior candidates for doctoral study are identified and encouraged from among the graduates of the master's program.

I. The Scholarship Sequence

The scholarship sequence includes provision for encouraging an attitude of scholarship and for the search for truth and meaning in the relationships of technology and man. It involves the study of philosophies of education, science, mathematics, and technology.

II. The Higher Education Sequence

The higher education sequence is directed to the preparation of teachers for higher education. The undergraduate program provided for orientation and try-out experience; the master's program gave attention to the preparation for initiation into college-level teaching.

III. The Leadership Sequence

> The doctoral leadership sequence builds on the same sequence begun on the master's level but calls for a concentration on leadership development in the fields of scholarship, philosophy, administration, research, and publication.

IV. The Research Sequence

> The research sequence emphasizes a mastery of research materials and processes essential in a profession. This mastery is attained by means of experience in high level basic and applied research. Concentration here may lead to assignments in full-time research within the profession.

V. The Publications Sequence

> The publications sequence implies a concern for the development of technical and professional literature for industrial arts as drawn from its research, from that of science and industry which is applicable to industrial arts, and from psychology, education, and other appropriate fields.

INDUSTRIAL ARTS AND THE UNIVERSITY

Industrial arts is seen here as a university-level program for liberal arts purposes. Its cultural function comes into strong play. It becomes essential to the full enlightenment of the student because of its challenges to search for the truth in technology. When the industrial arts profession senses the liberating qualities of its program, it will become even more enthusiastic about its potential for service. The immediate obstacle to the inclusion of industrial arts as liberal arts in the university is the time-worn notion that there is but one road to wisdom—through liberal arts in the classic tradition of science, mathematics, history, language, literature, and philosophy. We who believe in the liberating qualities of industrial arts must prove that another road to wisdom remains open—that of the study of man's material culture.

THE TECHNICAL INSTITUTE AND COMMUNITY COLLEGE

The role of the new industrial arts in the technical institute and community college includes that of providing teachers for technical subjects as well as for curricula in the form of content. The student preparing to teach in a technical institute may be an industrial arts education major who seeks greater technical-scientific competence with a view toward teaching in such an institute. Or the student may have already acquired a strong technical background elsewhere but may need further preparation for teaching and instruction in methodology. The common inclusion of technical courses in community college offerings, which are usually introductory, applied, or recreational in nature, suggests that this institution can use a graduate of industrial arts teacher-education who has, in addition to the technical background, the necessary competence in working with adults.

INDUSTRIAL ARTS CRAFTS—TECHNICAL PROGRAM

The crafts-technical program is intended to provide collegiate level instruction in crafts and technical fields for persons who intend to be professional craftsmen, industrial technicians, or technologists. Typical of these are potters, ceramic technicians, furniture craftsmen, wood technologists, graphic arts specialists, welding technicians, silversmiths, electronic technicians, and the like. The courses would provide training, retraining, and refresher instruction in terminal, one-year, two-year, or longer programs.

The instructional preparation in the technical fields can be included within the pattern of industrial arts teacher education. Additional course provision must also be made for specialization and preferably for cooperative training programs with industry to achieve higher specialization in the appropriate study field.

INDUSTRIAL ARTS PROFESSIONAL RECREATION

Industrial arts recreation is the answer proposed herein to the problem of discretionary time originating from the technology. Before technology reached its recent stages of development no such time problem existed; with an advancing technology an increasing leisure is becoming a national problem. At the time of this writing some labor unions are seeking a thirty-hour week.

The three divisions, school, community, and private agency, identify the basic areas for recreation service for industrial arts as well as for the professional preparation of recreation leaders. The program leading to professional recreation in industrial arts can be provided within the program of industrial arts teacher education. There will of necessity be some differences, however. The liberal arts base should prevail as well as the block of courses in fundamentals of technology. (See chart, Fig. 8-1.) The professional leader of industrial arts recreation needs a broad familiarity with materials, tools, processes, and machines. He needs the manufacturing sequence along with the fundamentals courses in transportation, power, construction, electronics, and research and development without the necessary concentration in two or more of these courses, as is the case for the teacher education student. In addition, his preparation should include experience in "manual arts"—those activities employing materials and hand processing, such as weaving, braiding, clay modeling, and others useful in camp and institutions. The professional education block includes those courses in education, methodology, and organization and administration appropriate to the field of recreation.

INDUSTRIAL ARTS PROFESSIONAL THERAPY

The program in industrial arts professional therapy prepares specialists in the fields of occupational therapy and rehabilitation and also equips them to help the mentally retarded and mentally ill. Work with materials and processes has been long recognized for its therapeutic values in hospitals and for its means to educating the mentally handicapped. The proposal here to include training in therapy in a program of preparation for professional workers grows from a realization that industrial arts activities have values that are not generally understood. The program of preparation can be carried on within the framework of industrial arts teacher education and supplemented with special technical courses applicable to various human weaknesses and with courses recommended by the medical profession.

PREREQUISITES FOR INDUSTRIAL ARTS

The practice, to accommodate students of all levels of intelligence in one course in industrial arts, in the new program is neither possible nor recommended. Certain courses in the high school sequence, for example, will not only appeal to different levels of interest and intellect but have different requirements for success. As earlier recommended, certain of the courses would have prerequisites of physics, chemistry, mathematics, sociology, or economics. Similarly, the junior high school sequence could be considered as prerequisite to the high school program. If this line of logic is sound, a set of high school prerequisites may likewise be justified for entrance into industrial arts teacher education.

The issue of prerequisites is a debatable one, and whether or not they are employed may have to be decided in specific situations. However, there are several considerations within the idea. One is that since the overall program of industrial arts is to a degree graded and continuous, the greatest good for the student is realized when he progresses accordingly. Another is that this type of program should command greater educative respectability than one in which any student can take any course at any time. The inference here, too, is that any single course may not be all things to all students. For the less than normal, the course may have to take on the quality of manual arts. Also implied is that no one teacher should be expected to handle both the diversity of subject matter on any one level and the full range of students.

When teacher education can build on what the student has had in school, it should be able to provide a higher level of teacher preparation. Suppose that entering college freshmen came with the background of industrial arts as proposed for the twelve years of schooling. Teacher education would properly then build on this rather than start from the beginning or duplicate it. Trends in college entrance requirements indicate that high school graduates are increasingly being held to such prerequisites as English, mathematics, social studies, and sometimes drafting for engineering students. We might well examine the wisdom of similar requirements in science and industrial arts for our freshmen entering teacher education.

In Reflection

The over-all program for the new industrial arts has a completeness extending beyond that common in today's applications. Because of its extensiveness, it may appear rather formidable and even impossible. And yet it may even serve to backstop and support the teacher and his administrator who on their own have already begun to build in this direction; and many have started. Obviously, such a program must have the right teachers and leadership. At this very time in the history of the profession we are facing a crucial problem which if not effectively solved will have long-term deteriorating effects. Because of other pressures, college-bound students in high school are routed away from courses in industrial arts. The assumption is that these courses are better reserved for those not college-bound, that they are not of sufficient intellectual stature to be essential for college preparation. But where then shall we get the students who will become industrial arts teachers, especially the kind needed in this new industrial arts? The new program should attract the college-capable student. It is designed for him as much as for the others. The college-level sequence as described shows a continuity and a relationship between levels which is not common today.

In all of the facets of the new industrial arts on the college level, the teacher education program is considered basic and common in the preparation of personnel to administer the respective facets. There are at least three good reasons for this, not the least of which is economy. With entirely separate leadership training curricula for each of the parts of the program, the undertaking would hardly be financially feasible. The duplication of facility and staff would be difficult to justify.

This leads to a second reason why the teacher education program is basic preparation for all involved in administering industrial arts. All programs on the college level have a strong core of unity and commonness. This begins at the point where it is agreed that American technology is the origin of industrial arts. And technology as the subject matter for the new industrial arts becomes the common factor. Of course, levels of technology ranging from the simple to the complex must be accounted for. The courses should be fundamental technology, and when they are, they serve equally well the future school teacher, college teacher, therapist, recreational worker, or others.

The third reason grows out of the second. For a generation or more special courses in art, drawing, mathematics, physics, and other subjects have commonly been included for industrial arts majors. This was under the assumption that, for example, an engineering grade of mathematics was not functional for an industrial arts teacher. Instead the student needed "shop math" because it was an applied mathematics. The same reasoning held for other of the substitute courses. They were often below the level of the courses for which they were substitutes and often took on the status of what today's student calls "Mickey Mouse" courses. The idea for these special courses, while implemented with the best of intentions, has reacted against us. The student himself can come to feel that he is scholastically inferior, that he is in an opportunity class, as it were. Forced to take the defensive on his own behalf, he argues that the original courses are not practical, but at the same time he may wonder if he is not in a field which is geared to lesser students. Thus, it is better for both student and program that he take the first-line courses which students in other fields take. The maturer students themselves tell us that. Within the curriculum for industrial arts teacher education, then, if all technical courses are centered in technological fundamentals, they will be as appropriate for one teaching field as another. Why should not the student himself be expected to, and expect to, make specific applications of the content to the situations as they present themselves. This is the mark of educative liberation, to enable one to search for the truth wherever he is and to find his own freedom in his search.

TO DISCUSS, TO DEBATE, TO DECIDE

1. Does any real advantage exist in trying to see industrial arts as a complete program?
2. What happened to mechanical drawing in the new program?
3. What is the difference between a course in auto mechanics and one in transportation?
4. Where should the new industrial arts program start? In the public school? In the teacher's college?
5. Should the doctorate lead to a doctor of philosophy degree in industrial arts or in education?

6. Why should graduate study include instruction and experience in writing?
7. Should industrial arts in the elementary school have a subject matter of its own or should it be completely integrated with other courses? Should it be content or teaching method?
8. Justify industrial arts as liberal arts for the university student in the arts and sciences.
9. How can the school industrial arts program serve as a community center? Would this be a good idea?
10. Should the industrial arts teacher expect to do all of the teaching in his adult program? Why?

(Above) A new development in steel rolling mills. Compact but complete, this automatic mill turns out stainless steel strip down to .005 inch thickness. Note the rolls in the center foreground. (Courtesy: United States Steel Corporation.)

(Right) Machine spinning a circular tank top. These two highly skilled workmen control the machine as it shapes the material over a wooden mold. Contrast the qualifications of these two men with those operating the automatic mill shown above. (Courtesy: Aluminum Company of America.)

The New
Industrial Arts:
Its Facilities

The control of fire was presumably the first great step in man's emancipation from the bondage of his environment. . . . For the first time in history a creature of Nature was directing one of the great forces of Nature. And the exercise of power must react upon the controller. . . . He was asserting his humanity and making himself.

—V. Gordon Childe, *Man Makes Himself.*
(C. A. Watts & Co. Ltd.)

The facilities for the new industrial arts may rightly be as new as the curriculum; their specifications will rightly be drawn from within the curriculum. They, too, will reflect technology and all together will provide a technological environment within an educational atmosphere. The new laboratory is more than a rearrangement of the old facilities. It includes representation of technical processes not heretofore commonly found in industrial arts. The issue of unit shop versus general shop is now forever resolved. These have served their day and will no longer be needed.

PACKAGE LABORATORIES. The goal in the identification and specifications of facilities will preferably be the development of *package laboratories.* Because a common curriculum is accepted for the new program, there is advantage in a standardizing of facilities to include at least the basic components. Once the components of these facilities are agreed upon, they become packages. For example, there may be such a package for the construction laboratory, the power and transportation laboratory, and the others. With these a particular community's industrial arts curriculum and facility need not be custom-made from the ground up, as once was assumed to be desirable. The time has passed when each new teacher can properly insist on remodeling or rearranging the laboratory to suit his personal whims. Along with the equipment package should come recommendations and standards for laboratory housing which carry the architectural approval of the American Institute of Architects.

The complete package now should include equipment specifications and quantities, proposals for equipment arrangement to fit typical laboratories, and architectural specifications and recommendations for the housing. Probably many items of equipment in this package will be uncommon to traditional industrial arts. Some will be difficult to find; some will require design, development, and manufacture.

This packaging of facilities at once relieves the local teacher of his traditional responsibility for proposing equipment for a new laboratory as well as for its planning. No longer will he be required to plan the facilities and then to convince the architect and the school administration to adopt his recommendations. Now he can concentrate on his program development and implementation and on his teaching, the true jobs for which he is employed. Such a standardization will also unify the program, which should result in a general strengthening of industrial arts.

The laboratory proposals to follow are included as points from which the implementation of the new program can begin. They are embryonic only, and we suggest that extensive research and experimentation start here for the design of a national laboratory project. This could promote the highest of excellence for new physical facilities. This unity in excellence is a challenge to the creative experts in laboratory design in the profession. Too much is at stake to leave laboratory development in the hands of the individual teacher; the teacher has enough to do in curriculum development.

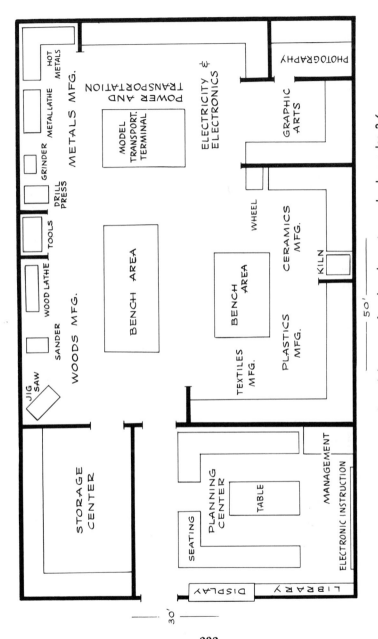

Fig. 9-1. The technology laboratory for the elementary school, grades 3-6.

303

THE TECHNOLOGY LABORATORY FOR THE ELEMENTARY SCHOOL

The technology laboratory for the elementary school should be furnished with equipment of such size, capacity, and simplicity that the child can efficiently and safely operate it. It should be entirely functional equipment rather than toys. Much of it may have to be especially designed and manufactured until it becomes easily available. The laboratory as proposed in Fig. 9-1 requires 1500 square feet of floor area and can accommodate up to 25-30 children.

One of the difficult problems in furnishing a laboratory for children is the great range in their physical sizes. Hand tools usable by sixth graders may be too heavy for first graders and too difficult for them to use. Bench heights, to date at least, are not readily adjustable. Tool manufacturers when making tools for children have generally done no more than reduce the sizes. They have not redesigned tools to make them more easily operable. A hand saw that has been cut in size to twelve inches does not cut any easier.

Machines for the lower grades serve to introduce the child to the machine technology, which is appropriate for industrial arts to do. Machines also enable him to gain a greater degree of control over materials than he can normally get with hand processes. Typical major items of machines and machine-type equipment include the following:

MANUFACTURING AND CONSTRUCTION

Woods	*Metals*	*Textiles*
Jig saw	Machine lathe	Spinning wheel
Sander	Drill press	Weaving loom
Wood lathe	Foundry	Printing equipment
Miter box	Grinder	Dyeing equipment
Drill press	Forge	Sewing machine

Plastics	*Ceramics*
Oven	Wheel
Buffer	Kiln
Die casting machine	Molds
Extruding equipment	Enameling equipment
Molds	Jigger

POWER AND TRANSPORTATION

Small engines	Transformers
Electric train	Wind tunnel
Electric motors	Meteorological station

COMMUNICATIONS

Electronic	*Graphic Arts*
Instruments	Typewriter
Coders and decoders	Printing press
Mock-ups	Papermaking equipment
Local transmitters	Photographic equipment

Several items in the above list are appropriate for use by children in the lower elementary grades. These include: typewriter, hand printing press, papermaking equipment, camera and photographic processing equipment, jig saw, miter box, drill press, loom, potters wheel, radio, mock-up, electric train, and the like. Each floor-type machine may be mounted on lockable casters to permit easy portability for demonstrations and movement to homerooms. The design and development of such equipment would make excellent projects for students in industrial arts teacher education. Eventually manufacturers could take over production.

The Technology Corner

The technology corner serves the elementary classroom in grades one and two. All package units are of a roll-away type and contain the basic materials and facilities essential for demonstrations and pupil work. The equipment provided serves also in studies of other areas, such as transportation, communications, housing, and recreation. The laboratory of technology may serve all six grades, or only the upper four, or just the upper two. There are good arguments for the homeroom teacher or for the industrial arts teacher and the homeroom teacher together carrying on these studies in the classroom in the lower grades. We recommend that the technology corner be a part of the first- and second-grade classrooms and that the activity be in the charge of the classroom teacher assisted by the

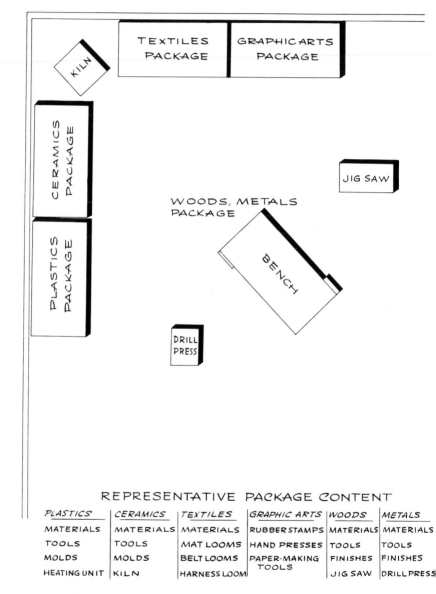

REPRESENTATIVE PACKAGE CONTENT

PLASTICS	CERAMICS	TEXTILES	GRAPHIC ARTS	WOODS	METALS
MATERIALS	MATERIALS	MATERIALS	RUBBER STAMPS	MATERIALS	MATERIALS
TOOLS	TOOLS	MAT LOOMS	HAND PRESSES	TOOLS	TOOLS
MOLDS	MOLDS	BELT LOOMS	PAPER-MAKING TOOLS	FINISHES	FINISHES
HEATING UNIT	KILN	HARNESS LOOM		JIG SAW	DRILL PRESS

Fig. 9-2. The technology corner for the classroom, grades 1, 2.

industrial arts teacher, who serves best as the chief resource person. For grades four through six we suggest that the pupils work in the laboratory under the instruction of the industrial arts teacher, assisted by the classroom teacher. This arrangement of team teaching has proved effective although other arrangements may be equally so. Bear in mind, however, that since a body of subject matter is available for industrial arts in the elementary school, the program requires a teacher prepared for it and a laboratory for its application and utilization.

The Manufacturing Laboratories

The manufacturing laboratories are proposed for grades 7, 8, and 9 within the pattern of the complete program already identified. The groupings of industries for study in the laboratories were decided on with consideration for the value of analogous activities in the same laboratory and with a concern for the maturity of the students. Other combinations may be equally effective, however. Certain groups of industries are analogous to all others and in some, student maturity is no particular key to selection. In this plan the three laboratories are necessary to give adequate representation to the manufacturing industries. Students spend a year in each. This arrangement is called Plan A for purposes of comparison with an alternate proposal, Plan B, discussed below. Advantages of Plan A include the possibility of a more complete selection of equipment for each industry in a laboratory of the same floor area as in Plan B. Some will reason that teaching in a laboratory with four or five industries would be more efficient than in one with twelve. This may not necessarily be true because different methods of class organization would logically be employed.

Laboratory 7:

Graphic Arts	*Paper*	*Leather*	*Textiles*
Printing	Manufacture	Fabricating	Weaving
Photography	Packaging	Dyeing	Fabricating
Publishing	Decorating	Decorating	Decorating
Drawing			

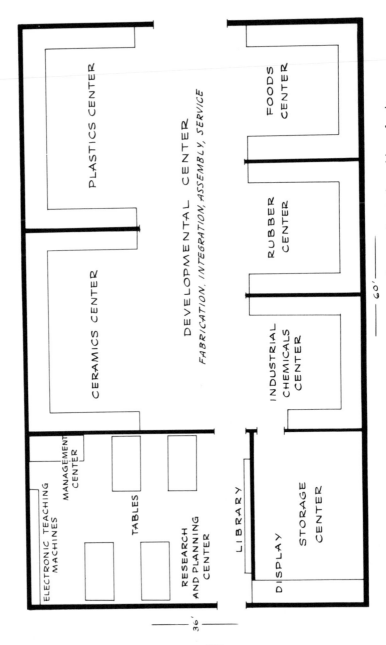

Fig. 9-3. Manufacturing laboratory 7: ceramics, plastics, chemicals, rubber, foods.

308

Laboratory 8:

Ceramics	Plastics	Rubber
Clay working	Casting	Casting
Glass working	Molding	Molding
Enameling	Fabricating	Fabricating

Chemicals	Foods
Compounding	Manufacturing
Testing	Appliance service
Utilization	

Laboratory 9:

Metals	Woods	Tools and Machines
Machining	Machining	Design, development
Casting	Fabricating	Machining
Forming	Finishing	Fabricating
Fabricating		Assembly

Plan *B* has the three laboratories as before, but each has the full complement of facilities for study of all of the industries. This plan has an advantage in that a school can install one such laboratory at a time and thus keep pace with student enrollment. When compromising is done, and this is common in industrial arts program development since we often tend to settle for less than what every American child needs, Plan *B* will probably be involved. Some of us will suggest that the industries about which we know little or nothing be excluded and the offerings narrowed. Some will insist that certain of the industries are more important and, therefore, a selection should be made. This argument is impossible to support except as an economy measure. For example, the metals industries employ more persons and the gross annual value of its products is greater than in the leather industries. Consequently, it can be reasoned that the former is the more important. The key to the argument and to its resolution is in the word *important*. Does economic importance alone give stature to an industry within the whole of technology? If you think so, reread the chapter on technology.

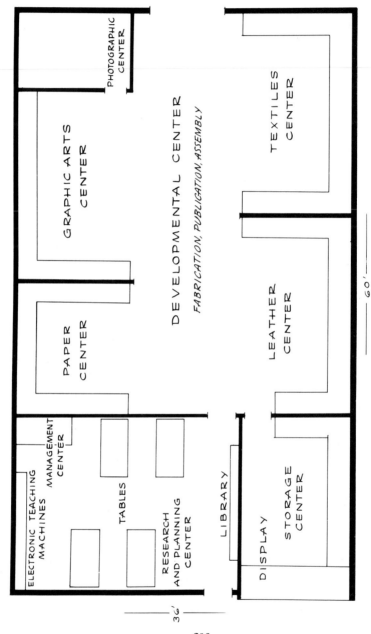

Fig. 9-4. Manufacturing laboratory 8: paper, leather, textiles, graphic arts.

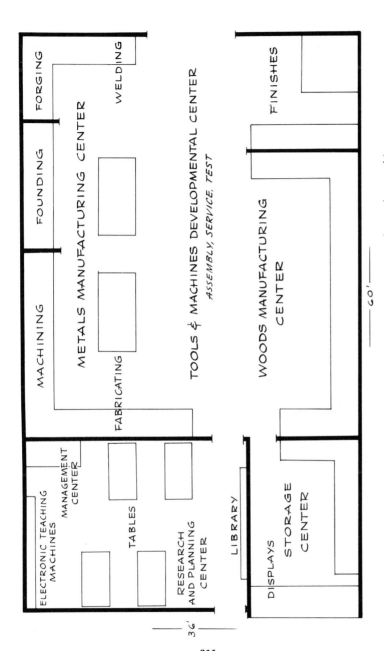

Fig. 9-5. Manufacturing laboratory 9: metals, wools, tools, machines.

Economic arguments do not disprove the fact that leather shoes, not wooden clogs or plastic sandals, are symbols of civilization for most of the world's people. Bare feet are useful for climbing trees, but shod feet give men dignity and status in all the world. Let us be careful then in singling out certain of the industries as being more important. If it must be done, let us first decide on what basis they will be considered more important, and here we must not overlook the social values. All of the industries included here in the three laboratories are basic; they have already survived the selective process. Many others have been excluded.

Operation of the laboratories in either plan assumes two different patterns. Each can be organized as a single laboratory, in the true sense of the term, with the student having access to any of its facilities in the development of his project. This method promotes projects which display an integration of materials, processes, and thinking. All students are given general instruction covering all of the industries involved. Beyond this they are given individual instruction toward specific problems within their individual projects. The second method considers each facility as including several smaller, branch laboratories in which the student works for a period of time before moving on to another. This is reminiscent of the rotation system in the general shop. The theory here is that the student does not have to complete a project or required work in each of the industries in order to benefit maximally from his experience in this program. When the student knows that he can draw on the entire laboratory for his study, he thinks of greater projects and sees greater challenges.

The Power and Transportation Laboratory

The study of the power and transportation industries is carried on in the same laboratory because of their close relationship although separation into individual quarters can be justified. Facilities for the study of electrical power, while previously included in the power industries analyses, are now included in the electrical-electronic laboratory, discussed below, because of their relationship to electronics equipment. Equipment for the power and transportation laboratory includes models, mock-ups, cut-aways, live and dead power

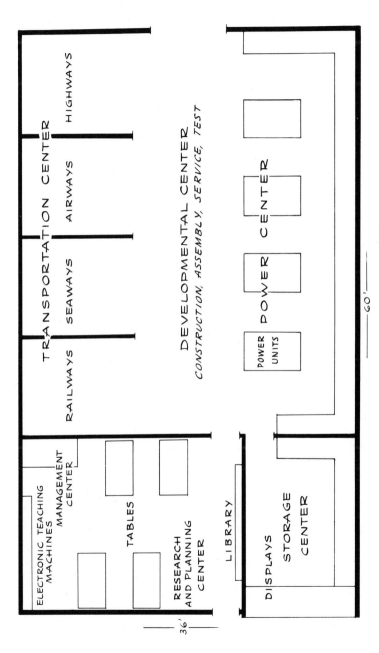

Fig. 9-6. The power and transportation laboratory.

313

plants, sub-assemblies, tools, machines, and facilities for disassembly, service, assembly, and construction. The program has the breadth suggested in the industries analyses, but it also provides opportunity for concentration of study in narrow fields. Class organization may be most effective with small groups of students making studies in particular areas although there is opportunity for indvidual research and development.

TYPICAL FACILITIES FOR THE
POWER AND TRANSPORTATION LABORATORIES

Combustion Engines	*Airways, Space Transportation*	*Conveyors*
Assemblies	Powerplants	Industrial types
Mock-ups	Regulation, controls	Regulation, controls
Operation	Components	Commercial types

Power Transmission	*Seaways Transportation*	*Production*
Electrical equipment	Powerplants	Design
Mechanical equipment	Military, commercial equipment	Fabrication
Hydraulic equipment	Regulation, controls	Operation
Pneumatic equipment		

The Electrical-Electronics Laboratory

The electrical-electronics laboratory is industrial arts' provision for study of the respective industries as well as electrical-electronic applications in industry, the home, business, schools, the military, and the community. In addition to the necessary electrical-electronic devices and facilities, there are tools, machines, and equipment for the construction of parts and projects. Prerequisites for the course may well include physics and mathematics as well as the junior high school manufacturing sequence in industrial arts. Students having completed the course in research and development may find special interests in electricity and electronics, and vice versa.

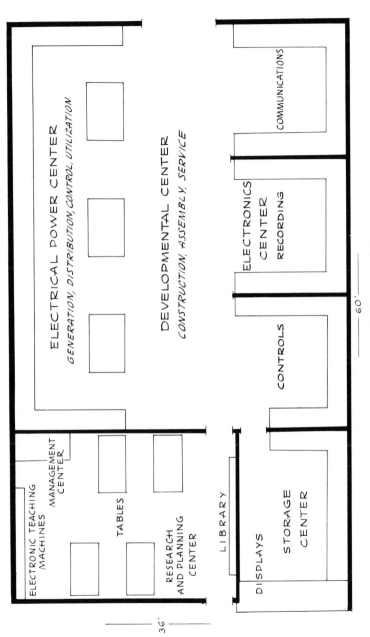

Fig. 9-7. The electrical-electronics laboratory.

315

TYPICAL FACILITIES FOR THE
ELECTRICAL-ELECTRONICS LABORATORY

Power	Communications	Controls	Recording
Generation	Radio	Industrial types	Tapes
Transmission	Telephone	Transportation	Discs
Utilization	Television	types	Photos
		Power types	

Household	Components	Materials	Production
Lighting	Amplifiers	Metalworking	Design
Heating	Oscilloscopes	equipment	Fabrication
Phonographs	Transmitters	Woodworking	Operation
		equipment	
		Ceramics	
		equipment	

The Construction Laboratory

The construction laboratory gives representation to the building industry. Within it facilities are arranged to study the industry literally from the ground up. In addition to the library and drafting provisions are models, mock-ups, and instruction panels illustrative of principles and practices. There are materials, tools, and machines for use in such activities as developing and testing structures, for construction and pre-fabrication, for three-dimensional model development of regional, community and neighborhood planning projects, for landscaping and home beautification. Also included are the instructional aids and equipment for the study of the construction industries. This laboratory is a center for instruction in the do-it-yourself program for adults.

TYPICAL FACILITIES FOR THE
CONSTRUCTION LABORATORY

Design	Structures	Electrical	Regional Development
Engineering	Materials	Lighting	Community planning
Architecture	Fastenings	Power	Neighborhood planning
Presentations	Prefabrication	Communications	Civic development

Air Conditioning	Decoration	Furnishing	Landscaping	Sanitation
Heating	Painting	Appliances	Earth moving	Water
Cooling	Papering	Furniture	Plantings	Waste
Ventilation	Paneling	Rugs	Community planning	Equipment

The Industrial Production Laboratory

The production laboratory is the center for demonstrating techniques of quantity production used by industry. Prerequisites for this course should include the junior high school manufacturing sequence. The typical facilities suggested offer the possibility of selection. We recommend, however, that the graphic arts group be included in all of the selections because it can produce the advertising, record forms, stock certificates, and packaging for any other of the manufacturing enterprises.

The class may be organized so that all of the students are involved in one production enterprise, as in ceramics or woods, for example, with the graphic arts' production correlated. Or they may be organized into two or more enterprises, each also using graphic arts. The nature of the item to be produced must be studied in advance in order to estimate the manpower and facility needs. When a product to be manufactured involves only a few operational processes or when some can be combined or made automatic, only a small group of students may be required. When two or more of such projects are to be operated simultaneously, each can be considered as a subsidiary of the parent company, the entire class. In any case the class is involved in the entire process from the selection of a suitable product, considering its marketability; the problem of finance, including the issuance and selling of stock; the production planning and the materials controls; the advertising and packaging design; the tooling-up; the marketing; and the declaration of profit or loss and the dissolution of the corporation. Frequent use of qualified resource persons from business and industry is desirable here in order to make the entire project as authentic, as business-like, and as successful as possible.

The product may originate in the research and development laboratory where it has been developed to the point that it is ready

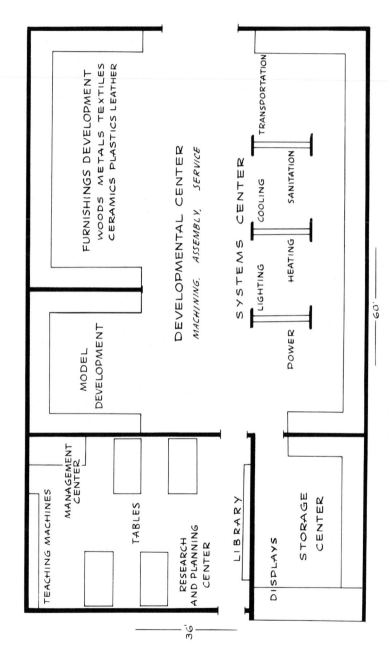

Fig. 9-8. The construction laboratory.

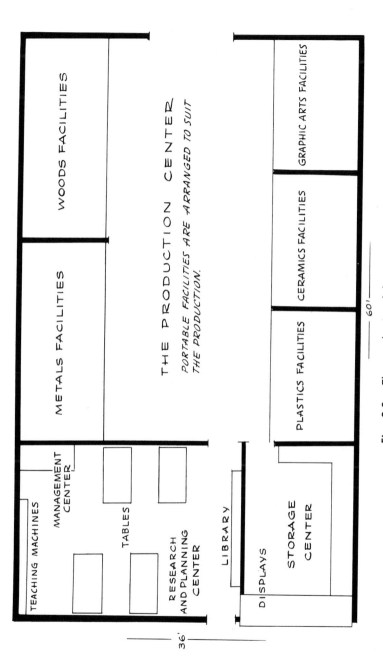

Fig. 9-9. The production laboratory.

for production. Jigs, dies, forms, molds, fixtures may have been designed and gotten ready for production in the tooling-up step. Similarly in research and development, students may have developed semi-automatic or even automatic controls to speed up production. They may have developed special equipment or machines adaptable to the project.

For the greatest effectiveness any production project undertaken requires the fullest involvement of the students. In view of the immense planning and the time-consuming preparation required before actual production can begin, the instructor may be tempted to shunt out some of the steps and concentrate on the technical and the manufacturing. Or he may be inclined to set up standardized production projects year after year. In either event he should reconsider such temptations in view of industrial arts' responsibility to its students. Industrial arts should not only permit students to carry out their own ideas but also hold them responsible for good ideas and

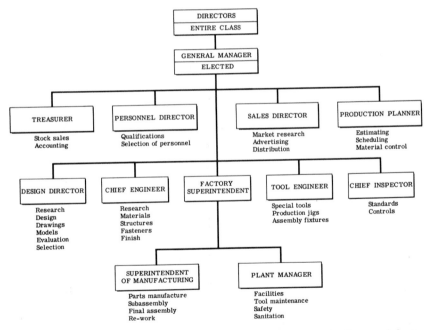

Fig. 9-10. Chart showing personnel requirements, organization, and flow of authority for an industrial arts production project.

correct execution. If the industrial arts teacher remembers this, he will likely prefer to function as the chief resource person for his classes rather than as general manager, personnel director, factory superintendent, and all of the rest of the supervisory staff, while the students function only as labor. The chart, Figure 9-10 shows a plan for organization of a manufacturing project in the production laboratory.

TYPICAL FACILITIES FOR
PRODUCTION LABORATORY

Woods	Metals	Graphic Arts	Ceramics
Machining	Machining	Printing	Clay products
Fabricating	Fabricating	Photography	Glass products
Finishing	Art ware	Publishing	Enamelware
		Drawing	
Textiles	Plastics	Rubber	Paper
Weaving	Die casting	Molding	Manufacturing
Printing	Forming	Coating	Fabricating
Dyeing	Extruding	Fabricating	Molding

The Industrial Management Laboratory

The industrial management laboratory houses the facilities for the study of industrial organization and management for senior high school students whose interests and aptitudes evidence a potential along management lines. It also has a place in teacher education programs. The classroom portion of the course is devoted to the study of principles and practices. Assistance is provided by resource persons from industry who can supply first-hand information on practices, problems, and solutions in the various areas of the field, ranging from personnel management to material control.

Student laboratory or try-out experience in management can be also arranged within the several industries laboratories beginning at the junior high school level. A student manager from the class may, as an example, undertake the development and operation of a system of materials control for one of the manufacturing laboratories as his own project.

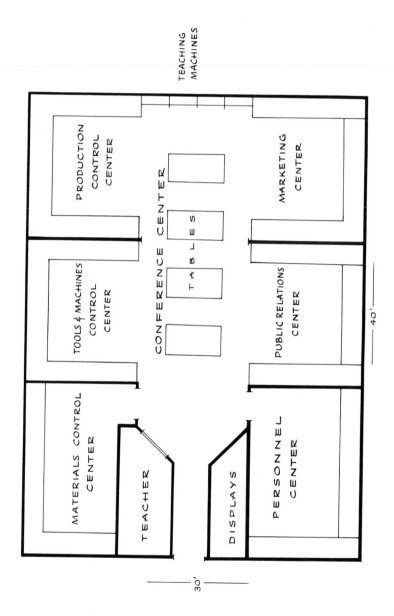

Fig. 9-11. The management laboratory.

Each of the line laboratories indicated on the chart, Figure 9-12, has a management branch center for the operation of that laboratory. The relationship between the main and the branch centers is two-way, suggesting that management problems originating at the lower level may be referred to the upper for study and experimentation in the branch centers.

Prerequisites for membership in the management class preferably include a background in one or more of the laboratories of industries plus courses from among economics, sociology, accounting, and psychology. Such requirements will probably permit only upperclassmen in high school or college to enroll, and this should be preferable.

TYPICAL FACILITIES FOR THE INDUSTRIAL MANAGEMENT LABORATORY

Material Control Center

Selection
Specifications
Purchasing
Inventory
Distribution
Accounting

Tools-Machines Control Center

Selection
Specifications
Purchasing
Inventory
Replacement
Maintenance record

Marketing

Consumer needs
Product sales
Advertising

Personnel Center

Instruction
Supervision
Organization
Goals, incentives
Evaluation
Promotion
Suggestions
Conferences
Timekeeping

Public Relations Center

Publicity
Exhibits
School relations
Community relations
Industrial relations

Production Control

Planning
Estimating
Scheduling
Engineering

THE INDUSTRIAL ARTS COUNCIL. The industrial arts council shown on the chart, Figure 9-12 is a body serving the entire industrial arts program in a school, or in several schools. Made up of industrial arts teachers, key students, representatives from among school administrators, and from industry, the body functions as a resource agency for assistance in major problems solutions, for program promotion and development, and for furnishing resource persons from industry and the community needed in the students' day-to-day study of technology. Such a body at once gives stature to the program and in itself is perhaps the most effective single public relations device upon which the new industrial arts can call.

The Research and Development Laboratory

The research and development laboratory is the center for actual, legitimate research and development on a student level. It houses

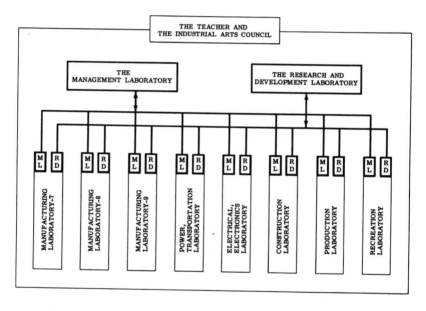

Fig. 9-12. This diagram shows the relationship of the main management laboratory to the management centers in each of the line laboratories. This same relationship holds for the research and development laboratories and the research and development centers in the same line laboratories. This relationship is integrative in that communications and controls flow in both directions, as indicated, for an over-all increase in efficiency. "ML" and "RD" identify the line or branch centers.

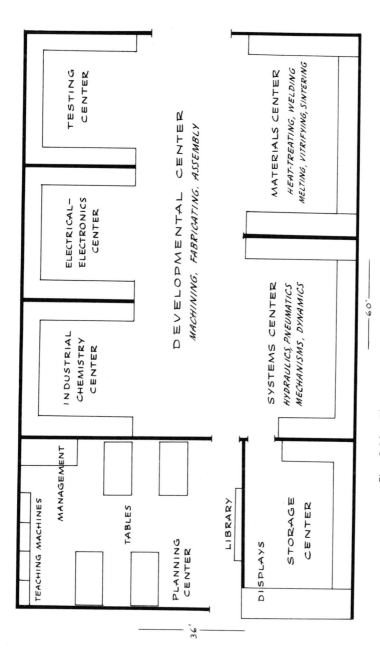

Fig. 9-13. The research and development laboratory.

the facilities for researching and developing materials, processes, products, systems, circuits, and the like, which are carried on by superior students. From this program come developed ideas which may be suitable for quantity production in the manufacturing or production laboratories. While ideas are being developed here, the students enrolled in line laboratories may also be engaged in experimental development in their projects. Ideas suggested on this level may be referred to the research and development laboratory for test, problems analysis, or development. The chart, Fig. 9-12, shows this two-way relationship.

The research and development laboratory serves the activity when it is offered as a unit course, as should be the case in the large school system and in teacher education. When set up in this way, the laboratory requires its own equipment and operates with a minimum of dependence on the other line laboratories. Its facilities are suited to a range of researching as wide as the extent of the industries in the new industrial arts. In general, the equipment will be of the laboratory type, capable of accommodating small quantities of material but representative of basic industrial processes.

The items are drawn from five groupings of research and development activities: constructing, measuring, testing, recording, and controlling. Those suggested are proposed as a starter package. They are more typical than inclusive. As the program grows, other items are needed, including some of special nature which will often be constructed by the students. Adequate library, drafting, and study provisions are also provided.

A research and development unit program can be carried on in a cooperative manner without the special laboratory described above. This plan requires a classroom as a center for consultation and discussion with the instructor and the resource staff, but the student is permitted the use of the entire laboratory facilities in pursuing his problem. This plan is cooperative in that the research student is assisted when necessary by the respective laboratory instructors, who act as resource persons. This plan utilizes existing equipment but in most cases necessitates additional items peculiar to the activity.

The chart (Fig. 9-12) shows a branch research and development center in each of the line laboratories. This suggests that the research activity is an integral part of each course. As such, it has the advantage that an atmosphere of research and development can be made to permeate all laboratory activity. It has the disadvantage, however, that research and development cannot receive the emphasis it needs to demonstrate its full value.

In operation, the research and development program has students engaged largely in individual or small-group projects involving testing and experimenting, searching and discovering, which to them becomes pure or fundamental research among materials, processes, tools, materials, and the many curricular components derived earlier. Students are also involved in inventing and devising new or better applications of mechanisms, circuits, systems, and other aspects of applied research. Students carry their ideas here into full development with a view to adaption for production in the production laboratory. The entire activity is one of intelligence, ingenuity, resourcefulness, and imagination at work scientifically and creatively.

Prerequisites for enrollment in the unit courses in research and development are desirable. Such a program cannot be expected to reach high levels of results without a selectivity in admission. The student should have had background courses giving him familiarity with materials processing as well as with the industrial area or areas where he plans to concentrate his research. Ordinarily courses in mathematics, physics, and chemistry will be helpful, but not necessarily essential. A student with a generous gift of creativity and a desire to utilize it may have the essential qualifications for carrying on his proposed project. Each student desiring admission submits a carefully worked out prospectus of the project he wishes to undertake. It includes a description of the project with an identification of anticipated major problems, proposals for going about their solutions, a listing of facilities likely to be needed, and a justification for such an undertaking. Sketches and diagrams may help to illustrate his points. A special application form for this purpose is recommended both for its evidence of efficiency and for its suggestion of the importance attached to the course. The instructor or the group of cooperating instructors make their selections with the aid of personal information on the student supplied by school records or teachers.

The emphasis given here on the research and development program in industrial arts is for several reasons. In the first place, it shows real recognition of the spirit of technology—there is a better way. The student's challenge is to find it. He may not in all cases, but he grows just the same. Then it calls on the full range of youthful potential with all of its store of imagination in the search. It capitalizes on the urge to human differentiation and nonconformity through opportunity, encouragement, and assistance in development of unique expression. It demonstrates the unrealized intellectual possibilities in industrial arts and raises them to such level that superior students make formal application to participate in the experience; it also raises industrial arts to a plane of educative stature that school administrators and parents become literally excited about its possibilities and its results. It enables industrial arts to actually contribute to an advancing of technology and to utilize rather fully the natural powers of the human which have contributed to making America great. The program is a demonstration that industrial arts has a major contribution to make to the college preparatory curriculum. It represents the ultimate level in educative respectability for industrial arts because it draws on the full talents of the student

TYPICAL FACILITIES FOR THE
RESEARCH AND DEVELOPMENT LABORATORY

Constructing	Measuring	Testing
Fabricating	Balances	Microscopes
Forming	Precision	Magnifiers
Extruding	instruments	Balances
Pressing	Gauges	Meters
Rolling	Electrical	Physics
Machining	meters	apparatus
Laminating	Heat	Chemical
Fastening	indicators	apparatus
Polishing	Light meters	
Grinding	Computer	
Finishing	Dynamometer	

Recording	Controlling	Designing
Photo laboratory	Electronic equipment	Drawing
Photo copy	Mechanical equipment	Modeling
Micro photography	Hydraulic equipment	Testing
Macro photography	Pneumatic equipment	Library
Motion picture photography		
Sound recording		
Television		

The Recreation Laboratory

The industrial arts recreation laboratory is the provision made to serve community recreation needs through industrial arts activities. Facilities include hand and machine tools of essentially two basic types: those which are suitable for use in home hobby activities, and those which the hobbyist is less likely to have but frequently needs to complete his activity. This program is available with or without credit for students in the senior high school as well as for those in college. It is offered to adults and to youth no longer attending school.

TYPICAL FACILITIES FOR THE
RECREATION LABORATORY

Woods	*Plastics*	*Graphic Arts*	*Leather*
Machining	Casting	Bookmaking	Carving
Fabricating	Extruding	Printing	Tooling
Finishing	Forming	Photography	Tanning
Upholstering	Fabricating	Papermaking	Fabricating

Metals	*Ceramics*	*Textiles*	*Electrical Apparatus*
Machining	Pottery work	Weaving	Radio ham
Casting	Enameling	Printing	equipment
Fabricating	Glass blowing	Dyeing	Hi-Fi
Jewelrymaking	Plaster casting	Fabricating	equipment
			Servicing
			Experimenting

The Services Industries Laboratory

Study of the services industries seems most appropriate when integrated with the study of the other industries. The reasons are two: One is that the study of any of the other industries to be complete should include that of the respective services. The second is that a unit program on services to be meaningful takes on the nature of vocational training. Consequently, no services laboratory

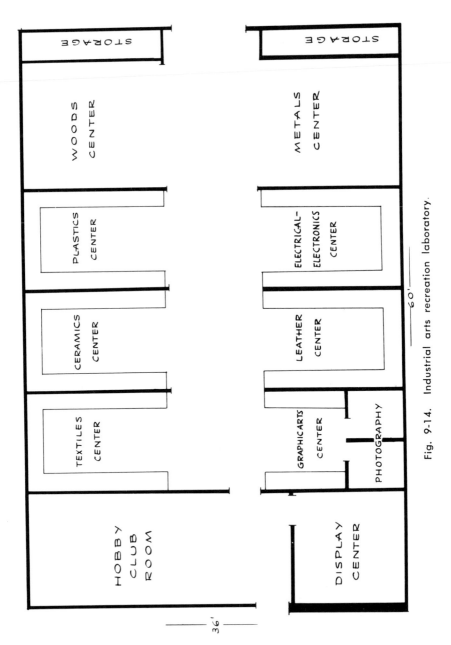

Fig. 9-14. Industrial arts recreation laboratory.

330

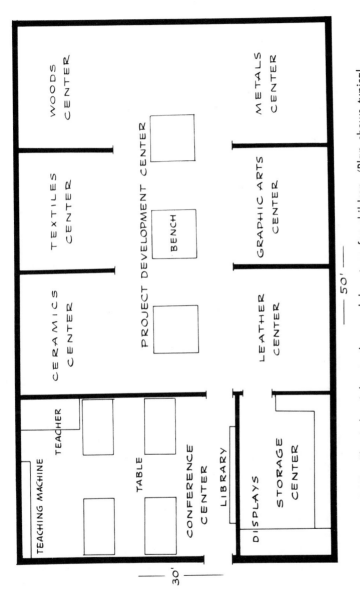

Fig. 9-15. The industrial arts therapy laboratory for children. (Plan shows typical centers only.)

331

as such is needed. Instead service centers are provided in the appropriate industries laboratories.

The Industrial Arts Therapy Laboratory

The facilities needed in therapy laboratories depend on the nature of the program and on the students being accommodated. Both mental and physical weaknesses and capacities are of concern. Equipment will generally be applicable to materials processing, complemented by other types according to needs.

TYPICAL FACILITIES FOR THE
THERAPY LABORATORY

Special Tools

Hand, arm, foot-operated tools

Industrial-type Machines and Tools

Industrial equipment for occupational training and rehabilitation

Special Machines

Power driven machines and machine tools adaptable to the operator

Typical Materials

Equipment to work with woods, metals, clay, textiles, paper, leather, plastics, reeds, fibers

In Reflection

New facilities for a new program are as essential as new wineskins for new wine. But one of the difficult problems will be to secure appropriate equipment which is not currently available. Throughout all of the equipment needs, emphasis is placed on machines in contrast to hand tools. A cooperative research and development program involving equipment manufacturers and the profession should assist in the provision of facilities designed for teaching and for learning. From this many new developments will be expected. The package concept suggests a type of efficiency and economic planning appropriate to industrial arts. The recommendation for an industrial arts council points out, among other things, the importance of technology as the content for industrial arts.

TO DISCUSS, TO DEBATE, TO DECIDE

1. Develop a list of equipment for a package laboratory for the elementary school.
2. Develop a list for a package laboratory for the junior high school manufacturing industries program.
3. Develop a list for a package laboratory for one of the programs on the high school level.
4. What items of equipment in any one package will not commonly be commercially available?
5. How can we get industry to produce equipment which meets the standards and needs of industrial arts?
6. What are the advantages of the package plan?
7. How could we get an acceptance of such packages by the profession?
8. Currently, the roughly 35,000 industrial arts teachers in the country have about the same number of different programs. Each teacher customarily thinks he knows best what should be done. Does this system strengthen or weaken industrial arts?
9. In the research and development program, what does industrial arts offer for the high I.Q. student?
10. Make a list of qualifications for the research and development teacher.

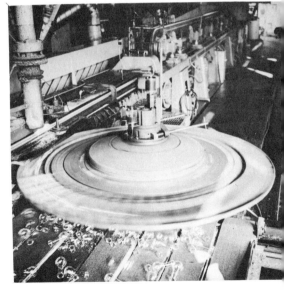

(Above) Glassblowing, the earliest of the processes for producing holloware in glass, became a highly skilled art. Here, in a replica, is shown the melting furnace made of clay and rock. A bellows furnished the needed air and charcoal, the fuel. Blowing by machine is one of today's basic processes. (Courtesy: Pittsburgh Plate Glass Company.)

(Right) The Corning ribbon machine is one of the fastest production machines in the world. It turns out bulbs at speeds up to 2000 per minute. The first machines used in the glass industry were mechanized hand processes. As demands for glassware increased and as entirely new products were conceived, new production techniques were developed. (Courtesy: Corning Glass Works.)

Some Reflections
on the New
Industrial Arts

I would recommend these three basic national goals in the technological area as part of the platform on which we can continue to build a strong nation and a better world:

Technological change should be used to improve men's lives. We have seen that it brings both progress and problems. Our goal must be to apply new technology so that it will improve the way men live and work. Necessary adjustment to an accelerating technology must be planned and carried out with human considerations paramount.

Technological change should be encouraged to meet our own increasing industrial needs, to stimulate our social and economic progress, and to face successfully the long-term challenge of international Communism.

Technological knowledge should be shared so that people throughout the world, particularly in the underdeveloped countries, may improve their lives and benefit from up-to-date technology.

—Thomas J. Watson, Jr., *Goals for Americans* (*The Report of the President's Commission on National Goals.* © 1960, by The American Assembly. Prentice-Hall, Inc., publisher.)

With time and an inclination to meditate upon the new industrial arts as conceived and proposed herein, many reflections capture the mind. Such reflections appear as highlights of the concept, and when collected, they become implications and even

335

a summation. Many more than those listed here come to mind as the proposal is studied and implemented.

On the Subject Matter

1. Technical fundamentals in subject matter are subject to change. This becomes the law of technological subject matter. No process, no matter how fundamental at one time, can be assumed to remain so indefinitely. The course of study must be inherently adaptive and flexible instead of rigidly calendared and metered. The legitimacy of our traditional fundamentals, such as planing a board into a square, rolling a wire edge, the western union splice, and many others, must be questioned.

2. Both breadth and depth in subject matter for any one student are essential to comprehension of the technology. A two-dimensional comprehension, which results from a mere surface exposure to an assortment of "areas," so typical in the general shop, and justified in the name of exploration, results in minimal understandings, superficial appreciations, and under-satisfied students. With penetration the student finds breadth; the deeper he penetrates, the broader his study and experience become. Depth produces narrowness only when we deliberately keep it so, but the inquiring mind knows no limits to its confines of search.

3. Subject matter is continuous and progressive. This is particularly evident in the curriculum for the public and private school, beginning with the elementary level. With a progressive subject matter the college freshman will not have to repeat what he has had in junior and senior high school industrial arts. He can begin where he is.

4. Reflective of technology, the new industrial arts serves the individual's educative needs as well as his work and his recreational needs. Finally now, industrial arts can become truly general education in the fullest sense.

5. New subject matter by itself will not assure a new industrial arts. It must be accompanied by a new spirit, a new sense of mission. This can be found within technology itself. To "beef up" the old industrial arts with new technicalisms is not the way to create a great new industrial arts; it only adds up to more of the

same. The fact that new oil added to the old makes more of the old becomes a good technological maxim.

6. The goal of the teacher cannot feasibly be that each student master all of the subject matter proposed, nor even that each student be exposed to it all, nor that the teacher himself be master of all he surveys. Technology did not accumulate in the lifetime of one man, nor with one man. Industrial arts initiates a study of technology which the student and the teacher must continue throughout their lifetimes if they are to find the wisdom and culture in technology. Only when the student takes the complete new industrial arts from elementary school through high school, including the appropriate study beyond, will he see technology in its full measure.

7. The total of the new subject matter stands as solid content around which industrial arts can then build its programs on all levels of schooling. This answers the question, "How can one tell what subject matter belongs in industrial arts?"

8. The new industrial arts subject matter takes on a complexity heretofore unknown. Principles, concepts, theories, relationships, systems, applications, computations, and other such components are not only as important as "how-to-do-it" or "how-to-make-it" but they are essential to a true understanding of technological subject matter. The challenge is to keep subject matter "first-handed" for the student, to let him make discoveries and inventions on his own. The problem will be to keep it from solidifying into secondhandedness as is the common practice in all of teaching. So much of the subject matter now taught in industrial arts is so secondhanded as to be technologically obsolete.

9. The mass of subject-matter content appearing with the industries and functions analyses and the curricular components emerges as from a literal explosion in knowledge. Much of it is new for us with new principles, concepts, and applications presenting new fundamentals. Now we will teach what we have not. The master list of curricular components serves as an encyclopedia of technological fundamentals.

10. Technology reaches and influences every community in the nation. The custom-making of industrial arts programs to fit individual communities is no longer necessary. This is not done in

other fields, such as English, mathematics, science, or economics.

11. The subject matter as derived will lead to a closing of the gap between industrial arts and the technology. As the gap closes, subject matter increases its contribution to an advancing of the technology through understanding and through the utilization of student head and hand potential.

On the Student

12. The new industrial arts is for all boys and girls; the latter are as much involved in the technological culture as are boys. Each person needs the new industrial arts. As an enlightened American he must know his own culture. Industrial arts is for the normal, above and below normal, for the young, and for the mature.

13. The student becomes a participant in the advancing of technology. Consequently, what he does in industrial arts must have educative and technological significance. The acquiring of technical knowledge is not enough. A concern also exists for meaning and application as guides for his own search for the truth.

14. The student is free to search, and is responsible for a continuing search, for a better way. Project selection and development is primarily student responsibility. Project selection is not left to whim, nor is its development left to trial and error.

15. The student is free to, is encouraged to, and is expected to advance as rapidly as he is able. Any course of study is based on the provision for the fullest development of the individual. The new program is geared to maximum human growth rather than lesser growth.

16. The student is free to deviate from accepted technical practices when he discovers or develops better or more appropriate ones. He is invited to try for a better joint than a mortise-and-tenon and a better way than coiling a pot of clay. He is expected to find ways and means to increasing efficiency in his own learning as well as in his own productivity.

17. The student is engaged in purposeful, planned exploring, in searching and discovering the technology, and at the same time he is engaged in making discoveries about himself. The realization of uniqueness is fully as significant in his growth and development as is a mastery of conformity.

On the Teacher

18. The role of the teacher in the new industrial arts is also new. He is now the chief resource person for the student. In this capacity he will draw on other resource persons as from industry, business, government, school, and college when they are needed.
19. The new teacher functions as administrator of the program, organizer of programs and activities, and promoter of their development within his school and community. He becomes consultant and counselor in contrast to pusher or policeman.
20. The new teacher is technically competent in science and technology. He is more scientist that tradesman, more creator than copier, more craftsman than machine operator. But as chief resource person, he is not expected to have all of the answers to student questions. Rather, he knows how to go about seeking out answers and where they may be found. He is the gifted generalist, not the jack-of-all-trades, or the narrow specialist.
21. The new teacher has a pedagogic proficiency enabling him to secure, identify, and assess growth and development in his students as individuals, along with a problem-solving ability.
22. The new teacher realizes that if he will develop creativity, he must teach creatively. Consequently, he himself is ever searching for the better way in his methodology. He will maintain a resourceful mind, ever stimulating, expediting, and raising the level of thinking by his students, and in so doing will himself experience a continuing growth.
23. The new teacher may be a man or woman. In the lower grades women may be preferred; in some upper grades they may be preferred when their qualifications equal or excel their competition.
24. The new teacher, young as he may be, has caught a vision of the great potential for good in technology, but he continues to search for evidence throughout his career. He understands the nature and value of research, and he encourages the attitude of research as a means to personal development.

On the Methodology

25. With subject-matter fundamentals subject to change, we can expect that teaching methodology will be subject to change

Fixed, inherited patterns of instructional techniques, once the practice, are now inappropriate.

26. The new methodology has its basis for learning in reasoning, problem-solving, creating, and constructing. Learning by doing, once the measure of good teaching, is no longer sufficient: emphasis must be on learning by individual, independent, imaginative thinking. Activity alone is not enough.

27. Teaching emphasis is on the realization of the individual potential of the student but within an atmosphere of general comprehension.

28. Creating begets creativity. The student is given full encouragement to think uniquely and to develop ideas expressive of distinctiveness. He is expected to make his own unique contributions not only to the discovery and development of his own capacities but to the advancement of his own school's industrial arts programs.

29. The new methodology is marked by a versatility and adaptability to the learning situation. The teacher is free to, and responsible for, employing the most effective methodology at the time and for the student.

30. The new methodology draws on technical, scientific, mathematical, economic, aesthetic principles and concepts as subject matter and effects understandings through applications in the project.

31. The new methodology is distinguished as liberating rather than disciplinary. This is the spirit of the technology. In the liberation of the student, the teacher finds a liberation. There is a teaching methodology to be developed from within the spirit of the technology: there is a better way.

32. Though the individual project is in a way tailor-made to suit the student, he will not go his way only. In all events, the student should travel on a broad, scenic boulevard and not on a one-way street.

33. Since the content of this industrial arts is technological, its study should appropriately be assisted by the maximum usage of technological means and media, including machines for teaching, television, working models and mock-ups, and the like.

On the Project

34. The project in the new industrial arts originates with the student as the expression of his search for a better idea, a better way.
35. The project is marked by originality and uniqueness rather than by effectiveness of reproduction.
36. Excellence in the project is relative to its technical respectability, its uniqueness, its involvement of the student, its expression of a better way.
37. The new project is identified by its meaning more than by activity. It has meaning for student and teacher and makes its contribution to both, as well as to technology.
38. The new project is essentially an intellectual experience which draws on the highest levels of the intellect and is effected through problem-solving, reasoning, creating, and constructing with materials.
39. The project becomes a strong measure of the success of the new industrial arts. It serves as both means and end.
40. As the student finds meaning in technology, he can be expected to become increasingly self-energizing, self-motivating in his project selection and development. Without this the project is busy work and is not a part of the new program.
41. The new industrial arts is much more than making things. Things which are made should be measured calculations of individual expression for purposes of finding better ways.

On the Facilities

42. The new industrial arts facilities provide a laboratory atmosphere within a technological environment. This is in contrast to a workshop or repair shop character.
43. The laboratory includes facilities representative of basic industrial materials, machines, energies, and principles. This does not necessarily require industrial production machines and equipment, although in certain instances these may be desirable. Rather, it suggests equipment which employs representative industrial principles. A student who understands, for example, an existent basic means for cutting a material will likely under-

stand the application of that process to another material and may be moved to search for a better one.

44. Most instructional emphasis will properly be given to machines and machine tools rather than to hand tools. Instruction in hand tools, when essential, may best follow or supplement instruction in machines. Machine literacy is representative of a higher level of human intellect than is that of hand-tool skill.

45. Equipment for the new industrial arts, while reflective of industry, must be so designed as to be most functional for student use. Industrial arts researchers will wisely team up with industry for the development of such equipment.

46. The new facilities are not involved in the worn-out controversy on the merits of the general shop versus those of the unit shop. They originate within the curriculum and the pedagogic requirements of the new program without commitment to earlier forms.

On Teacher Education

47. Since the new industrial arts will require superior teachers, an effective program of student orientation and guidance must be carried on in the secondary school. Such a program will be most effective if it is one which operates cooperatively with teacher education.

48. Teacher education will logically initiate a program of selection of students and maintain a functional guidance program in order to assist students into suitable fields of concentration.

49. Teacher education must maintain a continuing experimental program in methodology so as to prevent a sedimentation of practice and to demonstrate the significance in a searching for better ways.

50. Teacher education will be involved in a continuous curriculum revision in order that subject matter can be kept as fresh as technology.

51. Teacher education will carry on a continuing program of research and development in school-type instructional facilities, cooperatively with industry.

52. The new teacher education must carry on an intensive and extensive program of individual student research and development.

53. The new teacher education will include as areas for concentration preparation for teaching on all levels of industrial arts. This is in contrast to the usual practice of preparation largely for junior and senior high school instruction.
54. The search for leadership must be intensified. It should begin in the secondary school. The means for identifying and developing leadership must be studied. The leadership needed will not just happen; it must be planned and prepared for.
55. Since the new industrial arts can be no better than its teachers, teacher education curricula must be re-examined and revised to attract the kind of men and women needed.

On the Skill Objective

56. Contemporary technology has effected a changing concept of skill. The new skill has acquired an intellectual quality. Manual performance is not enough.
57. Manual dexterity is seen as a means to ends rather than an end; however, in industrial arts recreation the latter may be just. Manual dexerity contributes through technology an increasing control over man's environment.
58. The new skill is a composite of competences: creative, constructive, problem-solving, scientific, technical. Craftsmanship assumes greater dimensions requiring higher levels of technical comprehension and scholarship, constructional competence, engineering creativity, and servicing ingenuity.

On Industry

59. Industry becomes the great technological resource for the new industrial arts by providing resource persons, literature, materials, equipment, research, research assistance.
60. Industry provides the basic subject matter for the new industrial arts. No one industry is considered dominant in terms of the subject matter it provides.
61. A working liaison with industry is essential to a fully functioning program. Industrial arts must take the initiative in developing this liaison. When industry understands, it can be expected to respond.

On Implementation of the New Industrial Arts

62. A period of transition from the old to the new industrial arts is essential, but it should be shortened by every possible means. Nothing is to be gained by extending it; rather, much is to be lost. Time is against us already.

63. The transition should begin on all levels. Those who insist on teacher education as the point of origin of the new program would extend the period of transition. Research and experiment on all levels of the program should begin wherever men and women can handle it.

64. The major concern is for the implementation of the new industrial arts, not how much can be salvaged from the old.

65. A nationwide system of pilot model programs on all levels is the key to efficient, expeditious promotion.

66. In any one school or school system with an existing program, the transition from old to new need not be disturbing. The first and psychologically strongest move is to launch a research and development program, preferably in a unit course, along with an integrated application in existing courses. This is already being proved in numerous exemplary programs.

67. An all-out effort must be made by teachers and teacher educators for our own technological upgrading. No one should resist the new because he feels that its acceptance may reflect poorly on what he has been doing. It is more to his credit that he is alert and responsive to new ideas. Let us not, however, jump from the old to the new without a realization of new and greater horizons for industrial arts and a dedication to study and search for its potential as our guides in the leap.

68. Immediate redirection of industrial arts in the high school is necessary in order to attract college-bound students. They are the source of teachers and leaders for industrial arts. They cannot be obtained from the noncollege-bound group.

On Program Standardization

69. A commonness of basic subject matter over the United States is expected, but within a framework of continuing change. Only by this unity will industrial arts achieve the stature of educative

respectability it must have. An American program of industrial arts is needed, just as other subject fields have.

70. A standardization of equipment and facilities should properly be expected since the physical plant derives from the curriculum. Such standardization will simplify laboratory planning and lower equipment costs.

On Evaluation

71. With the new industrial arts operating on a national scale, evaluative measures can become standard. Efficiency and excellence can thus be increased.

72. With a standardization of program a system of national accreditation becomes possible and applicable to both school and college.

On American General Education

73. General education in the United States can, with the new industrial arts, become more general when it more completely reflects the contemporary culture.

74. The new industrial arts is in itself essentially general education for a people in a material culture.

75. Industrial arts now has definite substance and meaning characterized by order and unity. Up to now it has meant something different to everyone: the teacher-educator, the teacher, the student, the administrator, the parent, and the industrialist. Each was free to view industrial arts as being as big or as little as he chose, and he still could be right. With the new industrial arts the measures of its goodness can be consistent as they never have been, and the qualities of its goodness, intelligible to all.

On the Profession of Industrial Arts

76. The profession encompassing the new industrial arts has greater responsibilities than commonly accepted. It must so re-educate itself that the new program can be understood, implemented, and promoted.

77. The profession with a system of associations, committees, and

the like must give leadership, direction, and support to an improved professional literature.

78. Similarly, the profession must stimulate extensive research, applicable to the new industrial arts.

79. The profession must accept the prerogative of setting standards for itself. These will apply to all levels of the program. In accordance with the established standards, the profession is responsible for meeting them and assuring that they are met. This necessitates a national plan for accreditation.

80. The profession itself must accept the responsibility for the professional status of its membership. It will have to accept the responsibility for selling itself on a better program; this is the province of no other group.

81. Industrial arts will have as its all-encompassing goal the advancing of technology through the elevation of the human, and the elevation of the human through an advancing of technology.

NEEDED RESEARCHES ORIGINATING IN THE NEW INDUSTRIAL ARTS

Before a fully functioning program of the new industrial arts can be developed, much more needs to be known. The new proposal, while aimed at solving many problems, creates others. In the spirit of technology, however, it is reassuring to know that what one man conceives another can construct. The following are some of the major researches necessary for a deeper understanding of the new industrial arts and its implementation.

Researches in Curriculum

1. A complete and detailed derivation of subject matter must be made for each level of instruction. This involves further analyses of the industries categories, of the curricular components, and of the functions of the new curriculum. We must be able to identify clearly and draw off the subject matter. Then we can put our label on it with confidence.

2. Courses of study, teachers' guides, and student guides must be developed after the subject-matter derivations.

Researches in Resources

3. An extensive selection of new textbooks will be required. Research should establish standards and content structures for these texts, as well as guides for their preparation. Able authors must be recruited and interested publishers secured for a cooperative textbook operation.
4. A continuous searching of industrial researches and publications must be made to find resource material useful for the new industrial arts.

Researches in Facilities

5. Equipment specifications must be drawn for each laboratory. For those items not now available, design and development of pilot models suitable for manufacture by industry should begin in industrial arts. The assistance of industrial research and design should be solicited. Out of this will come our equipment packages.
6. Cooperative research with architects should be initiated so that architectural design, specifications, space allotments, and floor plans can be reduced to highly functional, economical packages readily adaptable to school plants.
7. A complete selection of machine-type equipment must be developed for the elementary and junior high school programs.

Researches in Teacher Education

8. The problem of student selection is still with us in teacher education. Effective selective processes must be established and adopted now. The teacher for the new industrial arts must possess unique qualities. These must be identified.
9. Teacher education curricula must be developed which will turn out teachers and leaders who not only understand the new industrial arts but know how to promote, guide, and effect its development.

Researches in Graduate Education

10. In view of the new undergraduate teacher education, what should be the nature of the master's program? Can one program serve both for development of the master teacher and of the leader-administrator? Such questions require researching.
11. In view of both the new undergraduate and the new master's program, what should be the nature of the doctorate? Is there not a place for scientific-technological study?
12. The need for re-training and upgrading teachers for the new program is imperative; the implementation of such training programs needs profession-wide study.

Researches in Methodology

13. With the teacher in his new role as chief resource person, the traditional teacher-pupil relationship needs re-thinking.
14. New class organization systems and techniques must be devised consistent with the new role of the teacher and student.
15. The identification and development of teaching methods directed to the fullest student utilization of creative imagination, and employing technological innovations to increase teacher efficiency must accompany the new subject matter.

Researches in Evaluation

16. Standards, methods, devices, systems for evaluation will be essential to measure growth and development in the student as well as in the overall program. It will be necessary to identify program strengths and weaknesses.
17. Standards, methods, and devices necessary in state, regional, and national accreditation must be devised. It is the responsibility of the profession to continually assess itself. Without accreditation, industrial arts commands little educative respect.

Research in Promotion

18. A nationwide promotional campaign stressing the new industrial arts as essential for the education of Americans in an age of

technology will be necessary to create public acceptance and demand. The story of this new education must become public conversation through paper-cover books, popular magazines, newspapers, television, and all such media. All of such material will require an extensive research program.

19. Actual justification of the new industrial arts for public consumption will require careful research.

Researches on the Gifted Student

20. We must find out how to attract, to challenge, and to teach the gifted student. Without him much of the new industrial arts can never be implemented. Without him in the program, it will never gain full educative stature.

21. On the collegiate level, we must find out how to attract and hold superior students including the honors group, not only in industrial arts teacher education but also in industrial arts as liberal arts education.

Researches on Value of Industrial Arts

22. To reiterate our earlier stand, we need to have a sound, solid base on which to construct a new, vital industrial arts and from which to project all facets of its program. This can rest on the technological and human postulates. But these must be researched so that the contributions of individual bases, for example, the psychological, the scientific, the moral and spiritual, the aesthetic, the cultural, and the social can be established. Out of such studies we should find the truth about the values of industrial arts. This would indeed be a glorious day.

In Retrospect
and in Projection

Any curriculum proposal has at least as many questions as answers. This does not, however, neutralize the effort. Because the answers may have been above or beyond the accepted, even to the point of being far out in space, the level of the questioning may have been raised. When this happens, the proposal has brought good. It is the author's hope that some of this type of relation and reaction will result from the proposal contained herein.

IS IT NEW? Is the new industrial arts really new? Some say that it is not. Some insist that it has been going on all the time. The author makes no claim here that what is proposed has never been thought of previously or that parts of it are not already in operation. However, in its entirety, it is yet to be seen. But argument on the condition of its newness should not consume the little time that we have to put our house in order. Rather, let us accept technology as our own primary resource for industrial arts and build upon it and with it. We are not in position to quibble about trivia; witness the current national scene in industrial arts. Psychologically, we are wiser to launch out on a wholly new program. This will give us each the lift we really need and add confidence and assurance that we may now at last be headed in a direction that makes all-around good sense. The newness may suggest to students, parents, school administrators, and industry that industrial arts now has something more educatively essential. The launching of a new industrial arts is at this very moment timed perfectly with the current concern and effort at strengthening programs in all of the disciplines in school and college. Never has a more complete rethinking of curricula been in progress at any one time. This is our invitation to offer a new industrial arts. The author wonders if we will accept it.

WILL IT WORK? We in industrial arts are so typically and completely pragmatic in our thinking that we tend to measure everything, every project, every process, every idea by the same standard—will it work? We find our pride in practicality and take our refuge in rationalizing on issues the resolution of which must supposedly lie in their workability. The old quip that it is a good idea, but it won't work is the yardstick of the pragmatic pessimist. It is being used on the new industrial arts. The blind assumption with us always seems to be that if an idea won't work, it is not a good idea. In our sightlessness and in our refuge, we overlook the possibility that someone else may be able to make it work, even when we cannot. It is the author's conviction that there are many of us who can make the new industrial arts work. If an idea is good, it can be made to work. Let this be our guide. Technology records this evidence; industry daily demonstrates it. Let no teacher, no teacher-educator stand in his own light or in the light of another who would try to make the new industrial arts work. As soon as we do succeed, we will be able to move ahead to an even greater industrial arts.

A NEW NAME? Many of us have looked for a new name to attach to a better industrial arts even though this better concept had not yet been created. This is a natural reaction in times of exasperation and in the face of a declining acceptance. But a new label is not enough. We have been especially sensitive about names. Somehow we assume that those of manual training and manual arts are beneath us. But if we are fully honest, we will likely admit that their connotations still fit what we do as well as the proposal of "industrial arts" in October, 1904.

Many have been calling for a new name to accompany this new program of industrial arts. Adding a new name can only add to the overall confusion unless we are willing to see the program for its newness. The proposal here can stand on its own merits in the second half of the century without support from the first half. Any name for it seemingly will properly include the terms "industrial" and "technology" as being generally descriptive and easily understood. The name *industrial technology* would be acceptable except that it has already been adopted for other programs and uses. In combination perhaps the term *industrial arts and technology* may be appropriate where industrial arts refers to the arts and technics of industry and technology to their study. Thus the title of this work. However, someone can make a strong case for retaining the present label and then going all out to live up to it.

THE CHALLENGE STANDS

Technology becomes the primary resource for industrial arts only as we are able to understand it. If technology is considered to be merely the addition of more industrialization to existing subject matter, we have missed its meaning. If it is only making industrial arts more scientific, we have still missed its message. We can expect that many of us in a hurry to get moving toward technology will settle on these two notions as the means to making industrial arts technological. However, the rest of us must probe more deeply into this man-made phenomenon. Then we may discover, each of us, that inner drive, that spirit which frees man to think differently about materials. By probing this spirit of technology deeply, we see man employing his full potential in reasoning, in creating, a problem-solving, in constructing with materials and energies. We find him equipped and challenged by the Great Creator to serve all man with his materials mastery. We watch him as he uses materials to release men from bonds of ignorance, poverty, hunger, disease, and fear. And then we see him lifting his freed fellows to new heights of human existence. He is a busy man in the technology, ever wondering, weighing, and working with materials in the search for better ways. When we understand the meaning of technology, we find in it the spirit of man inspired by his Maker and expressing his fullest purpose in living. Without this spirit, technology is reduced to metals and woods and clays. With it the very metals and woods and clays come to life and become a part of every man's living. With this spirit industrial arts experiences a rebirth and takes on stature and meaning as it goes about helping every American to know his America and to discover and develop his own talents for serving his fellow man through materials.

TO DISCUSS, TO DEBATE, TO DECIDE

1. When the new industrial arts is functioning in any one school what effects, if any, may be noticeable on other subject fields, such as social studies, science, mathematics, English?
2. Where is the greater danger for industrial arts, in thinking too big about the program or in thinking too little?
3. Suppose a teacher teaches with the assumption that the limits of human potential in things technological are as yet unknown. How will his efforts and results differ from those of the teacher who limits the perspective of his students?
4. What techniques can a high school teacher use to attract superior students to his industrial arts?
5. Critically analyze this hypothesis: the superior industrial arts program in a high school attracts superior students.
6. List the responsibilities that a national professional organization has to the classroom teacher. Compare these with the responsibilities of the state and local organizations.
7. What suggestions do you have for soliciting the cooperation of industry to produce the type of equipment needed for the new industrial arts?
8. How much faith should the industrial arts teacher place in the intelligence of his students?
9. Evaluate the concept that the realization of uniqueness is fully as significant in human growth and development as is mastery of conformity.
10. How can excellence in a project be identified?

Selected References

1. Adams, Walter. *The Structure of American Industry.* New York: The Macmillan Company, 1954.
2. Allen, F. R. and others. *Technology and Social Change.* New York: Appleton-Century-Crofts, Inc., 1957.
3. American Academy of Political and Social Science. *Automation.* Annals Vol. CCCXL. Philadelphia: The Academy, 1962.
4. American Council on Industrial Arts Teacher Education. *Essentials of Preservice Preparation.* Yearbook 11. Bloomington, Ill: McKnight and McKnight Publishing Company, 1962.
5. ————. *Problems and Issues in Industrial Arts Teacher Education.* Yearbook 5. Bloomington, Ill.: McKnight and McKnight Publishing Company, 1956.
6. ————. *Superior Practices in Industrial Arts Teacher Education.* Yearbook 4. Bloomington, Ill.: McKnight and McKnight Publishing Company, 1955.
7. American Industrial Arts Association. *The New Industrial Arts Curriculum.* Newark, N. J.: The Association, 1947.
8. American Vocational Association. *A Guide to Improving Instruction in Industrial Arts.* Washington, D. C.: The Association, 1953.
9. Anderson, Lewis F. *History of Manual and Industrial School Education.* New York: D. Appleton and Company, 1926.
10. Ashby, Eric. *Technology and the Academics.* New York: St. Martins Press, 1959.
11. Bawden, William T. *Leaders in Industrial Education.* Milwaukee, Wis.: The Bruce Publishing Company, 1950.
12. Bell, Daniel. *Work and its Discontents.* Boston: Beacon Press, 1956.
13. Bello, Francis. "Industrial Research: Geniuses Now Welcome," *Fortune,* Vol. LIII, No. 1 (January 1956), pp. 96-150.
14. Bennett, Charles A. *Art Training for Life and for Industry.* Peoria, Ill.: The Manual Arts Press, 1923.
15. ————. *History of Manual and Industrial Education 1870 to 1917.* Peoria, Ill.: The Manual Arts Press, 1937.
16. ————. *History of Manual and Industrial Education up to 1870.* Peoria, Ill.: The Manual Arts Press, 1926.
17. ————. *The Manual Arts.* Peoria, Ill.: The Manual Arts Press, 1919.
18. Bode, Boyd H. *Industrial Arts and the American Tradition.* Columbus, O.: Epsilon Pi Tau, Inc., 1942.
19. Bonser, Frederick G. *Industrial Arts for Public School Administrators.* New York: Bureau of Publications, Columbia University Teachers College, 1930.

20. ———— and Lois C. Mossman. *Industrial Arts for Elementary Schools.* New York: The Macmillan Company, 1935. Reprint.
21. Bowden, Witt. *The Industrial History of the United States.* New York: Adelphi Company, 1930.
22. Burlingame, Roger. *Backgrounds of Power.* New York: Charles Scribner's Sons, 1949.
23. ————. *Engines of Democracy.* New York: Charles Scribner's Sons, 1940.
24. ————. *Machines That Built America.* New York: The New American Library of World Literature, Inc., 1955.
25. Chase, Stuart. *Men and Machines.* New York: The Macmillan Company, 1929.
26. Childe, V. Gordon. *Man Makes Himself.* New York: The New American Library of World Literature, Inc., 1958.
27. Conant, James B. *Modern Science and Modern Man.* New York: Columbia University Press, 1955.
28. The Conference Board (National Industrial Relations Conference Board, Inc.). *Nonagricultural Employment by Major Industries, 1947 and 1956.* Road Maps of Industry, No. 1106. New York: The Board, March 8, 1957.
29. ————. *Leisure Time and Leisure Spending.* Road Maps of Industry, No. 1080. New York: The Board, Sept. 7, 1956.
30. ————. *Research and Development in Private Industry.* Road Maps of Industry, No. 1056. New York; The Board, March 23, 1956.
31. Council for Technological Advancement. *Automation and Job Trends.* Chicago: The Council, 1955.
32. Cuber, John F., Ed. *Technology and Social Change.* New York: Appleton-Century-Crofts, Inc., 1957.
33. Cushing, Burton, *Fundamentals of Machines.* New York: Ginn and Company, 1943.
34. Davis, John E. *Rehabilitation, Its Principles and Practices.* New York: A. S. Barnes and Company, 1946.
35. Deck, William L. "A Resource Research in Electricity." Doctor's dissertation. Columbus, O.: The Ohio State University, 1955.
36. DeGarmo, E. Paul. *Materials and Processes in Manufacturing.* New York: The Macmillan Company, 1957.
37. Dewey, John. *Democracy and Education.* New York: The Macmillan Company, 1916.
38. ————. *School and Society.* Chicago: The University of Chicago Press, 1916.
39. Dewhurst, J. Frederic and Associates. *America's Needs and Resources.* New York: The Twentieth Century Fund, 1955.
40. Diebold, John. *Automation.* New York: D. Van Nostrand Company, Inc., 1952.
41. Drucker, Peter F. "America's Next Twenty Years," *Harper's Magazine.* March, April, May, June, 1955. Reprint.

42. Giedion, Siegfried. *Mechanization Takes Command.* New York: Oxford University Press, 1948.
43. Glover, John G. and William B. Cornell. *The Development of American Industries.* Englewood Cliffs, N. J.: Prentice-Hall, Inc., 1959.
44. Greenbie, Sydney. *Leisure for Living.* New York: G. W. Stewart Publisher, 1940.
45. "The Good Life," *Life,* Vol. XLVII, No. 26 (Dec. 28, 1959), Special Issue.
46. Griffith, Ira S. *Teaching Manual and Industrial Arts.* Peoria, Ill.: The Manual Arts Press, 1924.
47. Harder, D. S. *Automation—Key to the Future.* Detroit: The Ford Motor Company, 1954.
48. Jacobsen, Howard B., Ed. *Automation and Society.* New York: Philosophical Library, 1959.
49. Kessler, Henry. *Rehabilitation of the Physically Handicapped.* New York: Columbia University Press, 1953.
50. Klemm, Frederick. *A History of Western Technology.* New York: Charles Scribner's Sons, 1959.
51. McGraw-Hill Book Company. *Yearbook of Science and Technology.* New York: McGraw-Hill Book Company, 1962.
52. Mead, Margaret. *Cultural Patterns and Technical Change.* New York: The New American Library of World Literature, Inc., 1955.
53. Meyer, Harold and Charles Brightbill. *Community Recreation: A Guide to Its Organization,* 2nd ed. Englewood Cliffs, N. J.: Prentice-Hall, Inc., 1956.
54. Micheels, William J. and others. *The Minnesota Plan for Industrial Arts Teacher Education.* Bloomington, Ill.: McKnight and McKnight Publishing Company, 1958.
55. Muller, H. J. *The Uses of the Past.* New York: The New American Library of World Literature, Inc., 1959.
56. Mumford, Lewis. *Technics and Civilization.* New York: Harcourt, Brace & World, 1934.
57. Odum, Howard. *Understanding Society.* New York: The Macmillan Company, 1947.
58. Ogburn, William F., Ed. *Technology and International Relations.* Chicago: The University of Chicago Press, 1949.
59. Ohio State Department of Education. *Ohio High School Standards, Industrial Arts Education for Junior and Senior High Schools.* Columbus, O.: Ohio State Department of Education, 1947.
60. Oliver, J. W. *History of American Technology.* New York: The Ronald Press Company, 1956.
61. Olson, Delmar W. "A Classification of Industrial Arts Subject Matter: Derivation of Activity Areas for a Laboratory of Industries." Unpublished Thesis. Columbus, O.: The Ohio State University, 1937.

62. ———. *Technology and Industrial Arts*. Columbus, O.: Epsilon Pi Tau, Inc., 1957.
63. Polakov, Walter. *The Power Age*. New York: Covici-Friede, 1933.
64. President's Commission on National Goals. *Goals for Americans*. New York: The American Assembly, Columbia University, 1960. Prentice-Hall, Inc., publisher.
65. Richards, Charles R. "A New Name," *Manual Training Magazine*, Vol. VI, No. 1 (October 1904), pp. 32-33.
66. Rockefeller Brothers Fund, Inc. *The Pursuit of Excellence*. Garden City, N. Y.: Doubleday and Company, 1958.
67. Rogers, Anne. *From Man to Machine*. Boston: Little, Brown and Company, 1941.
68. Rusinoff, S. E. *Automation in Practice*. Chicago: American Technical Society, 1957.
69. Sarnoff, David and others. *The Fabulous Future: America in 1980*. New York: E. P. Dutton, 1956.
70. The Scientific American. *Automatic Control*. New York: Simon and Schuster, Inc., 1955.
71. Snedden, David and W. E. Warner. *Reconstruction of Industrial Arts Courses*. New York: Bureau of Publications, Teachers College, Columbia University, 1927.
72. Spriegel, William and Richard Lansburgh. *Industrial Management*. New York: John Wiley and Sons, Inc., 1955.
73. State Committee on Coordination and Development. *A Prospectus for Industrial Arts in Ohio*. Columbus, O.: The Ohio Education Association and The State Department of Education, 1934.
74. Subcommittee on Economic Stabilization of the Joint Committee on the Economic Report of the United States. Eighty-fourth Congress. *Automation and Technological Change*. Washington, D. C.: U. S. Government Printing Office, 1955.
75. Terry, George R. *Principles of Management*. Homewood, Ill.: Richard D. Irwin, Inc., 1956.
76. United States Department of Commerce, Bureau of the Census. *Annual Survey of Manufactures: 1953*. Washington, D. C.: U. S. Government Printing Office, 1953.
77. ———. *Census of Manufactures: 1947*, Vol. I, General Summary. Washington, D. C.: U. S. Government Printing Office, 1950.
78. ———. *Census of Manufactures: 1947*, Vol. II, Statistics by Industry. Washington, D. C.: U. S. Government Printing Office, 1949.
79. ———. *1958 Census of Manufactures*, Vol. I, Industry Descriptions. Washington, D. C.: U. S. Government Printing Office, 1961.
80. United States Department of Health, Education, and Welfare. *Industrial Arts, An Analysis of 39 State Curriculum Guides: 1953-1958*. Bulletin No. 17. Washington, D. C.: U. S. Government Printing Office, 1961.

81. United States Department of the Interior, Office of Education, Committee on Industrial Arts. *Industrial Arts, Its Interpretation in American Schools.* Washington, D. C.: U. S. Government Printing Office, 1937.

82. ———. *Improving Industrial Arts Teaching.* Conference Report, June 1960. Circular No. 656, OE-33022. Washington, D. C.: U. S. Government Printing Office, 1962.

83. Vance, Stanley, *American Industries.* Englewood Cliffs, N. J.: Prentice-Hall, Inc., 1955.

84. Van Loon, H. W. *The Story of Mankind.* New York: Pocket Books, Inc., 1958.

85. Vinson, Arthur T. *Automation in Industry.* Schenectady, N. Y.: Public Relations Services, General Electric Co.

86. Walker, Charles R. *Modern Technology and Civilization.* New York: McGraw-Hill Book Company, Inc., 1962.

87. Weeks, Robert P., Ed. *Machines and the Man.* New York: Appleton-Century-Crofts, Inc., 1961.

88. Western Arts Association. *The Terminological Investigation.* Indianapolis: The Association, 1933.

89. Whitehead, Alfred N. *Adventures of Ideas.* New York: The New American Library of World Literature, Inc., 1955.

90. ———. *Science and the Modern World.* New York: The New American Library of World Literature, Inc., 1956.

91. ———. *The Aims of Education.* New York: The New American Library of World Literature, Inc., 1955.

92. Wiener, Norbert. *Cybernetics.* New York: John Wiley, 1948.

93. ———. *The Human Use of Human Beings.* Garden City, N. Y.: Doubleday and Company, Inc., 1956.

94. Wilber, Gordon O. *Industrial Arts and General Education.* Scranton, Pa.: International Textbook Company, 1954.

95. Wilkie Brothers Foundation. *Civilization Through Tools.* Des Plaines, Ill.: The Foundation, 1954.

96. Wilkie, Leighton A. *The Dawn of This Age.* New York: The Newcomen Society in North America, 1959.

97. Wilson, Mitchell. *American Science and Invention.* New York: Simon and Schuster, 1954.

98. Woodbury, D. O. *Let Erma Do It: The Full Story of Automation.* New York: Harcourt, Brace & World, 1956.

99. Woodward, Calvin M. *The Manual Training High School.* Boston: D. C. Heath and Company, 1887.

Index

Index